Pearson Education

Test Prep Series for

AP® Environmental Science

Myra Morgan

To accompany:

ENVIRONMENT:
The Science Behind the Stories
AP® Edition
Seventh Edition

Jay Withgott • Matthew Laposata

Pearson

330 Hudson Street, NY, NY 10013

Product Manager, Science: Cady Owens
Sr. Content Analyst, Science: Thomas Hoff
Managing Producer, Science: Michael Early
Sr. Content Producer, Science: Margaret Young
Production Management and Composition: Ramkumar Palani, SPi Global
Rights & Permissions Manager: Ben Ferrini
Manufacturing Buyer: Stacey Weinberger, LSC Communications
Sr. Product Marketing Manager: Alysun Estes
Cover Photo Credit: Seng Chye Teo/Moment Unreleased/Getty Images

ISBN-10:   0-13-645145-4
ISBN-13: 978-0-13-645145-7

www.PearsonSchool.com/Advanced

1 2020

Brief Contents

About the Author

Myra Morgan has been actively involved in teaching for over 35 years as Head of Sciences at Miss Porter's School (CT), the Ethel Walker School (CT), and the Sage Hill School (Newport Coast, CA), in addition to earlier work in marine research for the EPA. She has worked for the National Math & Science Initiatives in Kentucky, Connecticut, and Massachusetts, and currently is the AP Environmental Science Content Director for MASS Insight Education & Research in Boston. Laboratory and field research have been an integral part of her teaching over the years, providing students the opportunity to study with her at the Bermuda Biological Station, at the National Undersea Research Center, and in the Gulf of Maine using ROV and submersible technology. Myra has been an Environmental Science and Biology College Board Consultant and an AP Reader for over 20 years. She has provided AP Summer Institutes and workshops throughout the country in both biology and environmental science and has served as an AP Mentor to many teacher cadres. Myra has been honored for her contributions to the sciences and the AP Program with an Advanced Placement Recognition Award from the College Board, the NABT Outstanding Biology Teacher Award, a RadioShack Science Teaching Excellence Award, the Teaching Chair of Distinction in Science (Miss Porter's School), and a Teacher Fellowship at the University of St. Andrews, Scotland. The Smith College Botanic Garden also receives the benefit of her enthusiastic and scientifically informed volunteer work, helping others to appreciate the beauty of nature and the importance of protecting our fragile environment.

Part I

Introduction to the AP® Environmental Science Course and Exam

Welcome to the exciting and rewarding journey that is the AP Environmental Science course! Of all of the AP science courses, AP Environmental Science is unique in that it focuses primarily on the relevant and pressing problems that face our species and the planet. It is an applied science that focuses on problem solving, understanding environmental issues by emphasizing *critical thinking,* and encouraging you to propose possible solutions by immersing yourself in the *science* behind the issues. Laboratory and field investigations also form an essential component of the course, as these experiences afford critical insights into how science is practiced, how environmental problems are studied, and how humans worldwide are affecting their environment.

Part I of this Test Prep Series for AP gives an overview of the *AP® Environmental Science Course and Exam Description (CED)*. It describes the big ideas, the specific learning objectives, and the science practices that are a part of this newly updated AP course. It also introduces specifics as to the types of questions encountered on the exam and provides helpful test-taking strategies. Finally, a correlation chart is included that shows where in the *Environment: The Science behind the Stories,* Seventh Edition text you will find the content that is connected to the specific learning objectives and skills required by the AP Environmental Science Exam.

Part II of this Test Prep Series for AP is focused on *Environment: The Science behind the Stories,* Seventh Edition, by Withgott and Laposata, and provides a review of the major environmental science topics. It gives an overview of important information found in each text chapter and also provides sample multiple-choice and free-response questions. ***These chapter summaries are not a substitute for the text, class discussions, or laboratory portion of the course;*** however, they do offer a review that will help focus your preparation for the exam.

Each Part II chapter summary is organized according to **"*You Must Know*"** and should be reviewed and studied before you attempt the practice multiple-choice and free-response questions provided. Finally, be sure to thoroughly review the answers and explanations to prepare yourself for the range of questions and depth of information you will encounter on the AP Environmental Science Exam. This thorough approach will support a solid understanding and a confident ability to *apply and connect* the major concepts in the AP Environmental Science course.

Part III contains all of the answers and explanations for the Part II multiple-choice and free-response questions. Finally, Part IV includes a practice test with answers and explanations.

AP Environmental Science: A Brief Course Description

Today, AP® Environmental Science is one of the most timely Advanced Placement science courses offered to qualified high school students. This course brings to life many topics in the news and creates an understanding of the science behind the many diverse environmental issues affecting all of our lives. Because of its interdisciplinary nature, AP Environmental Science is an excellent option for any student who has completed two years of a high school laboratory science: one year of life science and one year of physical science, often biology and chemistry. Because the course requires quantitative analysis, students should also have taken at least one year of algebra. Because of these prerequisites, AP Environmental Science will usually be taken in either the junior or senior year of high school.

The AP® Program is sponsored by the College Board, a nonprofit organization that oversees college admissions examinations. The College Board summarizes the goals of the AP Environmental Science course: "to engage students with the scientific principles, concepts, and methodologies required to understand the inter-relationships within the natural world. The course requires that students identify and analyze natural and human-made environmental problems, evaluate the relative risks associated with these problems, and examine alternative solutions for resolving or preventing them."

The interdisciplinary nature of AP Environmental Science embraces a wide variety of topics. Yet there are several major unifying themes/big ideas that cut across the many topics included in the College Board's course framework. Four big ideas serve as the foundation of the course, allowing students to make meaningful connections between topics. These big ideas are briefly described in the *AP Environmental Science Course and Exam Description (CED),* published by the College Board, 2019:

- **Big Idea 1: Energy Transfer (ENG)** Energy conversions underlie all ecological processes. Energy cannot be created; it must come from somewhere. As energy flows through systems, at each step, more of it becomes unusable.

- **Big Idea 2: Interactions between Earth Systems (ERT)** The Earth is one interconnected system. Natural systems change over time and space. Biogeochemical systems vary in ability to recover from disturbances.

- **Big Idea 3: Interactions between Different Species and the Environment (EIN)** Humans alter natural systems and have had an impact on the environment for millions of years. Technology and population growth have enabled humans to increase both the rate and scale of their impact on the environment.

- **Big Idea 4: Sustainability (STB)** Human survival depends on developing practices that will achieve sustainable systems. A suitable combination of conservation and development is required. The management of resources is essential. Understanding the role of cultural, social, and economic factors is vital to the development of solutions.

The *AP Environmental Science CED* also organizes the course into nine commonly taught units, which may be ordered in a variety of effective sequences. The percentage after each major unit reflects the approximate proportion of multiple-choice questions on the exam pertaining to that topic; thus, the percentage also indicates the relative emphasis that should be placed on these topics in order to best prepare for the AP® Exam. These nine units are briefly described below.

Source: Copyright © 2019 The College Board. Reproduced with permission. http://apcentral.collegeboard.com.

Unit 1: The Living World: Ecosystems **(6–8%)**

Unit 2: The Living World: Biodiversity **(6–8%)**

Unit 3: Populations **(10–15%)**

Unit 4: Earth Systems and Resources **(10–15%)**

Unit 5: Land and Water Use **(10–15%)**

Unit 6: Energy Resources and Consumption **(10–15%)**

Unit 7: Atmospheric Pollution **(7–10%)**

Unit 8: Aquatic and Terrestrial Pollution **(7–10%)**

Unit 9: Global Change **(15–20%)**

Finally, the *AP Environmental Science CED* summarizes the seven science practices that describe what a student should be able to develop during this course. These practices form the basis of the skills required on the AP Exam and are explained in detail in the College Board's *AP Environmental Science CED*.

Practice 1 *Concept Explanation:* Explain environmental concepts, processes, and models presented in written format.

Practice 2 *Visual Representations:* Analyze visual representations of environmental concepts and processes.

Practice 3 *Text Analysis:* Analyze sources of information about environmental issues.

Practice 4 *Scientific Experiments:* Analyze research studies that test environmental principles.

Practice 5 *Data Analysis:* Analyze and interpret quantitative data represented in tables, charts, and graphs.

Practice 6 *Mathematical Routines:* Apply quantitative methods to address environmental concepts.

Practice 7 *Environmental Solutions:* Propose and justify solutions to environmental problems.

The AP Environmental Science Exam

The AP Environmental Science Exam is two hours and 40 minutes in length and consists of two sections: a 90-minute multiple-choice section and a 70-minute free-response (essay) section. The exam is challenging and requires the ability not only to understand the *science* behind the environmental issues, but also to make important connections between issues, to design and analyze scientific investigations, and to propose solutions to environmental problems. For example, what do ocean acidification, tropical rainforest destruction, and using fossil fuels as an energy source have in common? Understanding the actual *evidence* for global climate change, being able to *analyze and interpret* scientific data tables, and then to offer *evidence-based solutions* to the many environmental issues discussed in the course: These are the assessment goals of the exam. You should be prepared to recall basic environmental facts and concepts, to apply these to the analysis of particular environmental problems, to make essential connections between environmental topics, to perform quantitative analysis, and to demonstrate an understanding of the science practices and learning objectives outlined in the course framework. A four-function, scientific or graphing calculator is allowed on both sections of the exam.

Section I of Exam: Multiple-Choice Questions

Section I of the AP Environmental Science Exam contains 80 multiple-choice questions that test both scientific facts and their application; this section will constitute 60% of your final grade. You will have 90 minutes to complete these 80 questions, so you should spend an average of a minute on each question, enabling extra time for the more challenging questions. *Multiple-choice scores are based only on the number of questions answered correctly.* Points are no longer deducted for incorrect answers so that students are encouraged to answer all questions. The AP Environmental Science Exam will contain both individual and set-based questions, each of which will be described below, with examples.

Individual Questions

The individual or traditional multiple-choice questions, requiring basic factual recall, can take different formats: straightforward questions with options; "least" or "most likely" options; or "reverse" multiple choice questions, where only one option is incorrect. Examples follow:

1. The level of ecological organization described by field ecologists when studying multiple interacting species that live in the same area is
   (A) the habitat.
   (B) the ecosystem.
   (C) the population.
   (D) the community.

   Answer: D. A community is made up of numerous populations of different species in a given area. In contrast, the ecosystem level would include the community of different populations *plus* the specific environmental factors (temperature, soil, moisture, light, etc.) in that area.

2. Which of the following is *not* a major greenhouse gas?
   (A) carbon dioxide
   (B) nitrous oxide
   (C) carbon monoxide
   (D) water vapor

   Answer: C. Water vapor, perhaps surprisingly, is the most common greenhouse gas, since it absorbs more infrared radiation from Earth than any other compound. Other greenhouse gases include carbon dioxide and nitrous oxide. Carbon monoxide (CO), although very toxic, is *not* a major greenhouse gas.

3. When the IPAT model is applied to the United States, the *least* important factor in determining the environmental effects of the U.S. population is
   (A) the value of P.
   (B) the value of A.
   (C) the value of T.
   (D) the values of A and T.

   Answer: A. The size of the U.S. population (P) is fairly insignificant compared to the great importance of affluence (A). Affluence is directly related to the consumption of Earth's natural resources, and it has been determined that environmental impact is not so much about the numbers of individuals, as about what those individuals are doing. The addition of 1 American has as much environmental impact as the addition of 4.5 citizens of China, 10 citizens of India, or 19 citizens of Afghanistan, all because individuals from affluent societies leave a considerably larger per capita ecological footprint.

Set-Based Questions

All set-based questions include stimulus material that might consist of *quantitative* data (data tables, charts, graphs), *qualitative* data (models or maps), or *text-based sources* of information to analyze. Since data analysis and interpretation are skills at the heart of doing science, this type of question occurs frequently. Often there is more than one question that makes use of the same data. These questions may also require that you do some calculations to determine the correct answer.

Following is an example of set-based questions using quantitative (graph) data:

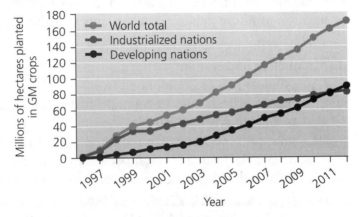

Growth of GM Crops, 1997–2012

4 Examining the graph between 2005 and 2009, there is evidence that
   (A) the rate of GM crop growth was being controlled.
   (B) the rate of increase of GM crops in industrialized nations was greater than in developing nations.
   (C) the rate of increase of GM crops in developing nations was greater than in industrialized nations.
   (D) the rate of growth of GM crops in both developing and industrialized nations was equal.

5. After examining the graph to determine the percent change of the world's GM crops between 2008 and 2011, one concludes that GM crops increased by approximately ___ during this time.
   (A) 160%
   (B) 80%
   (C) 40%
   (D) 33%

Answers: (#4) C. The question is asking for a comparison of *rates* of increase between industrialized and developing nations, not totals. The slopes of the two graph lines need to be compared between 2005 and 2009 in order to determine the rate of increase. One can visually see that the developing nations' graph line is steeper than that of the industrialized nation during this time, indicating a faster rate of growth. **(#5) D.** In order to determine the world's percent change in growth of GM crops between 2008 and 2011, one uses the following formula:

$$\% \text{ Change} = (\text{Final–Initial}) \div (\text{Initial}) \times 100$$
$$\% \text{ Change} = (160–120) \div (120) \times 100 = \mathbf{33.3\%}$$

Following is an example of set-based questions using a text-based source:

The Fukushima Daiichi nuclear disaster in Japan, caused by the Tohoku earthquake and subsequent tsunami, led to unsafe levels of radiation in Japan's soil and seafood. This disaster led to the immediate evacuation of thousands of people, in addition to re-evaluating the design and site location of future nuclear power plants worldwide.

6. Which of the following best describes the process of electricity generation at a nuclear power plant?
    (A) Nuclear power is generated from combustion of uranium, producing heat, causing water to generate steam, which turns a generator's turbine to create electricity.
    (B) Nuclear power is generated through fission, which releases a large amount of heat. This heat is used to generate steam, which turns a turbine that powers a generator, producing electricity.
    (C) Nuclear power is generated from Earth's thermal energy. The deep ground water can be turned to steam, which then turns a turbine to produce electricity.
    (D) Nuclear power is generated by fusion, a nuclear process bringing together radioactive atoms of barium and strontium, producing the highly desirable uranium fuel, a source of electricity.

7. At a nuclear power plant such as Fukushima Daiichi, in which of the following structures would a meltdown most likely lead to the accidental release of radiation?
    (A) cooling tower
    (B) containment dome
    (C) reactor core
    (D) backup generators

Answers: (#6) B. Although steam production is used to turn turbines, generating electricity, the source of the heat to make the steam is where answers A and B differ. Nuclear power's heat arises from fission of uranium, not the combustion of uranium. **(#7) C.** The reactor core is the structure that immediately surrounds the fissionable uranium. When excess heat cannot be dissipated safely, a reactor core meltdown occurs, leading to a release of radiation.

Section II of Exam: Free-Response Questions

Section II of the AP Environmental Science Exam consists of three free-response questions (FRQs), or essays, and constitutes 40% of the final grade of the exam. Each free-response question consists of several subparts, and since you will have a total of 70 minutes for this section of the exam, it is necessary that you watch the time very carefully so that you do not spend too long on any one essay.

Different subparts of each essay often are not of equal difficulty. Again, keeping track of the time is very important because each essay is worth a total of 10 points. Do not omit an entire essay just because a beginning subpart seems too challenging. Credit will be awarded for any of the subparts that you answer correctly.

Your answers to all free-response questions and their subparts must be presented in essay form. *Outlines, bulleted points, unlabeled and unexplained diagrams, or math work not shown are not given credit.* Again, each essay is scored on a scale from 0 to 10 points, and your performance on any single essay is evaluated independently of the other essays.

There are three different types of FRQs, described below:

Question 1: Design and analyze an investigation.

Question 2: Analyze an environmental problem and propose a solution.

Question 3: Analyze an environmental problem and propose a solution doing calculations.

FRQ 1: Design and Analyze an Investigation

This type of free-response question presents students with an authentic environmental scenario accompanied by either a model/visual representation or quantitative data, and it may assess a student's ability to analyze the data, describe potential responses to an environmental problem, critically analyze the investigation, or design an alternative investigation using scientific principles. A common mistake that students make is to simply repeat information given in the document as their answer rather than correctly providing new information and the requisite supporting detail.

FRQ 2: Analyze an Environmental Problem and Propose a Solution

This type of free-response question presents students with an authentic scenario accompanied by either a model/visual representation or quantitative data. This FRQ type will assess a student's ability to analyze these visual representations or data and to propose and justify solutions to the environmental problem under discussion. Your ability to earn points in this essay type will be determined by your *in-depth knowledge* and ability to support your statements with *specific scientific evidence.*

FRQ 3: Analyze an Environmental Problem and Propose a Solution Doing Calculations

This type of FRQ is often referred to as the math question. Quantitative data will be provided, which you will then be required to use in order to calculate your answers. Alternatively, a graph, diagram, or table/chart will be provided that will require quantitative analysis. *Don't give up* if you feel that you cannot do the math, as points can be earned on other parts of the question. Even though this is considered the math question, these questions typically have one or more parts not requiring calculations or graphing, but rather your specific knowledge of the environmental issue or concept to which the question refers. Remember to always *show your work* in your answer booklet for any calculation required, and also *provide the appropriate units* with each number. As with all free-response questions, you may be required to predict, identify, describe, explain, or discuss the topic in question, so you should *pay close attention to the word choice* used in each part of the question. Focusing on what type of verb is being used in the question can help you maximize both your time and ability to effectively earn points on this type of free-response question.

Grading Procedures for the AP Environmental Science Exam

The multiple-choice section of the exam is 60% of your total score. The raw score for this section is determined by crediting 1 point for each correctly answered question. It is important to answer all questions, as there is *no penalty for incorrect answers*. The free-response section counts for 40% of your exam grade. Each of the three essays is weighted equally, with a 10-point potential for each essay response. The raw scores of the AP Environmental Science Exam are converted to the following 5-point scale.

5–Extremely Well Qualified
4–Well Qualified
3–Qualified
2–Possibly Qualified
1–No Recommendation

Some colleges give undergraduate course credit to students who achieve scores of 3 or better on AP exams. Other colleges require that students achieve scores of 4 or 5. Each college and university sets its own AP credit and placement policies, and because these policies are individual and variable, it is important that you check the specific policies of the college or university for which you are interested on the College Board website (www.collegeboard.com/ap/creditpolicy).

Test-Taking Strategies for the AP® Environmental Science Free-Response Questions

- You will have 70 minutes to answer the three free-response questions. Since each essay is of equal value (10 points), dividing your writing time equally is important.
- **Read all questions** thoroughly before beginning to write. Determine which question you are most confident about. *Answer this question first,* so that *if* you run short of time on any question, it will be your most challenging one.
- **Write an essay!** Always answer in complete sentences. Outlines are unacceptable, and bulleted lists are not awarded any points and will not be graded. Diagrams will receive credit only if they are relevant, well-labeled, and connected to the text of your essay.
- **Read questions carefully.** Check to see whether there are comparisons to be made, an experiment to design, an *economic* advantage to describe, an *environmental* benefit to be explained, or data to be analyzed. Then do just that. Write a response that specifically answers the question that has been asked. Go into detail, defining terms as long as they are relevant to the subject and to the point. You will earn points only for sentences that *specifically* answer the question or provide illustrative examples.
- **Never make general statements.** For example: activity "x" causes "pollution," activity "y" is "bad for the environment." These statements are much too vague and will receive *no* credit. Follow through completely with your thoughts or examples, providing a full explanation for any term you use.
- **Label your answers** so there is no doubt where your answer is. All essays have very specific parts, such as *a, b, c,* or *i, ii, iii.* This also helps ensure that you have finished answering the question and can move forward to the next question.
- **Do not restate the question** in your answer, as it is a waste of your time. You also do not need to have an introduction or conclusion to your essay. Science writing is specific and concise.
- **If given a choice of topics to write about, make your choice** and stick with it. If two examples are asked for, give *only* two. No additional examples will be graded, and you earn no extra credit by providing more examples.
- **Write clearly and neatly** using a ballpoint pen with black or dark blue ink. Neatly cross out mistakes to save time, rather than erasing

or using white-out. If the grader cannot read what you wrote, you will receive no credit.

■ Try not to panic if you think you are somewhat unfamiliar with a question's topic. You will probably know something about the topic, so write what you know. **Do not give up and leave the entire question blank.**

■ **Routinely practice your math!** Math-based free-response questions can be challenging. However, if you practice these types of essays throughout the year, you will gain confidence and become more successful. Remember to **show your work** and **label all units** to receive credit on the math questions. Every AP Environmental Science student should be comfortable working with percent change, metric prefixes, basic algebra, scientific notation and exponents, and dimensional analysis.

AP Topic Correlation for *Environment: The Science behind the Stories*, Seventh Edition, by Withgott and Laposata

The following correlation is intended to help you prepare effectively for the AP® Environmental Science Exam. The 9 AP Environmental Science Units included in the Curriculum Exam Description (CED) describe the Big Ideas, Enduring Understandings, and the specific Topics in each Unit. Each unit's weight on the multiple-choice portion of the AP Exam is also shown.

Reference to the Course Exam Description (CED), located on the College Board's AP Central website (apcentral.collegeboard.org/courses/ap-environ mental-science), is recommended in order to understand the breadth and depth of each required topic. One can easily observe that all 9 Units include topics from several different text chapters, emphasizing the ***interconnectedness*** of content in this AP discipline.

This correlation lists the chapter and page location in the *Environment: The Science Behind the Stories, 7e* text for each topic. However, in order to understand the complexity of each topic, ***a complete reading of the text chapter in which the topic is located is essential.*** Part II of this Study Guide, with its focused chapter reviews and questions, will further support a thorough preparation and success on the AP Exam.

AP® Environmental Science Curriculum Framework		*Environment: The Science Behind the Stories*, 7e
Unit 1: The Living World–Ecosystems (11 Topics) 6–8% (AP Exam weight)		**Correlation with 7e text**
Big Ideas	**Enduring Understandings**	**Unit 1 Topics** are included in the following 7e Chapters and text pages:
Interactions Between Earth Systems (ERT)	**ERT-1**: Ecosystems are the result of biotic and abiotic interactions.	Introduction to Ecosystems, 61, 111–121 (Ch 3: Evolution and Population Ecology) Terrestrial and Aquatic biomes 94–101 (Ch 4: Species Interactions and Community Ecology) Biogeochemical Cycles (C,N,P, water) 121–129 (Ch 5: Environmental Systems and Ecosystem Ecology)
Energy Transfer (ENG)	**ENG-1**: Energy can be converted from one form to another.	Trophic levels, 81– 82, 373–374 Food Chains and Food Webs, 81–82 (Ch 4 Species Interactions and Community Ecology) Primary Productivity, GPP, NPP, 111, 114 Energy Flow and 10% Rule, 111–112 (Ch 5: Environmental Systems and Ecosystem Ecology)

Unit 2: The Living World–Biodiversity (7 Topics) 6–8 % (AP Exam weight)		**Correlation with 7e text**
Big Ideas	**Enduring Understandings**	**Unit 2 Topics** are included in the following 7e Chapters and text pages:
Interaction Between Earth Systems (ERT)	**ERT-2**: Ecosystems have structure and diversity that change over time.	Introduction to Biodiversity, 54, 69–71, 272–305 Ecosystem Services, 120–121, 311–312 Natural Disruptions to Ecosystems, 283–285 (Ch 11: Biodiversity and Its Conservation Biology) (Ch 3: Evolution and Population Ecology) Adaptation, 51–58 Ecological Tolerance, 67– 68 (Ch 3: Evolution and Population Ecology) Island Biogeography, 329–333 (Ch 12: Forests, Forest Management, and Protected Areas) Ecological Succession, 87–91 (Ch 4: Species Interactions and Community Ecology)

Unit 3: Population (9 Topics) 10–15 % (AP Exam weight)		Correlation with 7e text
Big Ideas	Enduring Understandings	Unit 3 Topics are included in the following 7e Chapters and text pages:
Interactions Between Earth Systems (ERT)	ERT-3: Populations change over time in reaction to a variety of factors.	Generalist and specialist species, 62 K and r-selected species, 68 Survivorship Curves, 68 Carrying Capacity, 67–68 Population Growth and Resource Availability, 66 (Ch 3: Evolution and Population Ecology)
Interactions Between Different Species and the Environment (EIN)	ENG-1: Human populations change in reaction to a variety of factors, including social and cultural factors.	Age Structure Diagrams, 195–196, 63 Total Fertility Rate, 198–199 Human Population Dynamics, 189–199 Demographic Transition, 199–201 (Ch 8, Human Populations)

Unit 4: Earth Systems and Resources (9 Topics) 10–15 % (AP Exam weight)		Correlation with 7e text
Big Ideas	Enduring Understandings	Unit 4 Topics are included in the following 7e Chapters and text pages:
Interactions Between Earth Systems (ERT)	ERT-4: Earth's systems interact, resulting in a state of balance over time.	Plate Tectonics, 35–41 (Ch 2: Earth's Physical Systems) Soil Formation and Erosion, 217–219, 229–237 Soil Composition and Properties, 217–219 (Ch 9: The Underpinnings of Agriculture) Earth's Atmosphere, 452–456, 107 Global Wind Patterns, 455–456, 605 (Ch 17: The Atmosphere, Air Quality, and Pollution Control) Watersheds, 397, 105 (Ch 15: Freshwater Systems and Resources)
Energy Transfer (ENG)	ENG-2: Most of the Earth's atmospheric processes are driven by input of energy from the sun.	Solar Radiation and the Earth's Seasons, 448,600 Earth's Geography and Climate, 455 (Ch 17: The Atmosphere, Air Quality, and Pollution Control) El Nino and La Nina, 427–429, (Ch 16: Marine and Coastal Systems and Resources)

Unit 5: Land and Water Use (17 Topics) 10–15 % (AP Exam weight)		Correlation with 7e text
Big Ideas	**Enduring Understandings**	**Unit 5** Topics are included in the following 7e Chapters and text pages:
Interactions Between Different Species and the Environment (EIN)	**EIN-2:** When humans use natural resources, they alter natural systems.	Ecological Footprints, 5–6, 16, 208 (Ch 1: Science and Sustainability) (Ch 8: Human Population) Tragedy of the Commons, 164–165 (Ch 7: Environmental Policy: Making Decisions and Solving Problems) Impacts of Modern Agricultural Practices, 219–223, 229–237 Irrigation Methods, 219–221 237 (Ch 9: The Underpinnings of Agriculture) Green Revolution, 245–247, 190, 215 Pest Control Methods, 251–254 Meat Production Methods, 247–250 (Ch 10: Making Agriculture Sustainable) Impacts of Urbanization, 336–357 (Ch 13: The Urban Environment) Impacts of Overfishing, 438–446 (Ch 16: Marine and Coastal Systems and Resources) Impacts of Mining, 649–658 (Ch 23: Minerals and Mining)
Sustainability (STB)	**STB-1:** Humans can mitigate their impact on land and water resources through sustainable use.	Introduction to Sustainability, 16–9, 153–155 (Ch 1: Science and Sustainability) (Ch 6: Ethics, Economics, and Sustainable Development) Integrated Pest Management, 254 Sustainable Agriculture, 266–269, 215 Aquaculture, 250, 444 (Ch 10: Making Agriculture Sustainable) (Ch 9: The Underpinnings of Agriculture) Sustainable Forestry, 324–325, 316–319 Clearcutting, 320, 312–316 (Ch 12: Forests, Forest Management, and Protected Areas) Methods to Reduce Urban Runoff, 109–110, 222, 397 (Ch 13: The Urban Environment) (Ch 15: Freshwater Systems and Resources)

Unit 6: Energy Resources and Consumption (13 Topics) 10–15% (AP Exam weight)		Correlation with 7e text
Big Ideas	**Enduring Understandings**	<u>Unit 6</u> **Topics** are included in the following 7e Chapters and text pages:
Energy Transfer (ENG)	**ENG-3:** Humans use energy from a variety of sources, resulting in positive and negative consequences.	Nonrenewable and Renewable Resources, 525–526 Global Energy Consumption, 526, 551–552 Fuel Types and Uses (wood, peat, coal, natural gas, and crude oil), 526–541 Distribution of Natural Energy Reserves, 526, 529–533 Fossil Fuels, 529–552, 525, 526 Nuclear Power, 564–575 (Ch 19: Fossil Fuels and Energy Efficiency) Energy from Biomass, 575–582 Hydroelectric power, 582–585 (Ch 20, Conventional Energy Alternatives) Solar energy, 597–602 Geothermal energy, 597–602 Hydrogen Fuel Cell, 613–614 Wind Energy, 602–607 (Ch 21: New Renewable Energy Alternatives)

Unit 7: Atmospheric Pollution (8 Topics) 7–10% (AP Exam weight)		Correlation with 7e text
Big Ideas	**Enduring Understandings**	<u>Unit 7</u> **Topics** are included in the following 7e Chapters and text pages:
Sustainability (STB)	**STB-2:** Human activities have physical, chemical, and biological consequences for the atmosphere.	Introduction to Air Pollution, 456–459, 566–567 Photochemical Smog, 468, 467–470 Thermal Inversion, 454–455 Atmospheric CO_2 and Particulates, 459, 470 Indoor Air Pollutants, 477–480 Reduction of Air Pollutants, 458–462 Acid Rain, 474–477 (Ch 17: The Atmosphere, Air Quality, and Pollution Control) Noise pollution, 352 (Ch 13: The Urban Environment)

Unit 8: Aquatic and Terrestrial Pollution (15 Topics) 7–10% (AP Exam weight)		Correlation with 7e text
Big Ideas	**Enduring Understandings**	<u>Unit 8</u> **Topics** are included in the following 7e Chapters and text pages:

Sustainability (STB)	**STB-3:** Human activities, including the use of resources, have physical, chemical, and biological consequences for ecosystems.	Sources of Pollution, 408–414
		Human Impacts on Ecosystems, 399–408
		Environmental effects of excessive fertilizers and detergents on aquatic ecosystems, 406–407
		Human Impacts on Wetlands and Mangroves, 398–399, 430
		Thermal Pollution, 413
		    (Ch 15: Freshwater Systems and Resources)
		    (Ch 16: Marine and Coastal Systems and Resources)
		
		Eutrophication, 110–111, 115, 221–222, 410–411
		Sewage Treatment, 415–417
		    (Ch 5: Environmental Systems and Ecosystem Ecology)
		    (Ch 9: The Underpinnings of Agriculture)
		
		Endocrine Disruptors, 362–363, 371, 377, 409–410, 412–413
		Persistent Organic Pollutants (POPs), 422
		Bioaccumulation and Biomagnification, 373–374
		    (Ch 14: Environmental Health and Toxicology)
		    (Ch 15: Freshwater Systems and Resources)
		
		Solid Waste Disposal, 620–621, 630–637
		Waste Reduction Methods, 623–627, 620, 621
		    (Ch 22: Managing Our Waste)

Interaction Between Different Species and their Environment (EIN)	**EIN-3:** Pollutants can have both direct and indirect impacts on the health of organisms, including humans.	Lethal Dose 50% (LD_{50}), 376–377 Dose Response Curve, 376 Pollution and Human Health, 368–372, 365–368 Pathogens and Infectious Diseases, 364–365 (Ch 14: Environmental Health and Toxicology)

Unit 9: Global Change (10 Topics) 15–20% (AP Exam weight)		Correlation with 7e text
Big Ideas	**Enduring Understandings**	**Unit 9 Topics** are included in the following 7e Chapters and text pages:
Sustainability (STB)	**SB-4:** Local and regional human activities can have impacts at the global level.	Stratospheric ozone depletion, 470–473 Reducing ozone depletion, 471–474 (Ch 17: The Atmosphere, Air Quality, and Pollution Control) The Greenhouse Effect, 488 Increases in Greenhouse Gases, 488–489, 491–494 Global Climate Change, 484–521 Ocean Warming, 425–427, 489–491 Ocean Acidification, 437–438, 504, 438 (Ch 18: Global Climate Change) (Ch 16: Marine and Coastal Systems and Resources)
Interactions Between Different Species and the Environment (EIN)	**EIN-4:** The health of a species is closely tied to its ecosystem, and minor environmental changes can have a large impact.	Invasive species issues, 75–76, 84–85, 291–294 (Ch 4: Species Interactions and Community Ecology) (Ch 11: Biodiversity and Its Conservation) Human Impacts on Biodiversity, 282, 288–294 Endangered Species, 296–297, 282–284, 288 (Ch 11: Biodiversity and Its Conservation)

Part II

A Review of Topics and Sample Questions

Part II is keyed to *Environment: The Science behind the Stories*, Seventh Edition, and provides a focused review of the major environmental science topics. It gives an overview of the important information found in each text chapter and also provides sample multiple-choice and free-response questions.

Each Part II chapter summary is organized according to **"*You Must Know*"** and should be reviewed and studied before attempting to practice the multiple-choice and free-response questions provided. *After* answering the practice questions, be sure to thoroughly review the answers and explanations located in Part III, so that you prepare yourself for the range of questions and depth of information you will encounter on the AP Environmental Science Exam. This thorough approach will support a solid understanding and a confident ability to *apply and connect* the major concepts in the AP Environmental Science course.

TOPIC 1

Environmental Science and Sustainability

Chapter 1: Science and Sustainability: An Introduction to Environmental Science

---

YOU MUST KNOW

- The terms *environment, environmental science, renewable natural resources,* and *nonrenewable natural resources.*
- The importance of ecosystem services, with specific examples.
- The connection/interplay between population growth and resource consumption.
- The meaning of ecological footprint and how to assess its impact.
- The scientific method and the process of science.
- How to judge the reliability of information sources.
- The concepts of sustainability and sustainable development.
- Specific examples and solutions being pursued with regard to sustainability.
- Strategies for sustainability: major approaches to building a sustainable future.

The terms environment, environmental science, renewable natural resources, *and* nonrenewable natural resources

- The **environment** is a complex entity of all living and nonliving things, including, in its broadest sense, the structures, urban centers, and other living spaces created by humans in the built environment.
- **Environmental science** is the interdisciplinary study (including natural and social sciences) of how the natural world works, how our environment affects us, and how we affect our environment—all using scientific methods to understand and solve environmental problems.
- **Renewable natural resources** are those that are replenished over relatively short periods. Sunlight, wind, and wave energy, for example, are perpetually replenished and essentially inexhaustible. Timber, water, and soil, however, can take months or decades to renew.

■ **Nonrenewable natural resources** such as mineral ores and crude oil are finite in supply—once depleted, they are no longer available.

Renewability of a natural resource is best viewed as a continuum, as even potentially renewable resources can be depleted if used faster than naturally replenished.

The importance of ecosystem services, with specific examples

■ **Ecosystem services** are essential processes carried out by naturally functioning ecosystems, supporting living things and making human economic activity possible.

■ Ecosystem services arise from the normal functioning of natural systems and are not meant for human benefit, yet we could not survive without them. For instance, if we degrade an ecosystem service, like a community's drinking water source, it may require a great deal of time and money to restore the original healthy water quality and deal with the health impacts experienced.

■ Specific examples of ecosystem services include the purification of air and water and essential cycling of nutrients by forests, plant pollination by animals, waste recycling systems provided by soil microbes, and global climate regulation by intact plant ecosystems.

The connection/interplay between population growth and resource consumption

■ The human population is currently approaching 8 billion, with 10 billion forecast by 2050.

■ The agricultural revolution (~10,000 years ago) and industrial revolution (beginning in mid-1700s) have fueled human population growth.

■ Population growth amplifies humans' resource consumption.

■ Resource consumption exerts social and environmental pressures. By mining energy resources and manufacturing more goods, we are consuming more of the planet's limited resources. Although some of the world's population may increase their affluence, this is not universally true, often creating economic disparity.

■ Expanding and intensifying world food production has come at a considerable cost:
  1) Approximately 50% of the planet's land surface has been converted for agriculture.
  2) Extensive use of pesticides and fertilizers has poisoned species, altered natural systems, and reduced Earth's biodiversity.
  3) Erosion and poorly managed irrigation have destroyed much cropland.
  4) Pollution from farmland/feedlots has polluted land, air, and water.

The meaning of ecological footprint and how to assess its impact

■ An **ecological footprint** represents the total area of biologically productive land and water needed to produce the resources and absorb or recycle the wastes (e.g., CO_2 emissions) of a given person or population.

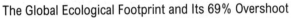

The Global Ecological Footprint and Its 69% Overshoot

- An ecological footprint can be calculated by answering specific questions regarding lifestyle and consumerism (www.footprintnetwork.org).
- Currently, humans are using more than 2.7 ha/person, creating a global ecological deficit of about 69%. That is, humanity is using renewable resources 69% faster than they are being replenished.
- Comparing human demand against biocapacity, it would take 1.69 years for the planet to regenerate the renewable resources that people use in just 1 year—demand is greatly exceeding nature's ability to provide ecosystem services.
- **Natural capital** is Earth's vast store of resources combined with the ecosystem services provided by the planet. This "capital" should be thought of as a bank account in which one leaves the principal intact and uses only the interest in order to live sustainably. Currently, we are drawing down Earth's natural capital faster than it is being renewed/replaced.
- The current U.S. ecological footprint is 8.1 ha/person (~20 acres) compared to China's 3.6 ha/person (8.9 acres) and India's 1.2 ha/person (2.9 acres).

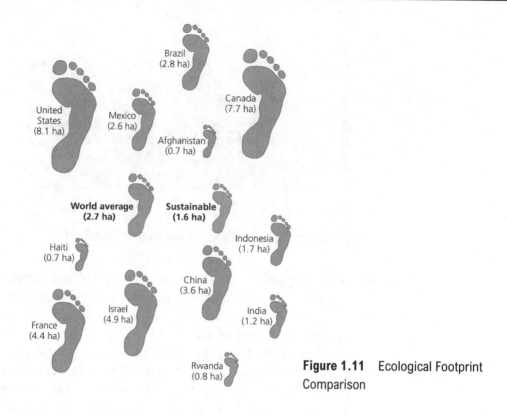

Figure 1.11 Ecological Footprint Comparison

The scientific method and the process of science

- The **scientific method** is a technique for testing ideas by making observations and asking questions, which lead to developing a **hypothesis** (a *testable* explanation).
- Using one's hypothesis to generate a prediction that can be tested forms the basis of hypothesis-driven science and scientific experimentation.
- A **controlled experiment** is one that tests the validity of a prediction or hypothesis, manipulating one variable at a time—the **independent variable.** The **dependent variable** (the one the scientist measures) produces the data necessary to support or refute the hypothesis.
- The **control** of an experiment is often the unmanipulated case, used for comparison.
- **Replication,** that is, repeating an entire experiment and offering multiple replicates of the result of that experiment, is essential for adequate and accurate data generation.
- In practice, scientists cannot always run *manipulative* experiments for all questions, especially those involving large spatial scales or long time scales (e.g., global climate change studies).
- **Natural experiments,** in which researchers test their hypotheses by looking for **correlation,** or statistical association among variables, are sometimes required. This type of experiment compares how dependent

variables are expressed in naturally occurring, rather than experimentally manipulated, contexts.

- Evidence based on correlation alone is not as strong as evidence based on manipulative experiments, but sometimes this is the only feasible approach given the nature of the research problem.
- Scientists record information from their experiments, specifically valuing **quantitative data** (information expressed by numbers).
- An essential part of **data analysis** often involves choosing an appropriate graph format (line, bar, scatter plot, or pie chart) to visualize data.
- **Statistical tests** are always necessary to objectively and precisely determine the reliability of data.
- After multiple experiments are performed, results are analyzed and the findings are documented and submitted for publication in scientific journals. **Peer review** determines whether work merits publication. Following publication, other scientists may attempt to reproduce the original results in their own experiments.
- If a hypothesis survives repeated testing and continues to predict experimental outcomes accurately, it may potentially be incorporated into *a theory*—a widely accepted, well-tested explanation of one or more cause-and-effect relationships that has been extensively validated by a great amount of research.

How to judge the reliability of information sources

- Society and world culture today are awash in information, including misinformation, from all kinds of sources. Environmental issues are often immersed in different political viewpoints, making it challenging to determine reliability.
- A key criterion in evaluating reliability of a source is to determine whether the information is *solidly based in evidence.*
- **Primary source** material is an original scientific research paper published in a peer-reviewed journal, presenting novel information that stands on its own.
- **Secondary sources** are articles or broadcasts produced by others about primary sources. Material that has "gone viral" through social media is often the most unreliable of secondary sources because it can be so easily altered along its path of transmission.
- When evaluating sources of information about science, an essential question is how many steps removed from the original research a source is. Other important questions to ask are *who* is presenting the information, and *why* is the information being presented?

The concepts of sustainability and sustainable development

- **Sustainability** is a guiding principle of modern environmental science that requires us to live in such a way as to maintain Earth's systems and its natural resources for the foreseeable future. Sustainability generally means sustaining human institutions and ecological systems in a healthy and functional state for a long period of time.
- Contributions of biodiversity and ecosystem goods and services are infinitely fundamental and valuable to sustainability.
- Protecting the environment against the ravages of human development is no longer the sole consideration of sustainable development. Finding ways to promote social justice, economic well-being, and environmental quality, all at the same time (triple bottom line), is the goal of modern sustainable development.
- **Sustainable development** satisfies our current needs without compromising the future availability of natural resources or our future quality of life.
- Energy choices (especially regarding fossil fuel consumption) will greatly influence Earth's future.
- Sustainable solutions are increasing: Innovative renewable energy resources are being developed, energy-efficiency efforts are gaining ground around the world, and agricultural reform and new environmental laws are reducing pollution and protecting the environment.
- The world's people have not benefited equally from society's overall rise in affluence; however, most people are now aiming to find solutions that foster economic advancement while protecting the environment and promoting social equity.

Specific examples and solutions being pursued with regard to sustainability

- **Audits** produce baseline data on how much an institution consumes and pollutes.
- **Waste reduction,** reusing, recycling, and composting are common sustainability efforts.
- **Green buildings** are constructed from sustainable building materials, are designed to reduce pollution, use renewable energy, and encourage efficiency in energy and water use. Buildings are responsible for 70–90% of a campus's greenhouse gas emissions, so building green is a current emphasis. *Leadership in Energy and Environmental Design* (LEED) standards are the agreed-upon standards guiding the design and certification of green buildings.
- **Water conservation,** especially important in arid regions, can include waterless urinals, "living machines" to treat wastewater, rain gardens for stormwater management, and low-flow showerheads.

- **Improving energy efficiency** can involve such measures as turning down hot water heater temperatures by 5 degrees, not powering unused buildings, and installing motion detectors to turn off lights when people are not in rooms.
- **Promoting renewable energy** can involve such measures as switching from fuel oil to carbon-neutral wood chips (reduces emissions by 40%), increasing solar power mix by installing PV solar system arrays, installing wind turbines, and purchasing "green tags" or carbon offsets (which subsidize renewable energy sources). Haverford College (PA) has achieved a 100% renewable energy status.
- **Reducing food waste** is being accomplished by campus dining services by composting food scraps, employing trayless dining, and establishing "farm-to-campus" programs that provide locally grown produce.
- **Promoting more sustainable food consumption** involves buying more locally grown food and organic produce and purchasing food in bulk with less packaging.
- **Promoting sustainable purchasing decisions** involves encouraging the purchase of energy-efficient appliances, recycled paper, certified sustainable wood, and nontoxic cleaning products and eliminating herbicides and fertilizers used on lawns, gardens, and golf courses.
- **Sustainable transportation alternatives** include promoting alternative fuels (e.g., natural gas and biodiesel) and alternative-fuel vehicles, bicycling, walking, and using public transportation.
- **Restoration of native plants, habitats, and landscapes** removes invasive species, enhances soil and water quality, and conserves water as vegetation is better adapted.
- **Carbon-neutrality as a major goal** involves reducing greenhouse gas emissions and/or employing carbon offsets to reduce the net amount of carbon released into the atmosphere to zero. College of the Atlantic (ME) was the first carbon-neutral campus.
- **Divestment from fossil fuel corporations** is a recent movement on many university campuses in which students are urging their administrations to divest from stock holdings of coal, oil, and gas industries. Unity College and Hampshire College became the first to formally divest in 2012.

Strategies for sustainability: major approaches to building a sustainable future

- **Consumer power:** Major approaches include expressing preferences through the political system, "voting with your wallet" for sustainably produced goods, and rethinking assumptions about economic growth as an ultimate goal.
- **Population stability:** The growth in population and per capita consumption need to be halted; both are unsustainable and will eventually encounter serious limiting factors.
- **Green technology:** Technology has traditionally increased environmental impact ($I = PAT$). However, new green technologies can help reduce impact: catalytic converters, recycling and wastewater

treatment technologies, and solar, wind, and geothermal energy technologies.

- **Local and global:** Promotion of local self-sufficiency and long-term thinking are critical criteria for sustainability.
- **Political engagement:** Ordinary citizens have power as well, if they choose to exercise it. You can exercise your power at the ballot box, by attending public hearings, by donating to advocacy groups, and by writing letters, sending e-mails, and making phone calls to officeholders.
- **Mimic natural systems** by promoting closed-loop industrial processes. For instance, transform linear pathways into circular ones, in which waste is recycled and reused, ultimately generating no waste.
- **Systemic solutions:** Promotion of solutions that focus on "big picture" solutions, not merely the symptoms of the problem. A systemic solution to our energy demands would involve developing an array of clean renewable energy sources instead of looking for more immediate/accessible fossil fuel sources.
- **Long-term perspective:** To be sustainable, a solution must work in the long term, as often the best long-term solution is not always the best short-term "political" solution. We must continue to build awareness that time is limited for turning around our increasing human environmental impact.

Multiple-Choice Questions

1. In terms of ecosystem services, sustainably managed ecosystems would
   - (A) provide enhanced and restored services over unaltered natural ecosystems.
   - (B) provide somewhat diminished or damaged services.
   - (C) provide more valuable services than converted ecosystems.
   - (D) restore the original biodiversity of ecosystems.

2. The world's average ecological footprint is 2.7 hectares/person compared to the U.S. average of 8.1 ha/person. The world is depleting renewable resources approximately ___% faster than they can be replenished; however, the U.S. impact alone is approximately ___ times greater than the world average.
   - (A) 69%; 3
   - (B) 50%; 2.7
   - (C) 30%; 5
   - (D) 69%; 2.7

Use graph below to answer questions 3 and 4

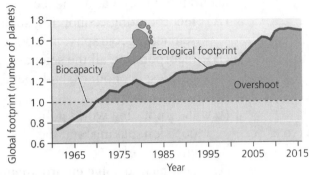

The Global Ecological Footprint and Its Overshoot

3. How much larger was the global ecological footprint in 2005 than in 1985?
    (A) 10%
    (B) 15%
    (C) 33%
    (D) 50%

4. A value of 1.2 ha/person for global footprint was first reached in the year
    (A) 1970.
    (B) 1975.
    (C) 1980.
    (D) 1990.

5. A controlled scientific experiment
    (A) often involves manipulating as many variables as possible in order to determine the factual basis of the relationship studied.
    (B) is always designed to generate new scientific hypotheses and advance science.
    (C) is an activity designed to test the validity of a hypothesis.
    (D) involves manipulating only the dependent variable and measuring the independent variable.

6. Ecosystem services
    (A) contribute to keeping ecosystems economically productive.
    (B) are focused on providing humans with the essential life services.
    (C) are separate from economic value and exist along a continuum from renewable to nonrenewable resources.
    (D) are economically valuable services provided by natural systems.

7. A well-designed and well-controlled experiment includes
    (A) a testable hypothesis, one independent variable, replicates, and a quantifiable dependent variable.
    (B) a testable hypothesis, several independent variables, one replicate, and a quantifiable dependent variable.
    (C) a testable hypothesis, one independent variable, replicates, and several quantifiable dependent variables.
    (D) a testable hypothesis, a quantifiable independent variable, one replicate, and a qualitative dependent variable.

8. Which of the following will lead to a more sustainable world culture?
   (A) increasing green energy production for everyone
   (B) increasing consumer growth for all developing nations
   (C) reducing overall consumption and halting population growth
   (D) assisting developing countries to achieve the U.S. ecological footprint

9. An ecological footprint is best described as showing
   (A) the major components of an average ecologist's footprint.
   (B) the total land area contaminated by the human population.
   (C) the amount of carbon emitted on average by industrialized countries.
   (D) the total biologically productive land and water area required to sustain a person or population.

10. Structures given a LEED platinum ranking are
    (A) inefficient and need to be renovated and upgraded to meet green standards.
    (B) especially high in heavy metal content.
    (C) exemplary in sustainable design, especially energy efficiency.
    (D) constructed to function sustainably without electricity from fossil fuels.

11. Environmental science is most accurately viewed as a science
    (A) incorporating economics, social sciences, geography, and policy.
    (B) incorporating all the sciences, politics, economics, and social sciences.
    (C) incorporating world politics, decision making, and the environment.
    (D) designed to solve environmental problems using current technology.

12. In a scientific experiment, the variable(s) that is/are manipulated "is/are"
    (A) the control, as this is the only quantifiable manner in which an experiment can be tested.
    (B) the independent variable.
    (C) the dependent variable.
    (D) are both the independent and dependent variable, one at a time.

13. It has been well documented that world population growth negatively impacts ecosystem services. The current world population is estimated to be closest to
    (A) 3 billion.
    (B) 7.2 billion.
    (C) 8.0 billion.
    (D) 10 billion.

14. Specific examples of potentially renewable natural resources are
    (A) forests, water, and soil.
    (B) timber, water, and mineral resources.
    (C) agricultural crops, soils, and natural gas.
    (D) tidal energy, water, and mineral ores.

15. Carbon-neutrality approaches refer to
    (A) reducing greenhouse gas emissions from fossil fuel combustion.
    (B) eliminating use of all carbon-based compounds.
    (C) cap-and-trade efforts currently employed by global enterprises.
    (D) becoming neutral with regard to renewable energy sources and negative with regard to nonrenewable energy sources.

16. Several of the least expensive ways to achieve a sustainable lifestyle include
    (A) employing an energy audit, carbon-neutrality, and personal divestment from fossil fuel corporations.
    (B) recycling, water conservation, and purchasing carbon offsets.
    (C) purchasing compact fluorescent bulbs, using biodiesel transportation, and eating local produce.
    (D) employing water conservation, recycling, bicycling, and eating local produce.

Free-Response Question

> In 1997, a team of scientists led by University of Vermont ecological economist Robert Costanza published a landmark paper, *The Value of the World's Ecosystem Services and Natural Capital*. Their study determined that the monetary value of Earth's ecosystem services (from 16 major ecosystems including forests, grasslands, and all other terrestrial and aquatic ecosystems) totaled at least $33 trillion per year. Prior to this important study, forests and ecosystems were thought to have value primarily for their *economic services* (e.g., lumber, paper, and other wood products from harvesting forests). As an example of their intrinsic value, the Costanza study estimated that the world's forests alone are providing us with *ecosystem services* worth at least $4.7 trillion per year.

a) Other than the recreation value provided by forests, identify and explain two of the primary ecosystem services provided by global forests.
b) Assuming that the ecological valuation of forests is estimated to be 400% greater than that estimated by the economic gain of directly harvesting the timber, what is the approximate economic valuation per year?
c) In 1997, the year this report was published, the global gross national product (the monetary value of all goods and services produced worldwide) was $18 trillion. In view of this fact, discuss with specifics the meaning of *sustainability* and its implications in the context of the Costanza study.

The Living World: Ecosystems and Biodiversity

Chapter 3: Evolution and Population Ecology

> **YOU MUST KNOW**
>
> - How evolution by natural selection generates and shapes biodiversity.
> - Reasons for current species extinction and Earth's known past mass extinction events.
> - Characteristics that make species vulnerable to extinction: K-strategists versus r-strategists; specialists versus generalists.
> - Levels of ecological organization, including habitat and niche.
> - Population characteristics used to predict population growth potential, growth rates, and survivorship curves.
> - Differences between exponential and logistic growth models.
> - Differences between density-dependent and density-independent factors.
> - Specific challenges and current efforts involved in conserving biodiversity.

How evolution by natural selection generates and shapes biodiversity

- Darwin's **theory of natural selection:** Organisms often produce excess young; individuals within each species vary in their traits; some individuals will be better suited to their environment than others and the genes/traits of these individuals that enhance survival will be passed on and become more prominent in future generations.
- **Mutations** and **sexual reproduction** produce the essential genetic variation upon which the process of natural selection acts.

- **Selective pressures** from the environment influence adaptation. Environmental conditions determine what pressures natural selection will exert, and these selective pressures affect which members of a population will survive and reproduce. Selection acts upon genetic variation, favoring certain variants best suited to the environment in which the organism lives.
- **Artificial selection** is the process of trait selection conducted under human direction, rather than environmental pressures, and has given rise to the wide diversity of food crops. Corn, wheat, rice, and most of the entire agricultural system are based on artificial selection.
- **Speciation** is the process by which new species are generated. Biological diversity, or **biodiversity,** refers to the variety of life across all levels of biological organization, including the diversity of species, genes, populations, and communities.
- **Allopatric speciation,** thought to be the main mode of speciation, occurs when an original population separates into *geographically isolated* populations that do not interbreed. As each separate population experiences differential selective/environmental pressures over time, it is possible that significant genetic differences will accumulate between these populations because of their differing environments. Allopatric speciation is confirmed when individuals from these formerly separated populations come back together and are unable to mate and produce viable offspring. The 18 living species of Hawaiian honeycreeper are examples of allopatric speciation. As new volcanic islands emerged and as forests expanded and contracted over the millennia, the original ancestral species population was split many times and came to live in new separated environments. The various honeycreeper species diverged from one another in this manner, evolving different body shapes, color, sizes, and unique feeding behaviors based on bill shape/length.
- **Sympatric speciation** occurs when a small part of a population becomes a new species because of reproductive isolation within the *same* geographic area. For example, populations of some insects may become reproductively isolated if they feed and mate exclusively on different types of plants in the same geographic area.
- Approximately 3.5 billion years of life on Earth have culminated in an estimated 3 million to 100 million species living today, with only 1.8 million species currently discovered and described. The vast majority of all species have become extinct over time.
- Speciation and extinction together determine Earth's current biodiversity, with **phylogenetic trees** providing an illustration of the relationships of these species and the history of life's divergencies and evolution.

Reasons for current species extinction and Earth's known past mass extinction events

■ Species often become extinct when environmental conditions change rapidly or severely enough that a species cannot genetically adapt to the change—the slow process of natural selection often does not have sufficient time to work. The current warming of our global climate is occurring too rapidly for most species to adapt, and many species may become extinct as a result.

■ **Small populations** often lack the genetic variation required to protect them against environmental change.

■ **Island-dwelling species** and other **small range populations** are particularly vulnerable because of the small areas and isolation by water, not allowing species movement if severe changes occur in their local environment. Half of Hawaii's native birds became extinct soon after humans introduced non-native rats, cats, and mongooses, as well as imported livestock such as cattle, goats, and pigs.

■ **Mainland "islands" of habitat** (such as remnant prairie surrounded by agricultural lands) can host endemic species that are vulnerable to extinction. Additional examples include the Yosemite toad, restricted to a small region of the Sierra Nevada mountains, and the Houston toad, occupying just a few patches of Texas woodland.

■ **Island-dwelling species** are particularly vulnerable to extinction because islands are smaller than mainland areas and are isolated by water, and fewer species reach and can inhabit islands. These vulnerable species often have a limited ability to escape predators that may have been introduced, or to restore their population numbers from "off island" if their numbers decline.

■ There have been five **mass extinctions,** the best-known occurring 66 million years ago (the K-T event), bringing an end to the dinosaurs. Evidence suggests that the impact of a gigantic asteroid caused atmospheric soot to blot out the sun, inhibiting photosynthesis and plant growth, causing plants to die and animals to starve. The mass extinction at the end of the Permian period, 250 million years ago, was even more catastrophic, and it is thought to have wiped out 75–95% of our planet's species during this one event.

■ During Earth's 4.6-billion-year history, there has been climate change, the subsequent rise and fall of sea level, the evolution of new species (adapting to gradually changing environments), followed by subsequent interspecific competition among species.

■ Human impact (especially the alteration of and destruction of natural habitats due to population growth, industrial development, and resource extraction and use) has profoundly affected current extinction rates, which the Millennium Ecosystem Assessment Report estimates to be 100–1000 times higher than background extinction rates and rising. Many biologists have concluded that Earth is currently entering its **sixth mass extinction** as a result of these diverse and negative human impacts.

Characteristics that make species vulnerable to extinction: K-strategists versus r-strategists; specialists versus generalists

- **K-strategists** are species having few offspring that are larger in size, require longer parental care, and reach maturity at a later age.
- **r-strategists** are species devoting energy and resources to producing many offspring in a relatively short time, with little or no parental care, that are small in size and come to maturity early.
- It is important to note that r-selected and K-selected species are two extremes on a continuum and that most species fall somewhere between these extremes.
- **Specialists** are species that can survive only in a narrow range of habitats that contain very specific resources. Because of these limitations on their specific way of life, they are more vulnerable to extinction when conditions change and threaten the habitat or resource on which they have specialized. The native Hawaiian forest birds, the various honeycreeper species, are a good example because each species has a unique bill shape exquisitely adapted for feeding on various insects/larvae that live on/in the wood of the native Hawaiian trees.
- **Endemic species** are those that occur nowhere else on the planet but in a very specific region. These species also face increased risk of extinction because their members often belong to a single, sometimes small, population. The Hawaiian state bird, the nēnē, is an example.
- **Generalists** are species with broad tolerances, able to use a wide array of resources, and succeed by being able to live in many different places with variable conditions. These species are often able to endure environmental change better than specialists, making them less susceptible to extinction; however, they may not thrive in any one situation as much as a specialist would. The common myna, a bird introduced to Hawaii from Asia, is an example of a generalist. Its unremarkable bill allows it to eat many types of food in many types of habitats, facilitating its spread through all areas where human development has altered the Hawaiian landscape.

Levels of ecological organization, including habitat and niche

- **Ecology** is the scientific study of interactions among organisms and of relationships between organisms and their environment.
- Living organisms are organized hierarchically, beginning with **species,** an organism or group of populations whose members share characteristics and freely breed with one another, producing fertile offspring. Moving up the hierarchy, one can study **populations** (a group of individuals of the *same* species that live in a particular area), **communities** (a set of populations of *different* species living together in a particular area), **ecosystems** (a community plus its nonliving environment and all interactions between them), and ultimately the **biosphere** (the sum total of living things on Earth and all areas inhabited by life).

Levels of Ecological Organization		
	Biosphere	The sum total of living things on Earth and the areas they inhabit
	Ecosystem	A functional system consisting of a community, its nonliving environment, and the interactions between them
	Community	A set of populations of different species living together in a particular area
	Population	A group of individuals of a species that live in a particular area
	Organism	An individual living thing

Hierarchical Levels of Life

- **Habitat** is the living and nonliving elements surrounding where an organism lives—its "address."
- **Niche** is an organism's use of resources and its functional role in a community, including habitat use, food consumption, role in energy flow/matter cycling, and all interactions with other organisms—its "profession."
- **Ecology** is studied at several levels: population, community, and ecosystem.

  1) **Population ecology** examines the dynamics of population change and helps us understand why populations of some species (such as endangered honeycreepers) decline, while populations such as humans increase.
  2) **Community ecology** focuses on patterns of species diversity and on interactions among species.
  3) **Ecosystem ecology** reveals patterns such as energy flow and nutrient cycling by studying both living and nonliving components of the ecosystem. Today's studies of how climate change is affecting various ecosystems around the world are examples of this level.
  4) **Landscape ecology** helps us to understand how and why ecosystems, communities, and populations are distributed across geographic areas.

Population characteristics used to predict population growth potential, growth rates, and survivorship curves

- **Population growth potential** attributes:
  1) population size
  2) density: number of individuals per unit area or volume
  3) distribution: spatial arrangement (random, clumped, or even)
  4) sex ratio: proportion of males to females
  5) age structure: relative number of individuals of each age group
  6) population: birth/death rates

- **Population growth rate:** to obtain an overall population growth rate, the total rate of change in a population's size per unit time, one must also take into consideration the effects of migration.

  - Crude birth rates (CBR) and crude death rates (CDR) are expressed per 1000 individuals per year.
  - (CBR − CDR) + (immigration rate − emigration rate) = population growth rate
  - ((births + immigration) − (deaths + emigration)) ÷ overall population size = growth rate

- **Survivorship curves:**
  1) Type I curves show low death rates during early and midlife, followed by death rates that increase sharply in older age groups.
  2) Type II survivorship curves show a constant death rate over a life span.
  3) Type III curves show very high death rates for young, then a lower death rate for the few individuals surviving to older age.

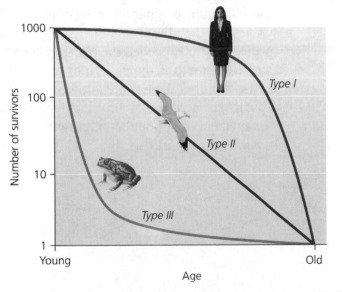

Figure 3.19 Survivorship curves show how an individual's likelihood of survival varies with age

Differences between exponential and logistic growth models

- **Exponential growth** occurs when a population increases by a fixed percentage each year and is pictured as a J-curve—growth under ideal conditions. It occurs in nature when a population is small, competition is minimal, and the organism is introduced into a new environment with abundant resources. The Eurasian collared dove is currently spreading across North America, propelled by exponential growth.

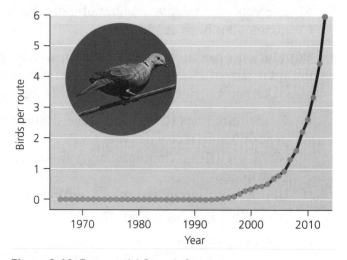

Figure 3.16 Exponential Growth Curve

- **Limiting factors** are the physical, chemical, and biological attributes of the environment that restrain population growth, restricting indefinite exponential growth.
- **Carrying capacity** is the maximum population size that a given environment can sustain. The interaction of limiting factors determines this maximum population size. With the global human population now surpassing 7 billion, many scientists are questioning whether our species has far exceeded the planet's carrying capacity for humans.
- **Logistic growth** is the pattern of growth in which a population initially grows rapidly, then more slowly, finally stabilizing at its carrying capacity as a result of limiting factors. This pattern is shown by an S-shaped curve of population growth over time.

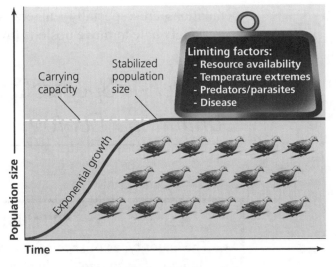

Figure 3.17 Logistic Growth Curve

Differences between density-dependent and density-independent factors

- **Density-dependent factors** are involved when death rates rise or birth rates fall as the overall population density rises. Examples include diseases and predation.
- **Density-independent factors** are involved when death rates do not change with an increase or decrease in population density. Examples include temperature extremes, floods, and fires.

Specific challenges and current efforts involved in conserving biodiversity

- **Introduced species** pose challenges for all native populations and communities. Island species are particularly vulnerable, as the Hawaiian islands have demonstrated (for example, the negative impacts from cattle, goats, sheep, pigs, alien grasses, shrubs, and trees have eliminated half [70 of 140 species] of all native Hawaiian bird species).
- Pressures from human development, resource extraction, and human population growth are speeding the rate of environmental change and altering habitats across the planet.
- The creation of national parks, followed by ecotourism, helps preserve biodiversity but cannot prevent all species extinction. Fundamental human behavior change with regard to energy and resource consumption needs to be taken more seriously to prevent further erosion of Earth's biodiversity.
- **Climate change** now poses an additional challenge. Traditionally people have sought to conserve threatened species by preserving and managing new tracts of land designated as protected areas. However, global climate change now is a threat, with temperature increases and shifting rainfall patterns causing areas *within* these protected areas to become unsuitable for the species they were meant to protect. For example, as global temperatures rise, island biota such as Hawaii's bird

populations are especially vulnerable, as mosquitoes and malaria are increasingly able to move upslope toward protected wildlife refuges.

Chapter 4: Species Interactions and Community Ecology

YOU MUST KNOW

- The major types of species interactions and how they compare.
- How to characterize feeding relationships and energy flow in the construction of trophic levels and food webs.
- The distinguishing characteristics of keystone species.
- Ecological succession and how communities can change over time.
- How to predict the potential impacts of invasive species, including solutions to biological invasions.
- Restoration ecology's goals and methods.
- The defining characteristics and significance of the major terrestrial biomes.

The major types of species interactions and how they compare

- **Competition** occurs when multiple organisms seek the same limited resource.

  - **Intraspecific:** competition between members of the same species.
  - **Interspecific:** competition between two or more different species. An example in the Illinois River of interspecific competition is the silver carp and bighead carp species (both invasive) competing with native fish populations for plankton, as all use this same food source.
  - **Fundamental niche:** the full niche of a species.
  - **Realized niche:** the niche that is displayed when, as a result of competition, an individual plays only part of its role or uses only part of its resources.
  - **Resource partitioning:** the evolutionary process by which species adapt to competition by using slightly different resources and/or using them in slightly different ways. For example, one bird species evolving behavior to become more active in the evening and another species becoming more active in the morning.

▪ **Predation** is the process by which individuals of one species hunt, capture, kill, and consume individuals of another species—the prey. Predation is a primary organizing force of community ecology (feeding relationships) and sometimes drives **cyclical population dynamics** (increases and decreases in the population of one species driving increases and decreases of another, such as hare and lynx population cycles).

▪ **Parasitism** is the interaction where one species derives benefit by harming (but usually not killing) another species; the parasitic sea lamprey (an invasive species in the Great Lakes) is an example, as they parasitize native lake trout.

▪ **Mutualism** is the interaction where both species benefit, each providing some resource or service that the other needs, for example, honeybees and flowering plants, and terrestrial plant species such as legumes and *Mycorrhizae,* a fungus.

▪ **Commensalism** is the interaction where one species benefits and the other species is unaffected, for example, remora and shark.

▪ **Herbivory** occurs when animals feed on plants; this is one of the most common species interactions in ecosystems.

How to characterize feeding relationships and energy flow in the construction of trophic levels and food webs

▪ Energy is transferred in food chains between trophic levels according to the **10% law,** with each trophic level containing just one-tenth the energy of the trophic level below it. Lower trophic levels generally contain more energy than high trophic levels.

Figure 4.11 Pyramid Relationship of Energy and Biomass

▪ **1st trophic level** contains producers, or autotrophs (those species capable of photosynthesis).

▪ **2nd trophic level** contains **primary consumers,** or herbivores.

▪ **3rd trophic level** contains **secondary consumers,** or carnivores.

▪ **4th trophic level** contains **tertiary consumers,** or top carnivores.

▪ **Detritivores** (millipedes, soil insects) scavenge dead organisms, feces, dead leaves, and wood, converting organic matter to inorganic compounds.

- **Decomposers** (bacteria, fungi) break down nonliving matter into simpler constituents, recycling nutrients back to the producers.
- **Biomass** refers to the collective mass of organic material making up a living organism(s). When quantitatively determining biomass for ecological studies, it is the total dry weight of the organism(s).
- Lower trophic levels always contain the most energy and generally contain the most biomass and number of individuals.
- A pyramid-shaped diagram best describes the energy flow between trophic levels in a community. The pyramid pattern illustrates why eating at lower trophic levels (vegan or vegetarianism) decreases a person's ecological footprint—because when we eat animals, we use up far more energy per calorie than we gain by eating plants directly.

The distinguishing characteristics of keystone species

- **Keystone species** have strong or wide-ranging impacts in their ecosystem, far out of proportion to their actual abundance. The removal of a keystone species from its community will have major ecological consequences.
- **Top predators** (wolves, sea stars, sharks, sea otters) are frequently considered keystone species and can promote **trophic cascades** (keeping species in intermediate trophic levels in check, while promoting species in lower trophic levels).
- Sea otter, sea urchin, and kelp forest relationships in the Pacific Northwest were extensively studied in the 1990s. Decline of the keystone sea otters (hypothesized to be caused by recent population increases in *Orcas,* killer whales) has set off a trophic cascade: Otters decrease and herbivorous urchins increase because their predators are fewer, and kelp forests decline due to overgrazing.
- Another example of a trophic cascade was the U.S. government's removal, by bounties, of wolves and mountain lions in the early 20th century. This resulted in a widespread explosion of the deer population. Large deer populations then overgrazed forest floor vegetation, eliminating tree seedlings and leading to major changes in forest structure across the United States.
- **"Ecosystem engineers"** physically modify the environment shared by community members (beavers, prairie dogs, ants, zebra, and quagga mussels).

Ecological succession and how communities can change over time

- **Ecological succession** refers to the transition in species composition that takes place in a given area over ecological time.
  - In **primary succession,** plants and animals gradually invade a region that is devoid of life and where soil has not yet formed, such as after a glacier retreats or after volcanic lava/ash spreads across a landscape. **Pioneer species** (lichens) begin this soil-building

process, eventually allowing grasses, shrubs, and the trees associated with the region's climax community to increase.

- In **secondary succession,** the existing community has been cleared or disturbed by fire, landslide, or farming; however, the soil is intact. An abandoned farm field will eventually return to a more diverse community of grasses, shrubs, and trees if no further disturbance occurs.

Time

Secondary Succession Occurs After Environmental Disturbance

- Communities may undergo **phase** or **regime shifts,** involving irreversible change if environmental disturbance is severe enough. An example is the many coral reef communities that have experienced the loss of herbivorous keystone fish species (due to overfishing). These reefs are now overgrown with algae and may never shift back to the original, coral-dominated state.
- Today, across large areas of western North America, entire forests are undergoing conversions due to catastrophic fires driven by climate change and past management policies by the U.S. Forest Service.
- Communities are now viewed most accurately as temporary/fluid associations of individual species, each species responding independently to their own limiting factors, the complexities of introduced species arriving into the community, and other complex factors.
- Ecological studies after the Mount Saint Helens volcanic eruption in Washington (1980) are providing new insights into the complexities and unpredictable nature of succession. Biological communities appear to recover from disturbance in ways that are dynamic and highly dependent on chance, not the linear path from pioneer species to hardwood forests once predicted.
- Scientists predict that human disturbance, climate change, and the introduction of non-native species will continue to create wholly new communities that have not previously occurred in nature.

How to predict the potential impacts of invasive species, including solutions to biological invasions

- **Introduced species** are non-native species, introduced (accidentally or deliberately) into a new area, often spreading widely, rapidly becoming dominant, with the potential for interfering with a community's normal functioning.
- The Asian carp is a recent example of a *deliberate* introduction (introduced to help clean up infestations of algae and parasitic snails in southern catfish farms). Asian carp populations quickly expanded and moved up the Mississippi, Ohio, and Missouri Rivers and into the Illinois River, threatening the native fisheries of the Great Lakes.

Figure 4.16   Asian Carp Modify the Aquatic Communities they Invade

- The zebra mussel demonstrates the variety of unexpected economic and environmental impacts that can result with an *accidental* introduction.
  - After zebra mussels were accidently introduced in the 1980s from the ballast water of ships coming from seas in Central Asia, phytoplankton and small zooplankton declined (zebra mussels are filter feeders) in the Great Lakes and other aquatic ecosystems where they became established.
  - Larvae and juveniles of open-water fish then declined (they also depend on phytoplankton and zooplankton).
  - Littoral (shallow-water) fish increased as zebra mussel shells provide habitat structure and their feces provide nutrients for many benthic species.

- Overall, the zebra mussel invasion has cost Great Lakes economies hundreds of millions of dollars.

- Introduced species may become **invasive species** when limiting factors that regulate their growth are absent (no predators and/or fewer competitors) and their population numbers increase dramatically (for example, chestnut blight fungus, European grasses introduced to the American west, zebra and quagga mussels throughout most American waterways, and kudzu in the American south).

- Total eradication of invasive species (involving physical removal and/or applying toxic chemicals) is often so difficult that managers aim merely to control populations by limiting their spread or impact. *Prevention* of the original introduction of non-native species is the best solution to this challenging issue; however, this approach requires constant monitoring and study of ecological relationships in the environment, including the activities of humans.

Restoration ecology's goals and methods

- **Restoration ecology** is the study of the historical conditions present in ecological communities as they existed before human alteration.

- Restoration ecology's specific goals and methods include reestablishing a wetland's ability to filter pollutants or recharge groundwater (Florida Everglades restoration) and reestablishing native prairie vegetation by weeding out invasive species and introducing controlled burning to mimic fires that historically maintained the community (tallgrass prairie restoration).

The defining characteristics and significance of the major terrestrial biomes

- **Biomes** are the major regional complexes of similar biological communities, often recognized by the indicator plants and animals occupying each.

- **Climate,** especially precipitation and temperature, determines the plant life in each biome, which in turn determines the animal life. Major terrestrial biomes include the following.

  - **Temperate deciduous forest:** fertile soils, deciduous trees (oaks, maples), and precipitation spread evenly throughout the year.

Figure 4.21b Washington, D.C. Climatograph

- **Deserts:** very sparse rainfall, extreme temperatures (hot or cold), and all plants and animals demonstrating water conservation adaptations.
- **Temperate grassland (prairie):** marked by too little rainfall to support trees, but with fertile soils, occasional fires, and large grazing mammals.
- **Tropical rainforest:** great biodiversity growing under constant, warm temperatures and high rainfall, but with nutrient-poor and thin soils.
- **Tundra:** marked by permafrost, cold temperatures, and little rainfall, producing a landscape of lichens and low vegetation, with no trees.

Figure 4.26b   Tundra Climatograph

- **Boreal/coniferous forest (taiga):** dominated by cone-bearing plants; acidic, nutrient-poor soils; long, cold winters; and moderate precipitation.
- **Savanna:** tropical grassland marked by high temperatures and distinct rainy seasons, with grazing animals concentrated near water holes.

- Altitude increases can create changes of precipitation and temperature, analogous to latitude changes, producing biomes ranging from desert to tundra.
- Understanding the reasons why biomes occur where they do allows for ecological restoration, which strives to undo some of the negative effects of human impact.

Chapter 5: Environmental Systems and Ecosystem Ecology

> ## YOU MUST KNOW
>
> - The nature of Earth's natural systems and how feedback loops work to maintain planetary homeostasis.
> - The specific causes and effects of eutrophication.
> - How to fully define an ecosystem and evaluate the interactions of its living and nonliving entities, especially with regard to productivity.
> - The fundamentals of landscape ecology, GIS, and ecological modeling.
> - How to assess ecosystem services and their benefit to our lives.
> - The major biogeochemical cycles (C, N, P, and water), including the source, sink, and importance of each nutrient to all living things.
> - How human activities adversely affect biogeochemical cycles, and possible approaches for improved resource management.

The nature of Earth's natural systems and how feedback loops work to maintain planetary homeostasis

- Earth's environment consists of complex networks of interlinked systems. These **systems** consist of both physical and biological relationships interacting with one another through the exchange of energy, matter, and information. Earth's natural systems include processes that shape the landscape, affect climate, govern interactions between species and the abiotic entities around them, and cycle chemical elements essential for all life.
- When all these planetary systems are working together naturally (*without* the effects of human intervention), natural processes will move in opposing directions at equivalent rates so that their effects create a balance, a state known as **dynamic equilibrium.** This tendency of a system to maintain constant or stable conditions is referred to as **homeostasis** and is a critical process to normal functioning of organisms, communities, ecosystems, and the biosphere.
- The Chesapeake Bay estuary and the Mississippi River watershed are examples of two complex systems with many interrelationships. Their interconnected environmental problems demonstrate the complexity involved in the analysis of and solutions to these problems.

■ For centuries, the Chesapeake Bay oysters kept this estuary's waters clear by filtering nutrients and phytoplankton from the water column. However, by 2010, the oyster fishery was reduced to 1% by overharvesting, habitat destruction, and agricultural pollution from excess nitrogen and phosphorus fertilizers. These complex and interrelated problems resulted in many hypoxic "dead zones" throughout this vast estuary. Now, strict pollution budgets aim to reduce N and P inputs, combined with oyster restoration efforts, in an attempt to restore the Chesapeake Bay to its former economic and biological productivity.

Figure 5.3 Chesapeake Bay Watershed

■ **Hypoxia** (low dissolved oxygen) in the Chesapeake Bay's estuary, resulting from excessive N and P fertilizer use in the adjoining watershed, illustrates one result of these complex system interactions.

■ All systems consist of interacting components that generally involve feedback loops. A **negative feedback loop** occurs when a system's output acts as an input that then moves the system in the opposing direction, toward stabilization (most systems in nature involve negative feedback loops). These negative feedback loops contribute to homeostasis and the overall balance and functioning of Earth's systems. **Positive feedback loops** have the opposite effect. Increased output leads to increased input, leading to further increased output and destabilization of the system (exponential population growth and Arctic sea ice/glacial melting are two current examples).

■ Approaching environmental issues in terms of systems is important in understanding how to avoid disrupting the many complex and interrelated Earth processes and in how to mitigate the disruptions already present. Earth's unperturbed ecosystems use renewable solar energy, recycle nutrients, and are stabilized by negative feedback loops.

The specific causes and effects of eutrophication

■ **Eutrophication** is the process of increased nutrient (N and/or P) enrichment → producing algal blooms → followed by eventual microbial decomposition of this increased organic matter → finally resulting in low oxygen levels/hypoxia and the suffocation of aquatic life, including shellfish, fish, and aquatic invertebrates.

Figure 5.5   Excess Nitrogen and Phosphorus Cause Eutrophication in Aquatic Systems

■ Eutrophication of freshwater systems is frequently caused by increased P (in the form of PO_4); in marine systems, increased N (in the form of NO_3) tends to be the cause.

■ Hypoxic "dead zones" are increasing, with approximately 475 currently documented worldwide, including one that forms each year at the mouth of the Mississippi River. This Gulf of Mexico "dead zone" and the seasonal hypoxic conditions in the Chesapeake Bay estuary are examples of the most serious cases in the United States.

How to fully define an ecosystem and evaluate the interactions of its living and nonliving entities, especially with regard to productivity

- An **ecosystem** consists of all living organisms and the nonliving attributes (temperature, water, sunlight, etc.) that occur and interact in a particular area.

- In all ecosystems, *energy flows in a one-way direction* from sun to organic compounds made through photosynthesis by producers, and exiting back to the environment in the form of heat during cellular respiration.

- In contrast, *matter is recycled within ecosystems* during feeding relationships involving producers and consumers and ultimately back to the nonliving environment when an organism dies and decays.

- **Gross primary productivity (GPP)** is the assimilation of energy into biomass by autotrophs during photosynthesis. A portion of this biomass is used by the autotrophs to power their own metabolism during cellular respiration.

- **Net primary productivity (NPP)** is the energy/biomass that remains after respiration (R) and is available for consumption by heterotrophs/consumers.

- $NPP = GPP - R$

- Ecosystems vary in their **productivity** (the rate at which autotrophs convert energy to biomass). Coral reefs, tropical rainforests, and swamps/marshes have higher productivity than the open ocean and deserts (when comparing g $C/m^2/yr$).

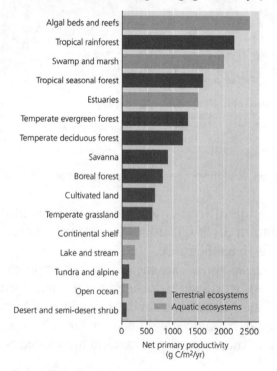

Figure 5.7 Net Primary Productivity for Major Ecosystem Types

The fundamentals of landscape ecology, GIS, and ecological modeling

- **Landscape ecology** approaches environmental problem solving on a broad, geographic scale that encompasses assessment of the multiple ecosystems involved. Landscape ecology deals with spatial patterns above the ecosystem level. This approach allows scientists to assess how landscape structure affects the abundance, distribution, and interaction of organisms. The current restoration of Chesapeake Bay's once-productive oyster industry is an example of a successful landscape ecology approach. It involves a temporary moratorium on oyster harvesting, construction of artificial reefs for young oyster larvae attachment, oyster aquaculture support, and avoidance of the introduction of non-native oysters.
- In any given landscape, there are often numerous ecosystem types and **ecotones** (transitional zones) consisting of **patches** spatially arrayed into a **mosaic** of habitats.
- **Conservation biology,** the study of the loss, protection, and restoration of biodiversity, must take into consideration all this habitat variety, particularly the fragmentation of habitat into small and isolated patches.
- **Geographic information system (GIS)** is a common tool for landscape ecologists, involving computer software that takes multiple types of data (geology, hydrology, vegetation, animal population, and human infrastructure) and combines them on a common set of geographic coordinates in order to more accurately assess environmental problems.
- **Ecological modeling** is the practice of constructing and testing models (simplified representations of complex natural systems) that aim to explain and predict how ecological systems function.
- Data from published scientific journals are used to establish the model's parameters. These assumptions are then used to predict the effects of different possible approaches to solving the problem.

How to assess ecosystem services and their benefit to our lives

- When ecosystems are undisturbed and functioning normally, they provide both goods (lumber, soil, fuel, metals, fiber, etc.) and **ecosystem services** (regulation of oxygen, carbon dioxide, temperature, precipitation, water supplies, etc.) essential to all life.
- Ecosystem services are the result of healthy ecological systems and the many negative feedback cycles that regulate and stabilize natural systems.

TABLE 5.1 Ecosystem Services

Ecological processes do many things that benefit us:

- ▶ Regulate oxygen, carbon dioxide, stratospheric ozone, and other atmospheric gases
- ▶ Regulate temperature and precipitation by means of ocean currents, cloud formation, and so on
- ▶ Protect against storms, floods, and droughts, mainly by means of vegetation
- ▶ Store and regulate water supplies in watersheds and aquifers
- ▶ Prevent soil erosion
- ▶ Form soil by weathering rock and accumulating organic material
- ▶ Cycle carbon, nitrogen, phosphorus, sulfur, and other nutrients
- ▶ Filter waste, remove toxins, recover nutrients, and control pollution
- ▶ Pollinate plant crops and wild plants so they reproduce
- ▶ Control crop pests with predators and parasites
- ▶ Provide habitat for organisms to breed, feed, rest, migrate, and winter
- ▶ Produce fish, game, crops, nuts, and fruits that people eat
- ▶ Supply lumber, fuel, metals, fodder, and fiber
- ▶ Furnish medicines, pets, ornamental plants, and genes for resistance to pathogens and crop pests
- ▶ Provide recreation such as ecotourism, fishing, hiking, birding, hunting, and kayaking
- ▶ Provide aesthetic, artistic, educational, spiritual, and scientific amenities

- ■ One of the most important ecosystem services is the cycling of essential nutrients in biogeochemical cycles.

The major biogeochemical cycles (C, N, P, and water), including the source, sink, and importance of each nutrient to all living things

- ■ The main factors of any biogeochemical cycle are the **reservoir** (place where materials are stored), the **flux** (rate at which materials move between reservoirs), the **source** (a reservoir *releasing more* materials than it accepts), and the **sink** (a reservoir *accepting more* materials than it releases). A model of the main components of a biogeochemical cycle is found below:

Figure 5.15 The Main Components of A Biogeochemical Cycle

- The **water cycle** affects all other cycles. The ocean is the main reservoir, holding 97% of all Earth's water; however, less than 1% is in a form readily usable (groundwater, surface fresh water, and rain). **Evaporation, transpiration, precipitation,** and surface **runoff** are the main processes determining the availability and location of Earth's water.
- The **carbon cycle** circulates carbon, the defining element of all organic compounds (carbohydrates, fats, and proteins). The photosynthetic process of autotrophs takes in CO_2 from the atmosphere, synthesizing these organic compounds. Plants are the major living carbon reservoir; however, sedimentary rock/fossil fuels are the largest fossil reservoir. CO_2 is returned to the atmosphere by the process of cellular respiration and the burning of fossil fuels.
- The **nitrogen cycle** moves nitrogen from the atmosphere through the living world. Nitrogen is an essential element required for making DNA, RNA, proteins, and enzymes.
  - The major reservoir of nitrogen (N_2) is in the atmosphere (nitrogen constitutes 78% of the atmosphere by mass); however, plants and animals cannot utilize this chemically inert form.
  - For nitrogen to become biologically available, **nitrogen fixation** ($N_2 \rightarrow NH_3$) must be carried out by symbiotic bacteria living in nodules of legumes (soybeans, peanuts). NH_3 then combines with H_2O to form NH_4^+ (**ammonification**). Other types of soil bacteria perform **nitrification**, changing NH_4^+ to NO_2^- and finally to NO_3^- (nitrates), which can be taken up by plants and subsequently consumed by heterotrophs.
  - **Denitrification,** which is carried out by other soil bacteria when organisms die, converts NO_3^- to N_2, thereby releasing nitrogen back into the atmosphere and completing the cycle.
- The **phosphorus cycle** is the only sedimentary cycle; phosphorus has no appreciable atmospheric reservoir. Because most P is bound up in rock and only slowly released, phosphorus is frequently a limiting factor for plant growth.

How human activities adversely affect biogeochemical cycles, and possible approaches for improved resource management

- Human activity affects every aspect of the **water cycle** through:
  1) deforestation, which intensifies surface runoff and erosion, reduces transpiration, and decreases infiltration, lowering groundwater tables.
  2) the emission of air pollutants, which changes the chemistry of precipitation.
  3) severe overdrawing of groundwater for drinking, irrigation, and industrial uses.
  4) damming rivers, slowing movement of water to the sea, resulting in increased evaporation and water loss from reservoirs.

- Human activity is affecting the **carbon cycle** through the burning of fossil fuels, which releases carbon dioxide and greatly increases the flux of carbon from the lithosphere to the atmosphere. Additionally, from cutting down forests, less vegetation results in less CO_2 being extracted from the atmosphere. Overall, the movement of CO_2 from atmosphere back to hydrosphere, lithosphere, and biosphere has not kept pace with *movement of CO_2 into the atmosphere,* resulting in the concerns behind today's global climate change and the highest CO_2 atmospheric reservoir the Earth has experienced in at least 1 million years.

- **Ocean acidification,** the process by which some of the excess CO_2 in the atmosphere is being absorbed by ocean water, is an additional concern of increasing atmospheric CO_2 levels. The lowering of ocean pH impairs the ability of corals and other shelled organisms to build exoskeletons of calcium carbonate and threatens the existence of coral reefs and many marine invertebrates.

- By learning how to synthesize ammonia (**Haber-Bosch process**) on an industrial scale, humans have effectively *doubled* the rate of nitrogen fixation on Earth, thereby increasing nitrogen's movement from the atmosphere to Earth's surface, overwhelming nature's denitrification abilities. When farming practices allow irrigation runoff and soil erosion, nitrogen (in the form of nitrates from synthetic fertilizers produced from the Haber-Bosch process) flows from farms into terrestrial and aquatic ecosystems. This leads to nutrient enrichment/pollution, eutrophication, hypoxia, and a greatly imbalanced **nitrogen cycle.**

- Humans are also affecting the natural **phosphorus cycle** by increasing amounts of this limiting factor in fresh water. Increases in phosphorus fertilizer use boost algal growth, also leading to eutrophication and hypoxic conditions.

- Tackling nutrient enrichment (CO_2, N, and P) will require diverse approaches because of our current heavy reliance on synthetic fertilizers in modern global agribusiness and on fossil fuels for energy. A *few* examples of possible approaches to control nutrient pollution in the Chesapeake Bay and Mississippi River watersheds are:

1) planting vegetation buffers around streams in the watershed to trap nutrient runoff.
2) restoring nutrient-absorbing wetlands along waterways.
3) increasing the practice of sustainable agriculture by reducing fertilizer use on farms and lawns with improved timing of fertilizer application.
4) improving technologies in sewage treatment plants to enhance N and P capture.
5) upgrading stormwater systems to capture runoff from roads and parking lots.

Chapter 11: Biodiversity and Its Conservation

YOU MUST KNOW

- How to characterize the scope of Earth's biodiversity.
- How to compare the natural background extinction rate with periods of mass extinction.
- How to evaluate the primary causes of biodiversity loss.
- The specific benefits of biodiversity.
- How to analyze the efforts to conserve threatened and endangered species.
- Specific examples of conservation efforts above the species level.

How to characterize the scope of Earth's biodiversity

- To date, of the 3–100 million species currently estimated by scientists, only 1.8 million species of plants, animals, fungi, and microorganisms have been described and named.

- Today, citizen science projects like Monarch Watch and the Christmas Bird Count, along with online data repositories like eBird and iNaturalist, have enlisted thousands of nonprofessional volunteers along with scientists in the field, adding to our knowledge of biodiversity worldwide.

- **Biodiversity** is a multifaceted concept including the variety of life across all levels of biological organization.

  - **Species diversity** focuses on the number or variety of *different* species in a particular region. **Species richness** (the number of different species) and **species evenness** (the relative abundance of different species) are important components to consider when evaluating species diversity.

  - **Genetic diversity** focuses on the differences in DNA composition between individuals of the *same* species, which provide the crucial raw material for adaptation to local conditions. Populations with low genetic diversity (cheetahs, bison, elephant seals) are more vulnerable to environmental change, disease, and ultimately to extinction. Low genetic diversity in our crop plants is also a prime concern today for humans.

  - **Ecosystem diversity** refers to the number and variety of ecosystems, biotic communities, or habitats within a specific area. A coral reef contains far more biodiversity than the same area of a monoculture cornfield. The Serengeti region of Africa holds a diversity of habitats including savanna, grasslands, seasonal wetlands, and rock outcroppings, contributing to the rich biodiversity in the area.

■ Some taxonomic groups—for example, insects—show much more species diversity (a high species richness) than others, such as birds and mammals.

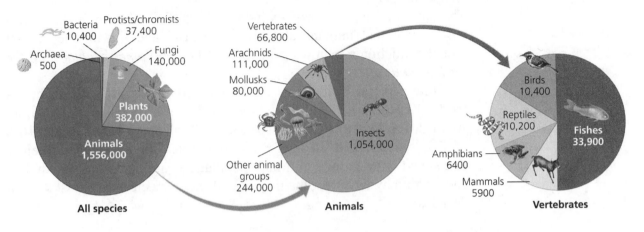

Figure 11.4 Uneven Species Distribution Among Taxonomic Groups: Insect Dominance

■ Measuring biodiversity is complex. Biodiversity is usually expressed in terms of species richness because this is the easiest component to measure. All estimates of biodiversity are incomplete because of the difficulty of estimating microbes, nematodes, fungi, protists, and soil-dwelling arthropods. Also, many areas of Earth still remain little explored (for example, tropical rainforests and ocean depths).

■ Biodiversity is unevenly distributed on Earth; however, species richness generally increases as one approaches the equator, a phenomenon known as the **latitudinal gradient.** This latitudinal gradient influences the species diversity of Earth's biomes, with tropical biomes showing more diversity than high-latitude biomes (boreal forests and tundra).

■ **Ecotones** are transition zones where different adjoining habitats overlap and intermix. These regions often tend to support a higher biodiversity than the individual habitats in isolation.

How to compare the natural background extinction rate with periods of mass extinction

■ **Extinction** occurs when the last member of a species dies and the species ceases to exist (for example, Costa Rica's golden toad, Mauritius's dodo, and North America's passenger pigeon). **Extirpation** occurs when a particular population of a species disappears from a given area, but not from the entire global population (for example, the black rhinoceros). Over time, extirpation is a process that often leads to extinction.

■ Extinction occurs naturally, at a very slow rate over geologic time. Paleontologists estimate that roughly 99% of all species that ever lived are now extinct. **Background rates of extinction** are currently estimated for mammals and marine animals to be one species vanishing per year for every 1–10 million species.

■ During Earth's five mass extinction episodes, extinction rates rose far above this background rate, often eliminating between 50% and 90% of all species per episode.

■ The current (sixth) mass extinction is different from all previous episodes in that humans are now the causal agent, with the current global extinction rate now estimated at *100–1000 times greater than the background rate.*

■ The International Union for Conservation of Nature (IUCN) maintains the **Red List,** an updated list of species facing high risks of extinction. As of 2019, 25% of mammal species, 40% of amphibian species, 16% of fish species, and 14% of all bird species on Earth are currently threatened with extinction. Many populations are declining worldwide, and Earth may have lost the majority of these species in the last several decades.

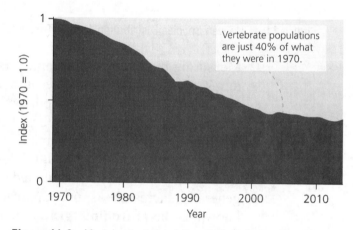

Figure 11.9 Vertebrate Animal Populations in Decline Worldwide

How to evaluate the primary causes of biodiversity loss

■ Five primary causes of population decline and species extinction have been identified by scientists: habitat loss, invasive species, pollution, overharvesting, and climate change. Each of these is further intensified by human population growth and increase in per capita consumption of resources.

■ Human disturbance of ecosystems and landscapes creates winners and losers among the world's plants and animals. "Winning species" tend to be generalists, able to fill many niches and tolerate disturbance (for example, the house mouse). In contrast, "losing species" tend to be specialists, rely on specific resources, and are very vulnerable to extinction (for example, Siberian tigers and pandas).

■ **Habitat loss** is the single greatest cause of biodiversity loss. Habitats are lost by outright destruction, moderate alteration, and, most frequently, **habitat fragmentation.** Farming, logging, and road building intrude into forested habitats, breaking up a continuous forest expanse into an array of fragments or patches.

■ Habitat loss affects all the world's biomes and is the primary source of decline for 80% of threatened mammals and birds.

■ Native American prairie biomes have been almost completely converted to agriculture (<1% remain), resulting in the extirpation of 82–99% of grassland birds. More than half of Earth's temperate forests, grasslands, and shrublands were converted by 1950.

Figure 11.15 Human Impact and Habitat Loss in World's Biomes

■ Globally, grasslands and forests of all biomes are experiencing the greatest habitat loss.

■ **Invasive species** are non-native species that thrive in areas where they are introduced, outcompeting, preying on, or otherwise harming native species (examples include the zebra mussel, Asian longhorn beetle, Asian carp, and European starling). Species native to islands are especially vulnerable to invasive species.

■ **Pollution** (air pollution, water pollution, and agricultural pollution from heavy metals, endocrine disrupters, oil, and other chemicals) is a substantial threat, although less significant in its effects than are habitat loss and invasive species. The once-abundant monarch butterfly has undergone dramatic declines due to herbicides, pesticides, and habitat loss along its long migration route.

■ **Overharvesting** today poses a threat for some top predators such as the K-selected African elephant and Siberian tiger, and also the r-selected shark species. To prohibit overharvesting, many governments have passed endangered species legislation and attempted to reduce **poaching** (the illegal killing of wildlife for meat and body parts).

- **Global climate change** affects biodiversity everywhere, not just in discrete locations. Organisms are being forced to shift their geographic ranges, and many (especially plants) are unable to move poleward fast enough. In the Arctic, where warming has been greatest, thawing ice is hindering the polar bear's ability to hunt seals.

- Scientists predict that a rise in global temperature of 1.5–2.5°C could put 20–30% of Earth's biodiversity at risk of extinction.

- Reasons for the decline of a population or species can be challenging to determine because of the many complex factors working together. A current example is the worldwide collapse of amphibian populations, as recent studies implicate habitat destruction, chemical pollution, fungal disease, invasive species, and climate change.

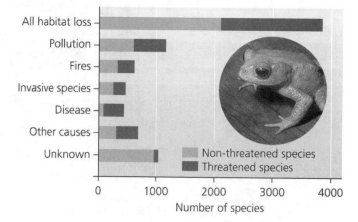

Figure 11.19   The World's Amphibians are Vanishing

The specific benefits of biodiversity

- Biodiversity provides the following:
  - **ecosystem services** that humans cannot replicate, including food, fuel, fiber, and shelter. Also, intact forests provide clean air, water, and a hydrologic buffer against flooding and drought. All of these ecosystem services are necessities that humans would need to pay for if nature did not provide them naturally.
  - **enhanced food security.** Currently, we get 90% of our food from just 15 crops and 8 livestock species, as compared to the approximately 7000 plant species and several thousand animal species in past history. Therefore, maintaining genetic diversity in our existing crops is essential.
  - **enhanced stability and resilience,** that is, the ability of ecosystems and communities to withstand the disturbance. Some species are more influential than others in an ecosystem's stability, and these

are often keystone species and/or top predators. Removal of keystone species, such as lions and leopards on the Serengeti or wolves, mountain lions, and grizzly bears in Yellowstone National Park, can significantly alter an ecological system with consequences that multiply as they cascade down the food chain (trophic cascade). These changes can then increase herbivore populations and dramatically decrease the natural vegetation in an area.

■ **valuable drugs and medicines** for humans (for example, the Pacific yew producing anti-cancer Taxol and *Cinchona* species producing the anti-malarial agent quinine).

■ **economic benefits** through tourism and recreation, particularly for tropical developing countries that have impressive species diversity.

■ an outlet for human's instinctive "love for nature" (**biophilia,** the term developed by Harvard professor emeritus E. O. Wilson).

How to analyze the efforts to conserve threatened and endangered species

■ **Conservation biology** is the scientific discipline devoted to understanding the factors that influence the loss, protection, and restoration of biodiversity.

■ **The Endangered Species Act (ESA),** passed in 1973, is the prime piece of legislation protecting biodiversity in the United States. This act forbids actions that destroy endangered species or their habitats and also forbids trade in products made from endangered species. The most notable successes of the ESA have been the comeback of the peregrine falcon, brown pelican, and bald eagle following the ban on the pesticide DDT; however, some opponents feel that the ESA values species over jobs. For example, in the Pacific Northwest, the northern spotted owl and marbled murrelet have slowed timber harvesting in the old-growth forests where these species live.

■ **The Convention on International Trade in Endangered Species of Wild Fauna and Flora (CITES)** protects endangered species by banning the international transport of organisms or their body parts. The 1990 global ban on the ivory trade is considered the biggest accomplishment of CITES to date, protecting both African elephants and rhinos.

■ The **Convention on Biological Diversity** (1992) has helped African countries achieve economic benefits from ecotourism at wildlife preserves such as Serengeti National Park. However, the Convention did not reach its 2010 goal of achieving a significant reduction of biodiversity loss. This has resulted in new goals being established for 2020, including cutting the loss of habitat by 50% and restoring at least 15% of all degraded landscapes.

■ Modern recovery strategies include **captive breeding** (California condor) and **reintroduction programs** (gray wolf to Yellowstone National Park). The newest approach involves investigating the potential of **cloning** endangered species.

- **Forensic DNA analysis** is now able to identify a species and its specific geographic region of origin. For example, recent research involving confiscated African elephant ivory has revealed the specific geographic areas where elephants are poached and the extensive crime network and countries involved in threatening this species.

Specific examples of conservation efforts above the species level

- Protecting communities and ecosystems is currently more challenging than protecting individual species because without protecting habitat, protecting endangered and threatened species does little good.
- **Umbrella species** (for example, the Serengeti's lions and wildebeest) are large species that roam great distances; they are often the focus of current conservation efforts because protecting them translates into protecting many species.
- **Flagship species** are large charismatic species used to promote biodiversity conservation (for example, the World Wildlife Fund's panda).
- **Parks and protected areas** set aside to remain undeveloped help to conserve habitat, communities, ecosystems, and landscapes. Currently, 15% of Earth's land area is in various types of parks, preserves, and wilderness areas. The Serengeti National Park and Maasai Mara National Reserve are two of the world's largest and most celebrated national parks.
- **Biodiversity hotspots** have been organized around geographic areas that support a great number of endemic (native/found nowhere else) species. To qualify, an area must have already lost 70% of its habitat as a result of human impact, be at risk of losing more, and must harbor at least 1500 endemic plant species (for example, Hawaiian Islands, Madagascar, Brazil).
- **Ecological restoration** attempts to mitigate the effects of environmental degradation, focusing on reestablishing basic processes (the cycling of nutrients and the flow of energy) that make an ecosystem function, along with bringing back the original population of plants and animals (for example, Illinois tallgrass prairie, Florida Everglades, Southeastern longleaf pine forests).
- **Community-based conservation** efforts are now being seen as the "key" to protecting global biodiversity because these efforts draw ecotourism, support local economies, and empower residents toward sustainable management of their local environment. East Africa's initiatives with the Masaai and other people of the region are positive examples of community-based conservation attempting to reverse the dramatic declines of endangered African wildlife. Tourist dollars and wildlife management authority have begun to be transferred to local villages and co-managed with Kenya Wildlife Service and international NGOs. It has become clear that in order to conserve animals and

ecosystems, the local people need to be stewards and feel invested in conservation.

■ One-fourth of the world's protected areas are now being managed using community-based conservation. In a world of rising human population and consumption, sustaining biodiversity will require locally based management that sustainably meets people's needs.

Chapter 12: Forests, Forest Management, and Protected Areas

YOU MUST KNOW

- The main ecological and economic contributions of forests.
- The history and current scale of global deforestation.
- The approaches to sustainable forest management in relation to fire, pests, and current global climate change.
- The major federal land management agencies and the lands they manage and protect.
- The various types of parks and protected areas.
- How to evaluate challenges for the effectiveness of parks and protected areas.

The main ecological and economic contributions of forests

■ Forests currently cover 31% of Earth's land surface.

■ The major forest types are boreal forests (primarily conifers of Canada, Scandinavia, and Russia), tropical rainforests, temperate deciduous forests, temperate rainforests, and tropical dry forests.

■ Because forests are ecologically complex, they provide many niches (canopy, subcanopy, understory, and snags) for organisms; forests are thus some of the richest ecosystems for biodiversity. As forests change over time through succession, the species composition of trees also changes, with old-growth forests containing more biodiversity than younger forests.

■ Forests supply us with many vital **ecosystem services** such as soil stabilization, flood prevention (through the slowing of rainfall's runoff), recharge of aquifers, water purification of streams and rivers (by acting as pollutant filters), moderation of precipitation patterns and climate (through photosynthesis and transpiration processes), enriched topsoil (by returning organic matter in the form of litter to soil), and carbon storage (in the form of organic matter produced through photosynthesis).

- **Carbon storage** (carbon sequestration) is now considered one of the most important ecosystem services because of its connection to global climate change. Carbon dioxide (taken in by all plants during photosynthesis and chemically changed into organic compounds) is the primary greenhouse gas contributing to global climate change. The more forests we preserve or restore, the more carbon (in the form of carbon dioxide) that can be kept out of the atmosphere, thus limiting climate change. When plant material is burned or when plants die and decompose, carbon dioxide is released. Therefore, when forests are destroyed, we contribute further to climate change. Forest destruction currently accounts for 17% of the world's greenhouse gas emissions.
- Forests provide many **economically valuable resources** such as medicines, dyes, fibers, food, and wood. Today, approximately 30% of all forests are designated for timber production.

The history and current scale of global deforestation

- **Deforestation,** the clearing and loss of forests, has been driven in nearly equal proportions by (1) farming, ranching, and mining, (2) logging, (3) slash-and-burn farming, and (4) wildfire. Currently, forest loss is greatest in the tropical forests of Central and South America, Africa, and Indonesia.
- Deforestation fueled the growth of the United States westward. Today there is very little **primary forest,** or **old-growth forest** (natural forests undisturbed by humans or natural disasters in 200 years or more), remaining in the lower 48 U.S. states. **Secondary-growth forests** (forests that have grown back from secondary succession once land has been cleared or cut) have smaller trees and lower species composition than original forests. The species composition, structure, and nutrient balance of a secondary forest are markedly different from the primary forest it replaced (smaller, younger trees, and less nutrients stored in trees' biomass).
- Developing nations, in need of economic revenue, are granting **concessions** (the right to extract a resource) to multinational corporations, which clear-cut forests to sell the wood and wood products. For example, throughout Southeast Asia and Indonesia today, primary forest clearing has been used to establish tree plantations of oil palms (palm oil is used in snack foods, soaps, and cosmetics, and also as a biofuel). Few animals live in oil palm monocultures, so destruction of primary forests means a staggering loss of biodiversity in these countries.

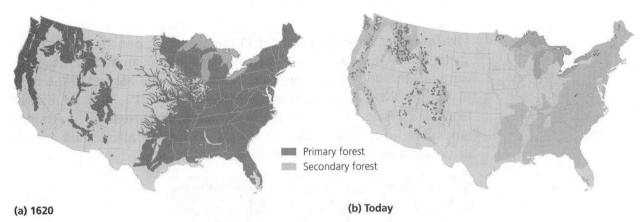

(a) 1620

(b) Today

Primary forest
Secondary forest

Figure 12.8 Areas of Primary Forest Have Been Dramatically Reduced in the U.S.

- Solutions to deforestation are emerging slowly.

  - **Conservation concessions** are a type of concession in which a conservation organization buys a concession and uses it to *preserve* the forest rather than cut it down.
  - **Carbon offsets** curb both deforestation and climate change. Wealthy industrialized nations pay poorer developing nations to conserve forests. In the international cap-and-trade system, the developing country gains income while the industrialized nation receives carbon credits to offset its emissions.
  - **Debt-for-nature swap** is an approach in which a conservation organization raises money and offers to pay off a portion of a developing nation's debt in exchange for that nation setting aside reserves, funding environmental education, and improving management of protected areas. The United States participates in this program through its 1998 Tropical Forest Conservation Act, forgiving Indonesia $30 million of debt in return for protecting the forested areas that are home to the Sumatran tiger and other species.

The approaches to sustainable forest management in relation to fire, pests, and current global climate change

- **Silviculture** is the professional practice of forest management. Forests are a potentially renewable resource *if* they are managed sustainably and not exploited too rapidly.
- **The U.S. Forest Service,** established in 1905, set aside a **national forest system,** which today covers over 8% of U.S. land area. This is public land set aside to grow trees, produce timber, protect water quality and wildlife habitat, and also provide recreational opportunities in a **multiple-use** and **maximum sustainable yield** approach. In reality, however, timber production/harvest has most often been the primary use.

- **Maximum sustainable yield (MSY)** is a guiding principle of resource management that aims to achieve the maximum amount of resource extraction without depleting the resource from one harvest to the next. In forestry, MSY argues for cutting trees shortly after they go through their fastest stage of growth (at intermediate age), maximizing timber production over time. However, forest ecology is altered and species that depend on mature tree habitats are eliminated.

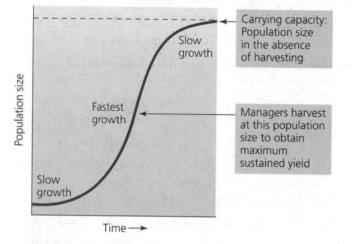

Figure 12.13   Maximum Sustainable Yield Maximizes Resources While Sustaining the Harvest in Perpetuity

- **Ecosystem-based management** attempts to manage the harvesting of resources in ways that minimize impact on the ecosystem and ecological processes. This is a more challenging approach to implement and allows succession to occur in some areas of the managed land.
- **Adaptive management** involves systematically testing different approaches and aiming to improve methods through time. This approach entails routinely monitoring the results of one's practices and adjusting them as needed.
- The vast majority (90%) of timber harvesting in the United States today takes place on *private* land owned by the timber industry and on the land owned by small private landowners.
- The U.S. timber industry focuses on **plantation forestry** in the South, where fast-growing tree species planted in **even-aged** monocultures dominate. This approach is quickly growing worldwide; however, ecologists view plantations more as crop agriculture than as a functional forest because biodiversity is lacking and susceptibility to the outbreak of pest species is common.

- Tree harvesting methods in today's forestry management plans include the following:
  - **Clear-cutting** is the most cost-effective harvesting method, but it has the greatest ecological impact because it involves cutting all the trees in an area, leaving only stumps.
  - In the **seed-tree approach,** small numbers of mature and vigorous seed-producing trees are left standing so they can reseed the logged area.
  - In the **shelterwood approach,** small numbers of mature trees are left in place to provide shelter for seedlings as they grow.
  - A **selection system approach** allows uneven-aged stand management because only some trees are cut at any one time; it is an approach unpopular with timber companies (more expensive) and loggers (more dangerous).
  - **Salvage logging** is the harvesting of trees for timber *after* a fire has burned a forest. A debate has arisen over whether the burned wood is more valuable left in place—for erosion control, wildlife habitat, and increased organic matter for soil. Recent studies have shown that salvage logging increases the risk of future severe fires.

- Past U.S. **fire policy** has been controversial, but scientists agree that there is a need to address the negative impacts of a century of fire suppression because many species and healthy ecosystems depend on fire. Catastrophic fires have resulted in the **wildland-urban interface** as a result of past fire suppression and increasing residential development along the edges of forested land. In 2018, the fast-moving Camp Fire destroyed the town of Paradise, California, and damaged several other communities, killing at least 85 people and destroying 19,000 buildings worth more than $16 billion.

- **Prescribed or controlled burns** clear away fuel loads, nourish the soil with ash, and encourage the vigorous growth of new vegetation. In the wake of major fires in California in 2003, **the Healthy Forests Restoration Act** was passed. This act encourages some prescribed burning; however, timber companies have mainly focused on the physical removal of small trees, underbrush, and dead trees (salvage logging). The negative effects of soil erosion and a lack of forest regeneration have often resulted from this approach.

- In 1976, the **National Forest Management Act** was passed, mandating that every national forest draw up plans for renewable resource management with more explicit emphasis placed on multiple use and maximum sustainable yield. In this **new forestry** approach, timber harvests have become more ecosystem-based, with attempts to recover plant and animal communities that have been lost or degraded in the past.

- ▪ **Sustainable forestry** is gaining ground, and **sustainable forest certification** (by the Forest Stewardship Council [FSC]) can now ensure the reliability and authenticity of these forest products by a "chain-of-custody certification" (meaning that all the steps from harvest to production have met strict standards). Specific attributes of FSC sustainable forestry include

  1) protection of rare species and sensitive areas,
  2) safeguarding of water resources from pollution and disease,
  3) control of soil erosion, and
  4) minimal use of pesticides.

- ▪ Slightly more than 6% of the world's forests managed for timber production are now FSC certified.

- ▪ **Global climate change** is now worsening wildfire risk by bringing warmer weather to North America and drier weather to western U.S. states. Fire also appears to be encouraging certain insect pests, particularly bark beetles, which are attracted to weakened trees. Millions of acres of western forest have been devastated, killing billions of conifer trees and leaving them as fuel for fires. As climate change interacts with pests, diseases, and management strategies, U.S. forests are being profoundly altered, with the original moist forests being replaced by drier woodlands, shrublands, or grasslands.

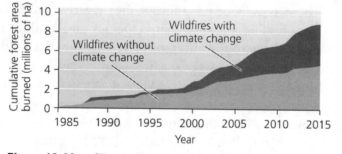

Figure 12.23a   Climate Change Drives Wildfires

The major federal land management agencies and the lands they manage and protect

- ▪ The **U.S. Forest Service** manages all federally owned **national forests.** This agency falls within the Department of Agriculture.

- ▪ The **National Park Service** (1916) manages all the **national parks** and seashores, monuments, historic sites, national recreation areas, and national wild and scenic rivers within the Department of the Interior.

- ▪ The **U.S. Fish and Wildlife Service** administers the **national wildlife refuges,** begun in 1903, and protects habitat for wildlife while also encouraging hunting and fishing. This agency falls within the Department of the Interior.

- ▪ The **Bureau of Land Management (BLM)** is the nation's largest landowner, managing 260 million acres spreading across 12 western states and consisting primarily of rangelands used for livestock grazing.

The various types of parks and protected areas

- **National parks, national forests, national wildlife refuges, and wilderness areas** form the central core of federally protected lands with an environmental connection in the United States.
- **Wilderness areas** are undeveloped lands initially set aside as a result of the Wilderness Act (1964), focusing on the preservation of undisturbed habitat, off-limits to development but open to hiking and other low-impact recreation. Wilderness areas have been established within national forests, national parks, and national wildlife refuges, and they are managed by the Bureau of Land Management (BLM).
- **Land trusts** are local or regional private nonprofit organizations that purchase land to preserve it in its natural condition. The Nature Conservancy, the world's largest land trust, uses science to select areas and ecosystems in the greatest need of protection.
- The **wise-use movement,** dedicated to protecting private property rights, opposes government regulation and promotes the transfer of federal lands to state and local control. This movement represents opposition to U.S. land protection policies and is especially prevalent in western states.
- Today 14.9% of the world's land area is designated for preservation in various types of parks, reserves, and protected areas. **Biosphere reserves** are tracts of land with exceptional biodiversity that couple preservation with sustainable development to benefit local people and are partly managed internationally by the United Nations (the Maya Biosphere Reserve, Guatemala, is an example). **World Heritage Sites** are another type of international protected area and are managed for their natural or cultural value (Serengeti National Park in Tanzania is an example).

How to evaluate the challenges for the effectiveness of parks and protected areas

- The current target for 2020 among nations under the **Convention on Biological Diversity** is for 17% of land area and 10% of marine and coastal areas to be set aside for protection. As climate change intensifies, biodiversity loss proceeds, and human population and consumption continue to grow, many scientists are calling for more ambitious targets.
- E. O. Wilson, esteemed scientist, is currently helping to lead the campaign for one-half of Earth's area to be protected. Wilson and other scientists supporting the Half-Earth Project argue that "the only way to reverse the extinction crisis is through a conservation 'moon-shot'... to keep half the land and half the sea of the planet as wild and protected from human intervention."
- **Habitat fragmentation** is a central issue affecting wildlife in their protected areas today. Expanding agriculture, cities, highways, and other impacts routinely divide large, continuous expanses of habitat into small, disconnected ones in which many species cannot live. **Edge effects,** impacts that result because conditions along a fragment's edge are different from interior conditions, often are responsible for the

failure of a species to breed or for increased predator pressure. Many bird species that thrive in the interior of forests may fail to reproduce near the edge of fragments (for example, North America's temperate deciduous wood thrush).

- A 2015 research study has concluded that 70% of global forests now lie within 1 km (0.62 mi) of an edge, indicating the increased potential for the direct influence of humans, the incursion of non-forest species, and the modification of forest microclimates.

- **Island biogeography theory,** developed by E. O. Wilson and Robert MacArthur in 1963, explains how species come to be distributed in "habitat islands." The theory predicts an "island's" species richness, involving immigration and extirpation rates, based on the island's size and its distance from the larger/main reservoir of the species located in the unfragmented environment.

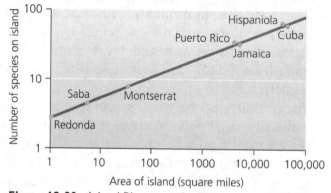

Figure 12.30 Island Biogeography Theory: Effect of Island Size on Species Richness

- Today, the *size* and *placement* in the landscape of protected areas are central issues in biodiversity conservation and protected area designation. Nicknamed the **SLOSS** ("single large or several small") **dilemma,** the question is whether it is better to make reserves large in size and few in number, or many in number but small in size. Wildlife corridors (protected land connecting fragmented "islands") may be one solution.

- In spite of worldwide efforts to increase the number of designated protected areas, global climate change now threatens to undo this investment. Species we had hoped to protect in parks may, in a warming world, become trapped in them. High-elevation and high-latitude species are most at risk from climate change because there is nowhere for them to go once a mountaintop becomes too warm or when an ice floe melts.

- In summary, in a landscape of increasing fragmented habitats, some organisms may be unable to travel from one fragment to another. In theory, connections between fragments (wildlife corridors) encourage gene flow and provide more habitat that will promote healthy populations. However, in response to the challenges of deforestation, fragmented habitats, and climate change, conservation biologists are now looking *beyond parks and protected areas* as they seek solutions for saving biodiversity.

Multiple-Choice Questions

1. Which statement best describes energy transfer in a food web?
   - (A) Energy moves from autotrophs to heterotrophs to decomposers, which convert it to usable form, which producers use again.
   - (B) Energy is transferred to consumers, which use it to synthesize food.
   - (C) Energy from producers is converted to oxygen, thus supporting consumers.
   - (D) Energy from the sun is stored in green plants and transferred to consumers through herbivory.

Use the graph below to answer questions 2–4.

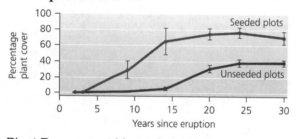

Plant Recovery at Mount Saint Helens

2. In the 30 years after the volcanic eruption of Mount Saint Helens, the data show that
   - (A) unseeded plots demonstrate primary succession.
   - (B) seeded plots demonstrate secondary succession.
   - (C) unseeded plots demonstrate that even a few organisms survived this natural disaster.
   - (D) seeded plots have twice the percentage of plant cover when compared to unseeded plots.

3. The approximate percent change in plant cover in seeded plots between 10 and 15 years after eruption was
   - (A) 100%.
   - (B) 30%.
   - (C) 15%.
   - (D) 1%.

4. Mount Saint Helens is an example that best demonstrates
   - (A) the complexity and unpredictable nature of ecological succession.
   - (B) that pioneer species are always lichens and mosses.
   - (C) the predictability of primary succession.
   - (D) how secondary succession progresses.

Use the figure below to answer questions 5 and 6.

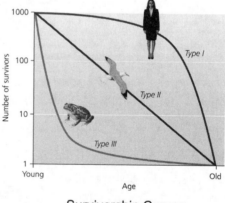

Survivorship Curves

5. The survivorship curve diagram shows that organisms that are Type III
   - (A) have high mortality when young.
   - (B) have high mortality when old.
   - (C) have a large number of offspring.
   - (D) have very few offspring that survive.

6. A polar bear would most likely show characteristics of
   (A) a Type I curve.
   (B) a Type II curve.
   (C) a Type III curve.
   (D) none of these curves.

7. When environmental conditions change, populations that are *most* vulnerable to extinction are
   (A) populations that have reached their carrying capacity.
   (B) large populations of small individuals living in urban areas.
   (C) large populations of medium-sized individuals living in rural areas.
   (D) populations of species that are specialized with regard to needed resources.

8. The climatographs of the tundra and desert biomes both
   (A) lack trees.
   (B) have relatively low precipitation on an annual basis.
   (C) lack birds as the dominant consumer.
   (D) have seasonally low temperatures.

9. A trophic cascade is the effect of ____ on ____.
   (A) flooding; terrestrial ecosystems
   (B) tertiary consumers; the abundance of primary consumers
   (C) producers; first-level consumers
   (D) top predators; one another

10. Eutrophication processes that have taken place in the Gulf of Mexico and other marine locations are caused primarily by
    (A) an overabundance of algal growth.
    (B) nitrates from agricultural applications.
    (C) pesticides from modern agriculture.
    (D) low oxygen levels resulting from decomposition.

11. Which of the following is an example of a positive feedback loop?
    (A) an increase in predators, resulting in fewer prey
    (B) the melting of Greenland's glaciers, resulting in sea level rise and continental flooding
    (C) the melting of Arctic sea ice, resulting in increased solar radiation absorption, and more sea ice melting
    (D) an increase in prey, resulting in an increase of decomposers

12. A marshland that contains elements of both the forest and a coastal marsh is called
    (A) an abiotic system.
    (B) an open system, exchanging nutrients.
    (C) an ecotone.
    (D) a closed system, maintaining all nutrients.

13. Island biogeography theory, developed by E. O. Wilson and Robert MacArthur in 1963, has many implications for
    (A) developing maximum biodiversity on remote islands around the world.
    (B) protecting the biodiversity of endangered island ecosystems.
    (C) planning wise use of island resources.
    (D) developing national parks of adequate size and with sufficient wildlife corridors.

14. Second-growth forests
    (A) are less abundant on Earth today than they were 200 years ago.
    (B) are forests that establish themselves after virgin timber has been removed.
    (C) are those forests in wilderness areas allowed to grow back after deforestation.
    (D) are forests whose timber has a second-rate economic value.

15. As scientists continue to study forest fragmentation, an important conclusion has been that
    (A) small forest fragments lose more species than large fragments.
    (B) large forest fragments contain more species and are more vulnerable to species loss.
    (C) forest fragments closer to one another lose more species overall.
    (D) climate change has neutralized forest fragmentation effects.

16. The normal functioning of an ecosystem requires that
    (A) energy be able to change forms, be recycled, and be decomposed.
    (B) energy be able to change forms, given that matter is not able to change forms.
    (C) energy be able to be recycled and matter be able to flow through biogeochemical cycles.
    (D) matter be able to be recycled and energy able to flow through ecosystems.

17. Assuming that the autotrophs in an ecosystem contain 500,550 kcal of energy, the third trophic level organisms could expect to contain approximately ___ of energy.
    (A) 50,055 kcal
    (B) 5005 kcal
    (C) 1/3 of 500,550 kcal
    (D) 2/3 of 500,550 kcal

18. The process of cellular respiration allows for the normal functioning of ecosystems by
    (A) taking in CO_2 and releasing $C_6H_{12}O_6$ and O_2 to other organisms.
    (B) taking in O_2 and releasing CO_2 and H_2O back to the environment.
    (C) taking in CO_2 and H_2O and releasing energy and glucose to organisms higher in the food chain.
    (D) taking in O_2 and releasing energy and glucose back to the environment.

19. Global climate change could be best thought of as a(n) _____ affecting a population's size.
    (A) logistical growth factor
    (B) exponential growth factor
    (C) density-dependent factor
    (D) density-independent factor

20. Introduced species can often be described as ___, outcompeting ___ species in a given region.
    (A) specialists; extinct
    (B) endemic; other
    (C) generalists; endemic
    (D) K-strategists; r-strategists

21. The specific biotic interactions of a Hawaiian honeycreeper, including the abiotic factors in this bird's high-altitude forest environment, are collectively referred to as its
    (A) trophic level.
    (B) consumption rate.
    (C) habitat.
    (D) ecological niche.

22. The energy content and biomass of ___ are the highest in any food web.
    (A) top carnivores
    (B) producers
    (C) small carnivores such as spiders and lizards
    (D) detritivores

23. The Everglades Restoration Plan in Florida
    (A) seeks to exterminate numerous invasive fish species and plants.
    (B) will restore natural levels of water flow by undoing numerous damming and drainage projects.
    (C) will result in serious depletion of drinking water supplies in south Florida.
    (D) will probably destroy much of the commercial fishing in the area.

24. Individuals of a single species fighting over access to a limited resource is an example of
    (A) intraspecific competition.
    (B) competitive exclusion.
    (C) resource partitioning.
    (D) interspecific competition.

25. The most productive ($g\,C/m^2/yr$) ecosystems in the world are
    (A) swamps and marshes.
    (B) boreal forests.
    (C) the open ocean.
    (D) temperate grasslands.

26. Humans have dramatically altered the movement of nitrogen from
    (A) producers to consumers through increased controlled burning.
    (B) oceans to soils.
    (C) soils to the atmosphere.
    (D) the atmosphere to aquatic systems on Earth's surface.

27. The rate at which biomass becomes available to consumers is termed
    (A) gross primary production.
    (B) ecosystem productivity.
    (C) cellular respiration.
    (D) net primary productivity.

Use the figure below to answer questions 28 and 29.

Species Richness and Forest Fragmentation Effects

28. Which of the following is the most likely hypothesis that scientists proposed for the results shown in the above graph?
    (A) Species richness tells scientists how many different species live in the study area.
    (B) Forest fragmentation promotes species richness.
    (C) Species richness does not correlate with forest fragmentation.
    (D) Species richness is adversely affected by forest fragmentation.

29. The approximate percent change in species richness from 1984 to 1991 was
    (A) an increase of 67%.
    (B) a decrease of 40%.
    (C) a decline of 67%.
    (D) a decline of 80%.

30. A population of grazing, deer-like mammals is found on a remote island in forested New Guinea. Which of the following information is most important in determining whether these mammals all belong to a single species?
    (A) that they share 99% of their physical traits
    (B) whether they can breed with one another
    (C) that the males all have similar antlers
    (D) whether the matings produce viable, fertile young

31. Wilderness areas
    (A) allow hunting as long as proper permits are acquired.
    (B) are biosphere reserves managed by UNESCO.
    (C) were set up under the wise-use and maximum sustainable yield approach.
    (D) are off-limits to all development but are open to low-impact recreation.

32. Introduced species can be deliberately or accidently introduced to a new environment. Many of these species become problematic because
    (A) they have large food supplies in a new habitat.
    (B) they have optimum climate conditions for growth.
    (C) few to no predators exist because they didn't evolve in the new habitat.
    (D) they have high birth and death rates, allowing them to overwhelm native species.

33. Forests provide many ecosystem services; however, the one that is receiving the most focus for climate change scientists is
    (A) protecting watersheds.
    (B) carbon sequestration.
    (C) habitat protection.
    (D) methane storage.

34. A population's growth rate is determined by knowing its
    (A) crude birth and crude death rates.
    (B) limiting factors.
    (C) crude birth rates, crude death rates, and migration rates.
    (D) survivorship curve type.

35. Zooplankton populations in Lake Erie and the Illinois River have declined by up to 70% since the arrival of zebra mussels because
    (A) zebra mussels block sunlight penetration into lakes and thus prevent zooplankton from photosynthesizing.
    (B) zebra mussels prey on zooplankton.
    (C) zebra mussels carry a parasite that kills zooplankton.
    (D) zebra mussels feed on cyanobacteria, which zooplankton need as a food resource.

36. In a New England white pine forest, the gross primary productivity (GPP) is 70 grams per square meter per day. Respiration loss is 30%. What is the net primary productivity for this forest?
    (A) 10 g/m^2/day
    (B) 21 g/m^2/day
    (C) 40 g/m^2/day
    (D) 49 g/m^2/day

37. A keystone species
    (A) is most often dominant in numbers in its ecosystem.
    (B) when removed, causes the removal of a trophic level in the ecosystem.
    (C) is most likely a top predator.
    (D) is most likely to be a producer on which all species ultimately depend.

38. Currently, one of the most serious human alterations of the water cycle is
    (A) due to deforestation and resulting erosion.
    (B) due to overdrawing groundwater for irrigation, industry, and drinking water.
    (C) due to damming waterways and the resultant disturbance to fish migrations.
    (D) due to burning fossil fuels and the resultant acid precipitation.

39. The largest reservoir of carbon in the carbon cycle is
    (A) located in the hydrosphere.
    (B) plant life.
    (C) sedimentary rock and fossil fuels.
    (D) located in the atmosphere.

40. "Dead zones" characteristic of the Chesapeake Bay estuary and many other locations worldwide most frequently result from
    (A) negative feedback loops.
    (B) invasive species of fish displacing native oysters.
    (C) a disrupted water cycle.
    (D) a disrupted nitrogen cycle.

41. Ocean acidification results from
    (A) increased use of artificial fertilizers.
    (B) increased pH due to high levels of carbonic acid.
    (C) lowered pH due to carbonic acid.
    (D) the increased availability of carbonate ions.
    (E) the dissolving of shelled organisms.

42. Earth's current biodiversity has most likely resulted from
    (A) high rates of mutation in the past millennium.
    (B) sympatric speciation.
    (C) current climate change pressures.
    (D) speciation minus extinction.

43. The *main* reason for the high species extinction rate that we see today is
    (A) global climate change.
    (B) invasive disease organisms.
    (C) overharvesting of Earth's valuable biodiversity.
    (D) habitat destruction.

44. The level of ecological organization described by ecologists when studying multiple interacting species that live in the same area is
    (A) the ecosystem.
    (B) energy flow.
    (C) the population.
    (D) the community.

Free-Response Question

At Hawaii's Hakalau Forest National Wildlife Refuge, biologists have been working for 25 years to understand the population change of native forest birds. Much of the region's forests had been cleared or fragmented for cattle ranching years earlier, and numerous introduced species had begun to thrive. In 1987, field biologists divided the refuge into 15 transect lines, with approximately 22 observation points along each transect. A standard method for estimating bird populations ("point counts" performed by stopping for an 8-minute bird count at each of the 22 observation points) was carried out. Data collection continued until 2012. Population density data for the Hawaiian 'apapane, a colorful Hawaiian forest bird, typify the data gathered at Hakalau Forest. Researchers used a statistical method to determine a "line of best fit" that most accurately represents trends in the data.

Population Estimates of 'Apapane in Hakalau Forest, 1987–2012

a) Like the endangered 'apapane, fully explain three *species characteristics* that would make other species particularly vulnerable to extinction.

b) Propose a hypothesis that these scientists used for this specific field investigation. Explain your reasoning.

c) Calculate the percent change of the Hawaiian 'apapane density between 1991 and 2012.

d) With continued forest protection, scientists predicted that the population of 'apapane would increase much more dramatically than it has. Explain one possible reason for the unexpected results that were found.

e) Describe three strengths of the experimental design for this field study at Hakalau Forest National Wildlife Refuge.

Environmental Decision Making

Chapter 6: Ethics, Economics, and Sustainable Development

YOU MUST KNOW

- Examples of how culture and worldview influence environmental decision making.
- The major approaches involved in environmental ethics.
- The principles of classical and neoclassical economics and their implications for the environment.
- The issues surrounding economic growth and the "limits to growth" economic models.
- How economic growth and progress can be measured, including the valuation of ecosystem services and full cost accounting.
- Specific ways in which individuals and businesses can help move our economic system in a sustainable direction.
- Examples of how sustainable development, which includes the "triple bottom line," is a growing global movement.

Examples of how culture and worldview influence environmental decision making

■ People with different worldviews and culture can study the same situation, yet draw dramatically different conclusions. Religion and spiritual beliefs are often among the most influential determiners.

■ In addition, political ideology, one's view on the proper role of government, and the level of scientific understanding in the culture also play critical roles in environmental decision making.

■ For example, two Costa Rican ranchers owning identical landholdings may make different management decisions: One might choose to receive government payments and conserve the forests on the land, whereas the other might opt to clear all the land for cattle grazing.

- Debates pitting economic arguments for harvesting forests (and other natural resources) versus ethical and environmental arguments for the preservation and restoration of forested lands (as is being actively practiced by Costa Rica's *Payment for Environmental Services* [PSA] program) are occurring in numerous places on Earth today. The PSA program recognizes four ecosystem services that forests provide:

  1) Watershed protection
  2) Biodiversity preservation
  3) Scenic beauty promoting recreation and ecotourism
  4) Carbon sequestration and the slowing of global warming

The major approaches involved in environmental ethics

- **Ethical standards** are influenced by the values and moral principles held by a person or culture and are the criteria that help differentiate right from wrong.
- Ethics and economics give us tools needed to pursue the triple bottom line: environmental, economic, and social sustainability.
- The value of something (a natural resource, such as clean water, or an animal, such as the whooping crane) can be **utilitarian** (i.e., it is valuable because it is *useful or beneficial* in some way), **intrinsic** (i.e., it is valuable *in itself*), or both.
- **Environmental ethics** is the application of ethical standards to relationships between people and nonhuman entities and involves issues of sustainability, environmental justice, and intrinsic values.
- An **anthropocentric** ethical view is one that is human-centered and often ignores the notion that nonhuman entities also have intrinsic value. An anthropocentrist evaluates the costs and benefits of actions solely according to their impact on people.
- A **biocentric** ethical view ascribes intrinsic value to all living things, including nonhuman life. A biocentrist might oppose an action if it would destroy or degrade plants and animals in an area, even if it would create jobs and generate economic growth.
- The **ecocentric** ethical view assesses actions in terms of their benefit or harm to the integrity of whole ecological systems, both living and nonliving. An ecocentrist might oppose an action after broadly assessing the potential effects on water quality, air quality, wildlife populations, and ecosystem services. This approach seeks to preserve the connections vital to the many complex ecosystem entities.
- The **preservation ethic** (preserving natural systems intact and for their own intrinsic value) was pioneered by **John Muir** in the early 20th century.
- The **conservation ethic** (advocating wise use of natural resources—a utilitarian standard) was pioneered by **Gifford Pinchot,** the first chief of the U.S. Forest Service.

- The damming of Hetch Hetchy Valley in Yosemite National Park, to provide drinking water for San Francisco in the early 1900s, was an early example of Pinchot's conservation ethic succeeding over Muir's preservation ethic.
- **Aldo Leopold's** "land ethic" called upon humans to include the environment in their ethical framework. By the mid-20th century, this framework had evolved toward an ecocentric outlook.
- In the 21st century, the concept of **environmental justice** has emerged, positing the importance of the fair and equitable treatment of all people with respect to environmental policy and practice, regardless of their income, race, or ethnicity.

  - Critics have characterized the attempts of Latino farm workers in California's San Joaquin Valley to achieve cleaner air (due to industrial agriculture's pesticide and feedlot emissions and windblown dust from eroding farmland) as important environmental justice issues.
  - Mountaintop coal-mining practices have long been the focus of environmental justice concerns for low-income white residents in the Appalachian region of the United States.
  - Uranium mining on Native American Navajo lands in the United States has also raised many of the same environmental justice issues.
  - The dumping of hazardous wastes by wealthy countries in poorer countries represents the international extent of environmental justice concerns.

- Questions of environmental justice, like questions of how to value ecosystem services, intertwine ethical issues with economic ones, and have become the primary focus of the modern drive for sustainable development.

The principles of classical and neoclassical economics and their implications for the environment

- **Economics** is the study of how people decide to use potentially scarce resources to provide goods and services in the face of demand for them.
- The **economy** (a social system that converts resources into **goods** and **services**) exists within the environment. The material inputs and the waste-absorbing capacity that Earth can provide to economies are ultimately finite; however, traditional economic schools of thought have viewed environmental resources as free and limitless, and wastes as something that can be endlessly exported and absorbed by the environment at no cost.
- The relationships among economic and environmental conditions are becoming widely recognized in the 21st century. In 2005, scientists with the Millennium Ecosystem Assessment concluded that 15 of 24 ecosystem services surveyed globally were being degraded or used unsustainably and that this degradation could easily disrupt national and

global economies. As a result, restoring ecosystem services is currently thought to be a prime avenue for alleviating a nation's poverty.

- **Classical economics,** a philosophy founded by Adam Smith, argues that self-interested economic behavior will benefit society as long as the behavior is constrained by law and private property rights, and is operating within a competitive marketplace.
- **Neoclassical economics** includes the psychological factors underlying consumer choices and considers supply, demand, costs, and benefits. Today's market systems operate largely in accord with the principles of neoclassical economics.
- **Cost-benefit analysis,** an approach of neoclassical economics, is used to evaluate public projects, assessing the capital costs that must be paid in order to gain benefits/value for a large group of people. If benefits exceed costs, the action goes forward; if costs exceed benefits, the project is not pursued. A major problem with this approach has been that monetary benefits are usually more easily quantified than environmental costs and benefits.
- Neoclassical economic models involve several assumptions that have often contributed to environmental degradation. These assumptions, briefly summarized, are the following:

  - Resources are infinite or substitutable; however, we live on a *finite* earth with *finite* resources.
  - Costs and benefits are **internal** (experienced by the buyer and seller alone); however, many transactions affect other members of society (those living "downstream" of the activity).
  - Future effects should be discounted; however, many environmental problems unfold *gradually* (resource depletion, pollution increase).
  - Growth is good; however, sociologists have coined a word for the way that consumption and material affluence often fail to bring contentment: *affluenza*.

The issues surrounding economic growth and the "limits to growth" economic models

- **Economic growth** is defined as an increase in an economy's production and consumption of goods and services.
- Today's mainstream economic theory assumes that growth is good and can continue forever; however, all matter and nonrenewable resources are finite.
- Today's mainstream economic theory often does not take into consideration **externalities** (costs affecting members of society other than the immediate buyer or seller). By ignoring these costs, economies often create a false idea of the true cost of a particular choice; for example, the air and water pollution generated from building and operating a factory are externalities.
- As human population and consumption continue to grow, it has become clear that natural resources are finite and that growth can continue only

when better technologies and approaches lead to improvements in *efficiency* of production.

■ The study by Meadows, Randers, and Meadows, *Limits to Growth: The 30-Year Update* (2004), shows that with policies aimed at sustainability (reducing human population growth, making resource use much more efficient, and placing greater emphasis on reusing and recycling resources), we can move toward a **steady-state economy** (an economy that neither grows nor shrinks, but actually mirrors natural ecological systems).

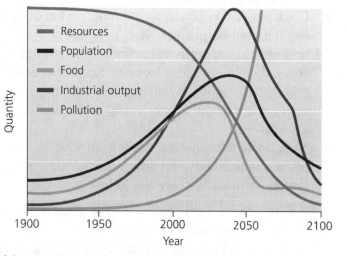

(a) Projection based on status quo policies

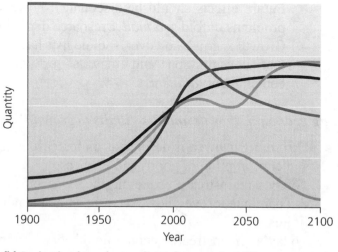

(b) Projection based on policies for sustainability

Figure 6.11a & b   Limits to Growth Modeling Projections

■ Every population in nature has a carrying capacity. **Ecological economics** maintains that civilizations, like natural populations, cannot permanently overcome their limits to growth and should not expect endless economic growth, but should support the principles of stability, steady state, and sustainability. This approach mirrors natural ecological systems. Today, many economists are concluding that future growth may be unsustainable if we do not *reduce* our demand for natural resources.

How economic growth and progress can be measured, including the valuation of ecosystem services and full cost accounting

■ **Gross Domestic Product (GDP)** is the total monetary value of final goods and services a country produces each year.

  ■ Because it doesn't account for **nonmarket values** (values not usually included in the price of a good or service such as ecosystem services), GDP is considered a poor measure of economic well-being.
  ■ GDP expresses all economic activity, both desirable and undesirable.
  ■ Pollution generally causes GDP to increase twice: once when a polluting substance is manufactured, and once when society pays for the cleanup.

■ **Genuine Progress Indicator (GPI)** differentiates between desirable and undesirable economic activity and is a more accurate indicator of a society's well-being. When compared with GDP, which has risen greatly, the GPI has remained largely flat for the past 35 years.

■ The GPI is an example of **full cost accounting** (also called true cost accounting) because it aims to account fully for all costs and benefits. Several U.S. states have begun using the GPI to measure progress and help guide policy. Costa Rica is also one of five nations working with the World Bank to implement full cost accounting.

■ Because the benefits of ecosystem goods and services lie chiefly in their nonmarket and intrinsic value, economists have historically failed to account for them.

■ In a major study (*Nature,* 1997), Robert Costanza estimated the value of the world's ecosystem services at more than $33 trillion ($153 trillion in 2019 dollars).

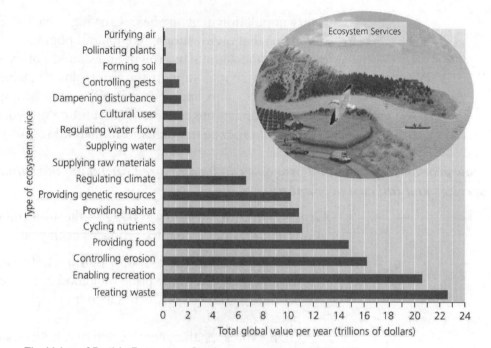

The Value of Earth's Ecosystem Services, estimated in 2007 dollars.

Data from Costanza, R. et al. 2014. Global Environmental Change.

- *The Economics of Ecosystems and Biodiversity* study published in 2010 describes the valuation of nature's economic worth as "a tool to help recalibrate (our) faulty economic compass" and attempts to set straight the essential importance of "biodiversity as the foundation of our economies."

Specific ways in which individuals and businesses can help move our economic system in a sustainable direction

- Consumer choice tied with improved environmental knowledge in the marketplace encourages businesses to pursue sustainable practices.
- **Ecolabeling** provides businesses with a powerful incentive to move toward more sustainable processes when these products are preferentially purchased. Examples include labeling tuna as "dolphin-safe," labeling recycled paper, and labeling organically grown food.
- Today, corporate sustainability has gone mainstream, with many of the world's largest corporations joining in. McDonald's, Intel, Toyota, Hewlett-Packard, IKEA, and Walmart are among those that are responding to sustainability concerns and modifying their operations through a variety of measures: using high levels of recycled materials in their manufacturing of new products, running alternative transportation programs for employees, increasing energy efficiency of their plants, reducing toxic emissions (including greenhouse gas emissions), and building green corporate headquarters using recycled materials, solar panels, green roofs, and enhanced insulation.

- Pearson Education, publisher of the Withgott/Laposata *Environment: The Science behind the Stories* textbook, is the first global media company to become climate-neutral, eliminating its net carbon emissions by installing solar and wind energy to power its facilities. Additionally, Pearson funds forest conservation efforts, has reduced its use of plastic and Styrofoam by 85% and 50%, respectively, and has been recognized by the Dow Jones Sustainability World Index for over a decade.
- **Socially responsible investing,** which entails investing in companies that have met criteria for environmental or social sustainability, is a fast-growing trend. Socially responsible investments of $11.6 trillion account for one-fourth of all U.S. investments in 2018.

Examples of how sustainable development, which includes the "triple bottom line," is a growing global movement

- **Sustainable development** centers on economic progress that maintains, not depletes, its resources for the future. The **triple bottom line** refers to a trio of goals made up of economic advancement, environmental protection, and social equity. Sustainable development occurs when there is significant overlap of social, economic, and environmental goals that have a long-range future in mind.
- Economic well-being and environmental well-being are compatible goals; however, some adjustments to the concept of unlimited growth must be made by using alternative ways of measuring growth. Recognizing the value of ecosystem services will play an essential role in environmental protection and conservation of resources.
- Monetary benefits of reducing greenhouse gas emissions to minimize climate change in the United States have been estimated to be between $235 and $334 billion (U.S. Environmental Protection Agency, 2015).

TABLE 6.2 U.N. Sustainable Development Goals

- End poverty in all its forms everywhere
- End hunger, achieve food security, and promote sustainable agriculture
- Promote health and well-being for all
- Ensure quality education for all
- Achieve gender equality and empower women and girls
- Ensure water and sanitation for all
- Ensure access to affordable, reliable, and sustainable energy sources
- Promote jobs and sustainable economic growth
- Build resilient infrastructure, promote sustainable industry, and foster innovation
- Reduce inequality within and among nations
- Make cities safe, resilient, and sustainable
- Ensure sustainable consumption and production
- Take urgent action to combat climate change and its many impacts
- Conserve marine resources
- Protect and restore terrestrial ecosystems and halt biodiversity loss
- Promote peaceful, inclusive, just institutions
- Renew partnerships for sustainable development

- **Sustainable Development Goals** were set forth by world leaders meeting at the United Nations in 2015; they describe 17 broad goals.
- Programs that pay for ecosystem services are one example of a sustainable development approach that seeks to satisfy a triple bottom line. Costa Rica's PSA program aims to enhance its citizens' well-being by conserving the country's natural resources, while compensating affected landholders for any economic losses.
- Valuation of ecosystem services, ecolabeling, ecotourism, corporate sustainability, and alternative means of measuring growth are all helping to bring economic and ethical approaches to bear on environmental protection and sustainable development.
- Growing evidence of climate change effects (Hurricane Sandy, coastal flooding in Miami, drought in the American Southwest) is providing the needed impetus to address climate change and true sustainable development.
- In summary, proponents of *strong sustainability* value the importance of natural capital (ecosystem services), insisting that human-made capital alone cannot substitute for natural capital and that we must not allow the natural capital of *essential* ecosystem services to be degraded and/or ultimately diminished.

Chapter 7: Environmental Policy: Making Decisions and Solving Problems

---

> ### YOU MUST KNOW
>
> - The nature of environmental policy and its societal context.
> - The role of science in creating environmental policy.
> - The institutions important to U.S. environmental policy.
> - A brief historical context for U.S. environmental policy, including several major U.S. environmental laws.
> - Specific approaches to creating environmental policy.
> - The major institutions involved with international environmental policy, including examples of major international treaties.

The nature of environmental policy and its societal context

- **Policy** is a tool for decision making and problem solving that makes use of information from science as well as values from ethics and economics.
- **Environmental policy** pertains to human interactions with the environment. Its aims are to promote human welfare and to protect natural systems by regulating resource use and pollution effects.
- Effective policy requires input from science, ethics, and economics. The 2015 landmark lawsuit *Juliana v. United States* is an attempt by 21 young Americans to test the legality of current U.S. policy on climate change. The lawsuit asserts that federal policies promoting fossil fuel use have violated the plaintiff's constitutional rights to life, liberty, and prosperity and have failed to protect essential natural resources. The lawsuit demands (1) that the courts order the federal government to stop subsidizing fossil fuels and (2) the swift drawdown of carbon dioxide emissions to 350 ppm by 2100.
- This pioneering case relies heavily on **public trust doctrine,** which holds that government is responsible for guarding and maintaining natural resources in trust for its public. As of late 2019, the case continues to be debated in the courts.
- What does the *science* on climate change tell us?

Figure 1   Mean global temperature and carbon dioxide concentrations from 1880–2020

■ A few of the major trends and impacts drawn from the work of thousands of scientists and compiled in numerous major reports (e.g., the Intergovernmental Panel on Climate Change (IPCC) and the U.S. government's *National Climate Assessment*) include the following:

1) Temperatures have been rising dramatically.
2) Precipitation patterns are changing globally.
3) Storms are becoming stronger and more frequent.
4) Ice in glaciers is melting at unprecedented rates.
5) Sea level is rising.
6) Ocean waters are becoming acidified.
7) Plants, animals, ecosystems, and agriculture are being affected in complex ways.

■ Policy is often required to protect resources held and used in common by the public; otherwise, a **tragedy of the commons** scenario may result. When publicly accessible resources are open to unregulated use (often because no one person, group, or nation "owns" the resource), these resources tend to become overused, damaged, or depleted. Garrett Hardin first articulated this important concept in his 1968 essay, "The Tragedy of the Commons." As a result of understanding this aspect of human behavior, restriction of use and some type of management (regulation, privatization, or cooperative efforts) are now central to environmental policy.

■ Effective environmental policy also addresses **external costs** (so that the people or the environment outside the transaction do not bear the harmful impacts created by the transaction) and **environmental justice** considerations.

■ Factors hindering effective environmental policy include political lobbying, campaign contributions, and vested interests. As a result, one cannot always take for granted that *science* will play a role in policy formation.

The role of science in creating environmental policy

■ Creating environmental policy is a multistep and time-intensive process involving many people and groups.

■ Several of the essential first steps involve the critical role played by science.

■ **Identifying the problem:** The environmental effects of climate change have required an understanding of many areas of science, including meteorological effects of weather, ocean current dynamics, global temperature fluctuations, and atmospheric chemistry. Assessing which factors are the critical ones is then essential for identifying the problem.

- **Identifying the specific causes of the problem:** Much of this scientific research takes place in the arena of risk assessment.
- **Proposing feasible solutions to the problem:** Much of this scientific research takes place in the arena of risk management in which scientists develop strategies to minimize risk.

- Sometimes science can be "politicized" when policymakers choose to ignore scientific data and allow political ideology alone to determine policy. The scientific community has claimed that politics are major determining factors in the area of U.S. climate change policy today. The Trump administration's pullout from the Paris Climate Agreement and the dismantling of Obama's Clean Power Plan are two specific examples of *politics* entering the realm of scientific and environmental policy making.

The institutions important to U.S. environmental policy

- Environmental law, or legislation, is created by Congress. Once laws are enacted, their implementation and enforcement are assigned to the appropriate executive agency. A few of the most environmentally important are listed below.

  - Department of the Interior—National Park Service, U.S. Fish & Wildlife Service
  - Department of Agriculture—U.S. Forest Service
  - Department of Commerce—National Marine Fisheries Service
  - Department of Health and Human Services—U.S. Food and Drug Administration (FDA)

**Federal Administrative Agencies
That Influence Environmental Policy**

EXECUTIVE OFFICE OF THE PRESIDENT

Council on Environmental Quality

DEPARTMENT OF AGRICULTURE (USDA)

Natural Resources Conservation Service
U.S. Forest Service (USFS)

DEPARTMENT OF COMMERCE

Bureau of the Census
National Marine Fisheries Service
National Oceanic and Atmospheric Administration (NOAA)

DEPARTMENT OF DEFENSE

Army Corps of Engineers

DEPARTMENT OF ENERGY (DOE)

Energy Efficiency and Renewable Energy
Energy Information Administration (EIA)
Federal Energy Regulatory Commission (FERC)

DEPARTMENT OF HEALTH AND HUMAN SERVICES

Centers for Disease Control and Prevention (CDC)
Food and Drug Administration (FDA)

DEPARTMENT OF THE INTERIOR

Bureau of Indian Affairs
Bureau of Land Management (BLM)
Bureau of Reclamation
Minerals Management Service
National Park Service (NPS)
U.S. Fish and Wildlife Service (USFWS)
U.S. Geological Survey (USGS)

DEPARTMENT OF LABOR

Occupational Safety and Health Administration (OSHA)

INDEPENDENT AGENCIES

Consumer Product Safety Commission
Environmental Protection Agency (EPA)
National Aeronautics and Space Administration (NASA)
Nuclear Regulatory Commission (NRC)

Source: U.S. General Services Administration, Washington, D.C.

- State and local governments also make environmental policy; however, if state or local policies conflict with federal policies, federal laws take precedence.
- California is an example of a state with strong environmental policy, particularly when it comes to clean air standards and climate change, passing the Global Warming Solutions Act in 2006. This legislation committed the state to bringing its greenhouse gas emissions down to 1990 levels by 2020. California met this emissions reduction goal four years early, achieving its target in 2016, even while adding 8.5% to its population.
- The Fifth Amendment ensures that private property shall not "be taken for public use without just compensation." A **regulatory taking** occurs when the government, by means of a law or regulation, deprives a property owner of some economic use of his or her private property. People often cite the takings clause in opposing regulations that restrict development on privately owned land.

A brief historical context for U.S. environmental policy, including several major U.S. environmental laws

- From 1780s to late 1800s: U.S. policy reflected the perception that Western lands were practically infinite and inexhaustible in natural resources. All policies encouraged settlers and land development (Homestead Act of 1862).

- From late 1800s to mid-20th century: As the U.S. continent became more populated and its resources increasingly exploited, public policies began to reflect elements of conservation, preservation, and mitigation of early land use (National Park Service Act, Soil Conservation Act, Wilderness Act).

- From mid-20th century to 2000: With continued development and industrialization, this era of environmental policy targeted pollution and has given us many of today's major environmental laws.

  - **National Environmental Policy Act (NEPA),** 1970: Often described as the cornerstone of U.S. environmental law, NEPA established the Council on Environmental Quality and the Environmental Protection Agency (EPA), and it required that an **environmental impact statement (EIS)** be prepared for any federal action (building an interstate highway or dam; logging) that might affect environmental quality.

  - **Clean Water Act,** 1977: Established the goal of creating "fishable, swimmable" waterways by setting maximum permissible amounts of pollutants that can be discharged into waterways and requiring permits for the discharge of these pollutants. Recent amendments have focused on stormwater pollution issues, requiring industrial stormwater discharges and municipal sewage discharge facilities to acquire permits prior to operation.

  - **Clean Air Act,** 1963, amended in 1970 and 1990: Established air quality standards for primary and secondary air pollutants and required states to develop specific plans for cleaner air, including the emission testing of automobiles.

  - **Endangered Species Act,** 1973: Identifies threatened and endangered species in the United States, puts their protection ahead of economic consideration, protects their habitat, and directs the U.S. Fish & Wildlife Service to prepare effective recovery plans.

  - **Comprehensive Environmental Response, Compensation, and Liability Act (CERCLA),** 1980: Established the Superfund for emergency response and remediation of toxic and hazardous waste sites.

  - **Resources Conservation and Recovery Act (RCRA),** 1976: The primary law pertaining to the disposal of solid and hazardous wastes, setting standards and requiring permits for "cradle to grave" management.

- **Safe Drinking Water Act,** 1974: Authorizes the EPA to set quality standards for tap water provided by public water systems and to protect drinking water from sources of contamination.

- The **Environmental Protection Agency** (EPA) has been the main U.S. agency working to develop solutions to pollution issues, conducting and evaluating environmental research, setting and enforcing standards for pollution levels, and monitoring overall environmental quality. Since the EPA's inception in 1970, it has played a central role in setting environmental policy.

- **Sustainability** (safeguarding functioning ecosystems), the raising of living standards for the world's developing nations (**environmental justice**), and addressing **climate change** solutions have been the focus of 21st-century U.S. environmental policy.

- Concerns over climate change and environmental justice have recently come together in the **Green New Deal,** proposed in 2019. This is a blueprint plan that puts forth 10-year goals for converting the U.S. power grid to 100% renewable sources, dramatically reducing greenhouse gas emissions, and reducing poverty with high-paying green energy jobs. Intended not as legislation, but as a way of addressing social equity and climate change issues, it is modeled on Franklin Roosevelt's New Deal set forth during the Great Depression of the 1930s.

Specific approaches to creating environmental policy

- Environmental policy is diverse and follows three major approaches: lawsuits in the courts, command-and-control policy, and economic policy tools.

- **Congressional legislation** and subsequent regulations from the appropriate administrative agencies, such as the Environmental Protection Agency (EPA), comprise the **command-and-control approach** in which the regulating agency prohibits certain actions, sets limits or standards, and threatens punishment for those violating these terms. This direct approach has brought U.S. residents and other nations cleaner air and water, safer workplaces, and other advances.

- Shortcomings of this top-down approach have led many economists to advocate alternative economic policy tools such as the following:

  - **Green taxes**—The "polluter pays" principle, which levies taxes on businesses that engage in environmentally harmful activities and products, provides a market-based incentive to *discourage/correct* the activity. Green taxes are common in Europe, where many nations have adopted the polluter pays principle.

  - **Subsidies**—The government provides an incentive (cash or tax break) intended to *encourage* a particular industry or activity. Subsidies can be used to promote environmentally sustainable activities, but they can also be used to support unsustainable ones such as fossil fuel corporations. In the United States from 1950 to 2010, $594 billion was given to fossil fuel industries in subsidies, whereas only $171 billion was granted to renewable resources.

- **Ecolabeling**—Sellers who use sustainable practices advertise this fact, hoping to win approval and sales from buyers.
- **Emissions trading**—The government issues marketable emissions permits to businesses that conduct environmentally harmful activities; the businesses then engage in buying and selling these permits to each other. Under a **cap-and-trade system,** an acceptable level of pollution is determined by the government, which then issues permits. A company receives credit for amounts it does not emit and then can sell this credit to other companies unable to meet the capped standard. The United States has employed the cap-and-trade system for dealing with the stricter SO_2 standards of the 1990 Clean Air Act amendments. Some environmental advocates oppose emissions trading because they view it as giving polluters a "license to pollute."
- **Market incentives** operate at the local level. Examples are (1) **charging** for waste disposal according to the amount generated and (2) issuing **rebates** to residents who buy environmentally efficient appliances, such as water-efficient toilets.

The major institutions involved with international environmental policy, including examples of major international treaties

- Worldwide, many nations have embarked on a new wave of environmental policy defined by two main goals: to develop solutions to climate change, an issue of unprecedented breadth and global reach, and to achieve sustainable development while raising living standards for the world's people.

- The **United Nations (UN),** today serving every nation in the world, has taken an active role in shaping international environmental policy.
- The **World Bank,** based in Washington, D.C., is one of the largest sources of funding for economic development worldwide, providing funding for irrigation infrastructure, dams, and other major development projects. Some World Bank projects have been criticized as unsustainable, often causing more environmental problems than they solve.
- The **European Union's (EU)** Environment Agency works to address waste management, noise, pollution of water and air, and habitat degradation for its 27 member nations.
- The **World Trade Organization (WTO)** imposes financial penalties on those nations that do not comply with its directives. Thus, the WTO can exercise authority in a nation's internal affairs. The UN and the EU, in contrast, do not exercise authority within the borders of their member nations.

- **Nongovernmental organizations (NGOs)** are becoming increasingly influential in their environmental protection advocacy role. The Nature Conservancy, Greenpeace, and Conservation International are just a few of these influential NGOs.
- International law arises from conventions or treaties (written contracts among nations) into which nations enter. Treaties such as the Paris Agreement and Montreal Protocol are global in scope and have been ratified by most nations.
- Some major international environmental treaties are the following:

  - **Convention on International Trade in Endangered Species of Wild Fauna and Flora (CITES),** 1975: Protects endangered species by banning their commercial trade as live specimens or wildlife products.
  - **Montreal Protocol,** 1989: This treaty's goal is to reduce the emission of airborne chemicals (CFCs) that deplete stratospheric ozone. Because of its effectiveness in decreasing global CFC emissions, it is considered *the most successful effort to date in addressing a global environmental problem.*
  - **Kyoto Protocol,** 2005: An agreement drafted in 1997 that called for reducing, by 2012, emissions of six greenhouse gases to levels lower than their 1990 levels. To date, the United States has refused to ratify this treaty, primarily on the basis of economics.

Multiple-Choice Questions

Use the figure to answer questions 1 and 2.

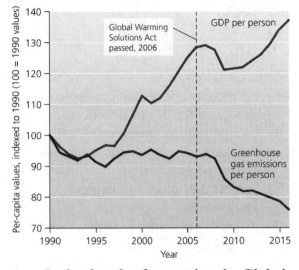

1. In the decade after passing the Global Warming Solutions Act,
    (A) California's greenhouse gas emissions were reduced by 50%.
    (B) California's GDP grew significantly although greenhouse gas emissions were in a steady state.
    (C) California's greenhouse emissions were reduced as the state grew economically.
    (D) California's greenhouse gas emissions and GDP are not shown to be correlated.

2. The percent change in GDP from 1995 to 2006 is approximately
    (A) 95%.
    (B) 34%.
    (C) 30%.
    (D) 15%.

3. The National Environmental Policy Act (NEPA)
    (A) puts all federal land under environmental protection.
    (B) requires compensation be given to anyone harmed by pollution from a business or corporate entity.
    (C) requires environmental impact statements for any federal project.
    (D) protects all endangered species from international trade.

4. A cap-and-trade system
    (A) allows industries to set their own levels for pollution emissions so that trading can continue.
    (B) has recently been repealed by Congress as useless in diminishing pollution.
    (C) specifies a certain cap on industrial pollutants that can be traded to other nations.
    (D) permits industries that pollute under the federal limit to sell credits to industries that pollute over the limit.

5. A cost-benefit analysis for a public project always includes
    (A) the internal costs.
    (B) the external costs.
    (C) the GDP.
    (D) the GNP.

6. Regarding environmental laws and the U.S. Constitution,
    (A) state laws take precedence over federal laws.
    (B) federal laws can override the Constitution if a waiver fee is paid.
    (C) fundamental environmental policy is always set forth by the Constitution.
    (D) federal environmental legislation always takes precedence over state laws.

7. A modern-day example of the "tragedy of the commons" would be
    (A) strip-mining in a national park or national forest.
    (B) use of herbicides and pesticides by industrial agriculture in California.
    (C) acid precipitation falling throughout the northeastern United States.
    (D) grazing sheep in a private park.

Use the figure below to answer questions 8 and 9.

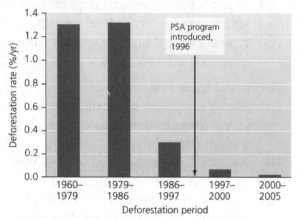

8. The graph indicates that forest recovery in Costa Rica
   (A) was not affected by the introduction of the PSA program.
   (B) had already dropped, indicating that other factors in addition to the PSA program were involved.
   (C) is complete and ecosystem services are now functioning.
   (D) was primarily caused by the PSA program.

9. Costa Rica's program to pay for ecosystem services (PSA) has inspired other nations to implement similar programs. This program can be seen
   (A) to promote intrinsic values and natural capital.
   (B) to value externalities and promote economic growth.
   (C) to be an anthropocentric approach for a country's environmental decision-making policies.
   (D) to be primarily concerned with environmental justice.

10. One of the most effective international environmental treaties to date is the
    (A) Kyoto Protocol.
    (B) Montreal Protocol.
    (C) CITES.
    (D) NEPA.

11. Which of the following accounts for the nonmarket value of goods and a country's overall desirable economic activity?
    (A) GDP
    (B) GAP
    (C) GPI
    (D) GNP

12. Modern environmental policy aims to
    (A) promote fairness among people and groups in the use of resources.
    (B) use natural resources for economically important industrial products.
    (C) protect the values of the legal landowner.
    (D) promote economic growth whenever possible.

13. The economic value of ecosystem services was studied and first estimated in the late 20th century by
    (A) Aldo Leopold.
    (B) Robert Costanza.
    (C) John Muir.
    (D) Gifford Pinchot.

14. Once an environmental law or regulation having to do with the timber industry has been passed, it is up to the ___ to carry out the enforcement of this legislation.
    (A) Environmental Protection Agency
    (B) Department of the Interior
    (C) Department of Agriculture
    (D) Department of Health and Human Services

15. An example of giving polluters a "license to pollute" is often the policy of
    (A) providing subsidies.
    (B) implementing green taxes.
    (C) providing market incentives.
    (D) cap-and-trade.

Free-Response Question

Read the following excerpt from a U.S. Environmental Protection Agency press release and answer the questions below.

> During the late 1980s, an environmental controversy began in Western Oregon, Washington, and Northern California that continues today. At stake were thousands of jobs and the future of old-growth (never been logged) coniferous forests, along with the many species that depend on these forests. Current estimates are that approximately 8% of old-growth forests remained in 2013. The endangered northern spotted owls depended upon preserving the old-growth forests of this region. The federal government proceeded to suspend logging in the 3 million remaining acres where the last 2100 owls live. The timber industry estimates that this halt to logging would cost them 33 billion dollars, with most of the losses borne by local logging companies and residents in Washington and Oregon. Conservationists dispute these numbers of economic loss, stating that there could actually be a *gain* in economic value, also adding that the northern spotted owl is an important umbrella species.

a) Explain the scientific reasoning and rationale for conservationists claiming an *economic gain* rather than an economic loss with this federal decision.

b) Describe one specific piece of environmental legislation that could apply in the above conflict, including the rationale of your choice.

c) Describe one *internal cost* and one *external cost* that might be associated with the timber industry, including your explanation.

d) Propose a solution to this environmental problem that could benefit both the timber industry and the owls. Be specific in your proposal, explaining *how* your proposal would benefit each side.

Human Population Dynamics

Chapter 8: Human Population

YOU MUST KNOW

- The scope of human population growth.
- The divergent views on population growth.
- How to evaluate the effects of human population growth, affluence, and technology on the environment.
- The fundamentals of human demography and the interpretation of age structure diagrams.
- The fundamentals of demographic transition.
- How poverty, the status of women, family planning, and affluence affect population growth.

The scope of human population growth

- The current world growth rate is approximately 1.1%; roughly 80 million people are added each year.
- With a 1.1% growth rate, the world population will double in approximately 64 years (**doubling time = 70 ÷ % growth rate**).
- The current world population, as of November 2019, is in slight excess of 7.7 billion.

The divergent views on population growth

- Current world population numbers are due to the many factors that have brought down death rates and infant mortality rates: improved sanitation, better medical care, increased agricultural output, and other technological innovations.
- Global birth rates have not declined as much as death rates; therefore, the human population has continued to rise.
- **Thomas Malthus** (1766–1834), British economist, predicted that human population size would eventually outgrow the available food supply if humans did not purposefully limit births.

- **Paul Ehrlich,** in his 1968 book, *The Population Bomb,* predicted that population growth would soon lead to famine, and conflict over scarce resources would eventually consume civilization by the end of the 20th century.
- These predictions have not fully materialized, primarily because of increased food production innovations, enhanced prosperity, and education/gender equality for women.
- Many nations are questioning whether continued population growth is positive, especially if it depletes resources, stresses social systems, and degrades the natural environment.
- China's current growth rate of 0.5% and the results of its one-child family policy have led to a shrinking labor force, an increasing number of older people, and too few women, leading to questions of whether China traded overpopulation for these unintended consequences.
- Population decline and population aging in additional countries have given rise to fears of possible future economic decline. The U.S. birth rate has reached its lowest level in history, and two of every three European governments now feel their birth rates are too low to sustain their economic growth.

How to evaluate the effects of human population growth, affluence, and technology on the environment

- The $I = P \times A \times T$ model summarizes how environmental impact (I) results from the interactions among population size (P), affluence (A), and technology (T).
- Environmental impact is most often equated to degradation of ecosystems by pollution and/or unsustainable resource consumption.
- Understanding the IPAT model clearly demonstrates that negative environmental effects are not caused solely by the numbers of humans (population size) in a given area, but are caused by what those numbers of humans are capable of doing (their rate of consumption of resources due to affluence and technology use).
- IPAT could be refined further by adding a fourth factor, sensitivity (S), to denote how vulnerable a given environment (e.g., arid lands, deserts, tundra) is to human pressures.
- Technology advances have allowed for increased efficiency, temporarily alleviating our strain on resources; however, all matter (land, water, natural resources) is *finite,* and *limits to population growth exist.*
- The size of Earth's carrying capacity is often debated, with estimates ranging from a conservative 1–2 billion humans living prosperously in a healthy environment to 33 billion living in extreme poverty with intensive cultivation and no natural areas remaining.
- China's growth in total population (currently 1.37 billion) exerts an unprecedented environmental impact (reduced air quality, overdrawn aquifers, high levels of soil erosion) resulting from increased affluence (A) and technology (T). The U.S. total population (currently at 331 million),

although significantly lower than China's, has a much higher level of affluence (A) and use of technology (T), currently resulting in a more significant impact (I) on Earth.

- The **Human Footprint Map** attempts to quantify human stresses/activity (e.g., population density, agricultural land changes, built environments, night-time light density, major roads and railway presence) on natural systems, using a scale from 0 to 50 (zero represents no impact from human activity).

- The human footprint score is a *very different measure than ecological footprint*, since it measures the degree of stress placed on a given area by human activities. By contrast, an ecological footprint is the area of biologically productive land needed to support an individual or a population.

- When examining Human Footprint Map changes from 1993 to 2009, researchers found that many nations were discovering ways to decouple population increases and economic growth from corresponding increases in environmental stress and degradation.

The fundamentals of human demography and the interpretation of age structure diagrams

- The principles of population ecology, which apply to animal and plant life, also apply to humans. **Demography** is the study of human populations, how they change with time, and the main factors causing this change.

- The following are the main factors useful for predicting population dynamics and environmental impacts.

  - **Population size,** the absolute number of individuals, is only one aspect in determining population dynamics.

  - **Population density** and **distribution** reflect the spatially uneven nature of human population on Earth. Temperate, subtropical, and tropical areas have the highest population density; therefore, these regions often bear the highest environmental impact.

  - **Age structure diagrams (population pyramids)** describe the number of individuals of each age class within a population and are especially valuable for predicting future population change. The width of each horizontal bar represents the number of people in each age class; a wide base indicates a population capable of future rapid growth or population momentum. An age structure diagram with approximately equal age classes from pre-reproductive through post-reproductive ages will remain stable and experience insignificant growth.

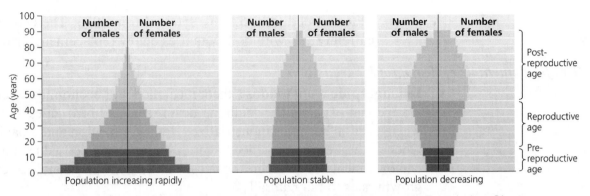

Figure 8.6 Age Structure Diagrams and Their Ability to Predict Human Population Change

- ■ **Sex ratios,** the ratios of males to females in a population, affect population dynamics. In most countries, this ratio is approximately equal when people reach reproductive age; however, currently in China, this ratio is strongly skewed in favor of males (because of cultural preferences and China's one-child policy).
- ■ **Birth and death rates, immigration, and emigration** also determine whether a population grows, shrinks, or remains stable.
  - ▪ Birth and immigration *add* individuals to a population.
  - ▪ **Crude birth rate (CBR)** is the number of births per 1000 individuals per year.
  - ▪ Death and emigration *remove* individuals from a population.
  - ▪ **Crude death rate (CDR)** is the number of deaths per 1000 individuals per year.
  - ▪ *Global* **population growth rate** $= (\text{CBR} - \text{CDR}) \div 10$

  A *nation's* **growth rate** $=$

  $$\frac{(\text{CBR} + \text{immigration}) - (\text{CDR} + \text{emigration})}{10}$$

  or, shown another way,

  $$\frac{(\text{births} - \text{deaths}) + (\text{immigration} - \text{emigration})}{10}$$

- ■ **Total fertility rate (TFR)** is the average number of children born per woman during her lifetime. **Replacement fertility** is the TFR that keeps the size of a population stable $(\text{TFR} = 2.1)$; if it drops below 2.1, the population size will shrink (in the absence of immigration).
  - ▪ Improved medical care (reducing infant mortality), increasing urbanization, and greater educational opportunities for women have recently pushed TFR downward in many nations.
  - ▪ TFR has dropped from 2.6 to 1.6 in many European countries, resulting in declining populations in these countries. In China,

TFR dropped from 5.8 in 1950 to 1.6 in 2015. The U.S. TFR is currently 1.7, with both countries below replacement fertility.

The fundamentals of demographic transition

- **Demographic transition** is a theoretical model of economic and cultural change that explains the declining death rates and birth rates that occur when a nation becomes industrialized. Industrialization and urbanization reduce the economic need for children, while education and empowerment of women decrease unwanted pregnancies, causing growth rates to fall naturally.
- There are four stages of the demographic transition model.
  - **Pre-industrial stage:** Death rates are high (disease is widespread), and birth rates are also high (people are compensating for high infant mortality).
  - **Transitional stage:** Death rates decline due to improved medical care and food production.
  - **Industrial stage:** Birth rates decline as a result of increased opportunities for women and access to birth control.
  - **Post-industrial stage:** The final stage in which both birth and death rates have fallen to low and stable levels.

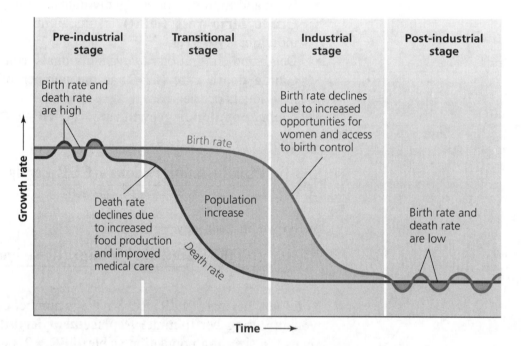

Figure 8.12 The Demographic Transition Model and Its Major Stages

- Many European countries, the United States, Canada, and Japan have already passed through demographic transition. It remains an unanswered question for Earth's environment whether developing nations will pass through these stages in the same manner as Western countries, as many nations in sub-Saharan Africa are experiencing demographic fatigue due to HIV/AIDS removing young members from their society and workforce.

- Most experts predict that China will continue to industrialize, grow its economy, and settle into a stable post-industrial nation with minimal population growth in future years.
- By comparison, India, with a TFR of 2.3 and growth rate of 1.4%, is predicted to overtake China, becoming the world's most populous country in several decades; as a result, India may not complete the transition to a fully industrial society.

How poverty, the status of women, family planning, and affluence affect population growth

- Poorer societies tend to show faster population growth than do wealthier societies. A vast majority of the next 1 billion people added to Earth's population will be born in the developing countries of Africa, Asia, and Latin America.
- Increasing female literacy is strongly associated with reduced birth rates in many nations.
- Perhaps the greatest single factor enabling a society to slow its population growth is the ability of women and couples to practice birth control with contraception.
  - Fifty-six percent of married women worldwide report using a modern method of contraception to plan or prevent pregnancy.
  - China has the highest rate of contraception use (84%) of any nation, slowing its growth rate down to 0.5%, primarily through its one-child policy.
  - Thailand has been successful in slowing its growth rate to 0.2% by using an education-based approach to family planning and increasing the availability of contraceptives.
  - Many African nations have rates at or below 15% contraception use; the region's TFR is 4.6.
- Affluent societies' intensive consumption often makes their ecological impact even greater than that of poorer nations with larger populations.
  - The addition of 1 American has as much environmental impact as 3.4 Chinese, 8 Indians, or 14 Afghans.
  - Our species has an ecological footprint 50% greater than what Earth can support—an amount termed the **biocapacity.**

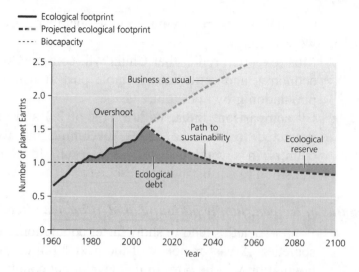

Figure 8.19 The Global Ecological Footprint of the Human Population

- Epidemics (such as HIV/AIDS) claiming many young and productive members of society influence population dynamics and can have severe social and economic ramifications. Africa is being hit the hardest and is struggling to advance through the demographic transition.
- China's past restrictive reproductive policies (their one-child policy) have led to a shrinking workforce, a rising number of older citizens, and an unbalanced sex ratio (many fewer females). Although overall affluence has improved, the future productivity of the nation may be compromised.

Multiple-Choice Questions

1. To determine the number of individuals that will be added to a population in a specified time, multiply the growth rate by the
   (A) number of immigrants.
   (B) crude birth rate.
   (C) original population size.
   (D) final population size.

2. If a country's age structure diagram looks like a pyramid, the population
   (A) will expand for at least one generation.
   (B) is demonstrating exponential growth.
   (C) is shrinking.
   (D) is expanding.

3. Which best describes the reason for the very rapid growth of the human population since the industrial revolution?
   (A) Humans have few offspring, but their young survive at a very high rate.
   (B) Technology has allowed the species to overcome some environmental resistance.
   (C) The biotic potential for humans has increased.
   (D) Climatic change favorable to humans has allowed our species to expand its range.

4. What is the first significant change that occurs in a country undergoing demographic transition?
   (A) Birth rates decline as a result of improved education for women.
   (B) Birth rates decline and emigration occurs, resulting in a gradually declining population.

   (C) Death rates decline as a result of improved food production and medical care.
   (D) Death rates and birth rates diverge, leading to a gradual population decline.

5. If the global population has a CDR of 12 and a CBR of 15, this would result in a growth rate of ___%.
   (A) 0.3
   (B) 3.0
   (C) 30
   (D) .03

6. The *most critical factor* in controlling human population growth is
   (A) decreasing the average number of births per woman.
   (B) controlling the length of one's reproductive life span.
   (C) decreasing the age of first birth for a woman.
   (D) decreasing infant mortality.

7. When the IPAT model is applied to China, the *most* important recent factor that has changed and is instrumental in determining the environmental effects of China's population is
   (A) the value of P.
   (B) the value of A.
   (C) the value of China's growth rate.
   (D) the value of TFR.

(a) Age structure diagram of Canada in 2019

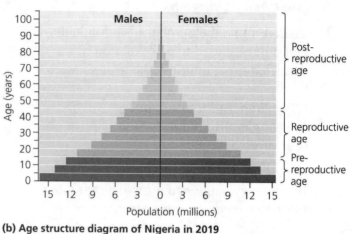

(b) Age structure diagram of Nigeria in 2019

Figure 8.7

Use Figure 8.7 to answer questions 8–10.

8. Looking at the figure, you are able to determine that
   (A) the population in (a) is growing rapidly.
   (B) the population in (b) is declining rapidly.
   (C) the population in (b) is growing rapidly.
   (D) the population in (a) is aging rapidly.

9. What is the population in (b) likely to experience in the near future?
   (A) resource depletion and decreased quality of life
   (B) a high infant mortality
   (C) lack of economic growth
   (D) a quick move through demographic transition

10. The population in (a) suggests that its total fertility rate (TFR) is
    (A) less than replacement level.
    (B) zero.
    (C) over 4.0.
    (D) now rising, but has been recently declining.

11. When the IPAT model is applied to the United States, the *least* important factor in determining the environmental effects of the U.S. population is
    (A) the value of P.
    (B) the value of A.
    (C) the value of T.
    (D) the values of A and T.

12. Replacement fertility
    (A) restores the population size after a catastrophic event.
    (B) is a contraceptive technique.
    (C) is below 2.0 in Latin America and the Caribbean.
    (D) is equal to 2.1 in stable populations.

13. If a population doubles in the course of 30 years, its growth rate would be close to ___%.
    (A) 4.6
    (B) 2.3
    (C) 5.0
    (D) 10

Use Table 8.4 to answer questions 14 and 15.

TABLE 8.4 Demographic Comparison: China and India

MEASURE	CHINA	INDIA
Rate of natural increase (% per year)	0.5	1.4
Total fertility rate	1.8	2.3
Women using modern contraception (%)	84	48
Infant mortality rate (infant death per 1000 live births)	10	34
Urban population (%)	59	34
Gross national income per capita ($)	16,760	7060

Data from Population Reference Bureau, *2018 World population data sheet.*

14. The key factor that demographers use to examine a population's *potential* for growth is
    (A) the rate of natural increase.
    (B) total fertility rate.
    (C) the percent of women using modern contraception.
    (D) gross national income per capita.

15. In 1950, India's growth rate was 2.7%. What is the *percent change* that India has experienced in its growth rate?
    (A) 1.3% decline
    (B) 48% decline
    (C) 93% increase
    (D) 1.3% increase

Free-Response Question

In January of 2019, the population of China was estimated to be approximately 1.39 billion, with an annual growth rate of 0.5%. In 1949, when Mao Zedong founded the country's current political regime, approximately 500 million people lived in China, the total fertility rate (TFR) was 5.8, and the country was mostly rural, undeveloped, and impoverished. Include all calculations and provide full explanations for the following questions.

a) Calculate the *percent change* in China's population from 1949 to 2019.

b) Describe/explain the *stages* of demographic transition China has experienced. Include specific evidence for each stage.

c) Describe the approximate shape of the base (pre-reproductive age class) of China's age structure diagram in 2019, as compared to the size of the reproductive and post-reproductive age classes. Include specific evidence.

d) Calculate the number of *additional* people China will have at the end of 2019.

e) Based on the current growth rate, calculate the *doubling time* for China's population.

Earth's Land Resources and Use

Chapter 2: Earth's Physical Systems: Matter, Energy, and Geology

---

YOU MUST KNOW

- The fundamentals of matter and chemistry and be able to explain their application to real-world situations.
- How water's unique chemistry supports the living world.
- The role of organic compounds in ecosystem function.
- How to differentiate among the basic forms of energy and explain the first and second laws of thermodynamics.
- The basics of photosynthesis, cellular respiration, and their importance to living things.
- How the basic geology processes of plate tectonics and the rock cycle shape Earth's landscape.
- Major types of geologic hazards and the approaches required to mitigate their impacts.

The fundamentals of matter and chemistry and be able to explain their application to real-world situations

- **Environmental science,** the broadest of all scientific disciplines, must include the study of **matter** (that which takes up space and has mass) in order to understand the underlying nature of environmental problems.
- **Chemistry** (the study of elements and compounds and how they interact) plays a central role in understanding most environmental issues. Examples:

  - How do gases such as CO_2 and CH_4 contribute to global climate change?
  - How do pollutants such as SO_2 and NO cause acid rain?
  - How do pesticides affect the health of wildlife and humans?

- **Law of conservation of matter:** Matter cannot be created or destroyed, but can be transformed into new substances.
  - The amount of matter on Earth is constant and is recycled in biogeochemical cycles.
  - Matter cannot be "thrown away" or made to disappear, even though it can change form.
- **Elements** (composed of only one type of atom and cannot be broken down into substances with other properties) and **compounds** (composed of two or more elements chemically combined in a fixed ratio) make up all matter.
- The elements C, H, O, and N make up 96% of living matter.
- **Isotopes** are atoms of the same element with a differing number of neutrons and mass.
- **Radioisotopes** change chemical identity as they shed subatomic particles, emitting radiation and decaying at a rate determined by their **half-life** (the amount of time it takes for one-half the atoms to give off radiation and decay). The 2011 Fukushima Daiichi nuclear plant accident released numerous types of radioisotopes (Cs-137 for example), contaminating the Pacific Ocean waters, sediment, and marine life for decades to come.
- **Ions** are charged atoms; their charge is due to an unequal number of protons and electrons. The changing radiation emitted by radioisotopes is called **ionizing radiation** because of the ions generated when striking molecules, affecting the stability and functionality of biological molecules such as DNA.

How water's unique chemistry supports the living world

- The **structure of the water molecule** is the key to its special properties: The two hydrogen atoms and the one oxygen atom bond together to form a **polar molecule**—the end bearing the oxygen has a slightly negative charge, whereas the end bearing the hydrogen atoms has a slightly positive charge.

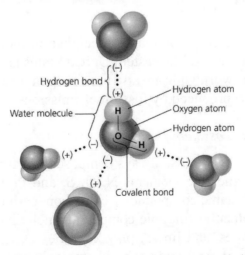

Figure 2.5 The Water Molecule and Its Hydrogen Bonds

- Because of water's polar nature, **hydrogen bonds** form between water molecules, giving the properties of **cohesion** (water molecules "sticking" to one another), a **high ability to dissolve** many substances, and a **high specific heat** (water can absorb a great deal of heat with only small changes in its temperature). These are properties that help to support life and stabilize Earth's climate.

- Some water molecules split apart, forming hydrogen ions (H^+) and hydroxide ions (OH^-). Solutions in which the concentrations of $H^+ > OH^-$ are **acidic (pH < 7),** whereas solutions in which $OH^- > H^+$ are **basic (pH > 7).**

- Pure water is neutral (pH of 7) and $[H^+] = [OH^-]$.

- The pH scale is logarithmic; each step from 0 to 14 represents a tenfold difference in hydrogen ion concentration.

Figure 2.8 The pH Scale

- Industrial air pollution makes precipitation more acidic. The pH of rain throughout most of the eastern United States now averages well below 5. The oceans worldwide are also becoming more acidic as seawater absorbs excess CO_2 produced by fossil fuel emissions.

The role of organic compounds in ecosystem function

- **Organic compounds,** always composed of carbon and hydrogen atoms, and sometimes the elements N, O, S, and P, are essential to all living things. Inorganic compounds lack carbon–carbon bonds.

- **Macromolecules** (organic compounds including proteins, nucleic acids, carbohydrates, and lipids) play key roles as energy sources (especially glucose: $C_6H_{12}O_6$) and are building blocks of living organisms.

- **Hydrocarbons** (organic compounds consisting solely of carbon and hydrogen atoms) are important to environmental science because they are the primary constituents of fossil fuels and all petroleum products.
- **Synthetic polymers (plastics)** are often long-lasting, are resistant to chemical breakdown, and play a large role in our manufactured products. These same characteristics also result in problems for wildlife, human health, water quality, and waste management.

How to differentiate among the basic forms of energy and explain the first and second laws of thermodynamics

- **Energy** is the capacity to accomplish work and change position, physical composition, or the temperature of matter. Geologic events (earthquakes and tsunamis) involve some of the most dramatic releases of energy in nature.
- **Potential energy** (energy of position) and **kinetic energy** (energy of motion) are two major forms.
- **The first law of thermodynamics** states that energy is always conserved (cannot be created or destroyed) but can change in quality during chemical reactions. The potential energy of water behind a dam will equal the kinetic energy of its eventual movement downstream.
- **The second law of thermodynamics** focuses on the conversion of energy (change in quality). It states that energy will always change from more ordered to less ordered, degrading in quality and increasing in entropy, so long as no force counteracts this tendency. The potential energy of wood (stored in its molecular bonds) transforms into heat, light, carbon dioxide, water vapor, and the residue of carbon, ash, and particulates after it is burned. All of these products are less ordered and higher in entropy than the concentrated energy stored in the original wood.
- Organisms maintain their structure and function by continually consuming energy, which flows through trophic levels in food chains and is never recycled. Energy must be constantly supplied to an ecosystem, usually by the sun.
- **Energy conversion efficiency** is the ratio of useful output of energy to the amount needed for input.
- **Energy transfer/flow** between trophic levels is typically only **10% efficient**.

The basics of photosynthesis, cellular respiration, and their importance to living things

- **Photosynthesis** is the process by which **autotrophs/primary producers** make organic compounds by converting light energy from the sun into chemical energy (sugars/food). Sunlight, life's primary energy source, powers the autotroph's chemical reactions, converting CO_2 and H_2O into the concentrated chemical energy of sugars ($C_6H_{12}O_6$), their food.

- **Cellular respiration** is the process by which most organisms release the chemical energy of sugars $(C_6H_{12}O_6)$ to provide energy for both plants' and animals' cellular activities. CO_2 and H_2O are also products of respiration. As in all energy conversions, the energy released per glucose molecule is only about two-thirds of energy input per glucose molecule; therefore, the energy conversion is not 100% efficient. This is a prime example of the second law of thermodynamics.

- Organisms at each trophic level use most of the food energy for their own life's needs (building new tissue, movement, essential chemical reactions, etc.).

- Only about 10% of the original energy at any trophic level is available to be passed up to the next higher trophic level, creating a pyramid of energy that is never inverted.

- Another significant energy source is **geothermal heat** generated deep within Earth as a result of radioactive decay. These radioisotopes produce heat that gradually makes its way to the surface, heating magma that erupts from volcanoes and drives plate tectonics. In underground locations where this energy heats groundwater, natural surface eruptions of steam can result.

How the basic geology processes of plate tectonics and the rock cycle shape Earth's landscape

- Earth's geology is dynamic, with very long periods of time involved in geologic processes, especially when compared to the length of a human lifetime.

- Earth is composed of distinct layers (**crust, mantle,** and **core**) that differ in composition, temperature, and density.

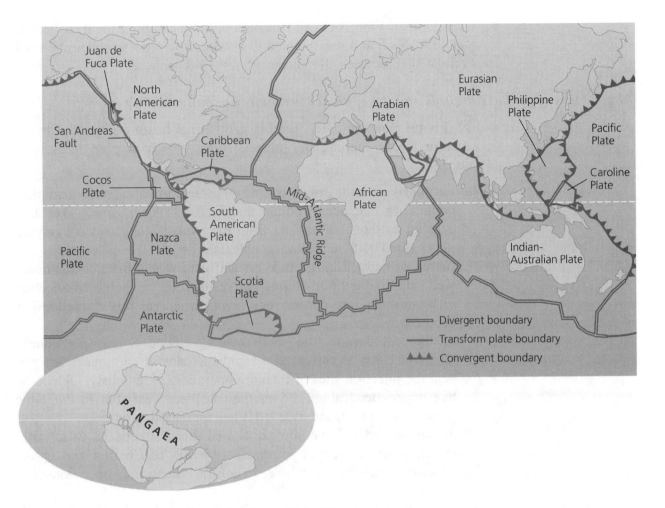

Figure 2.8   The Earth's Major Plates Involved in Plate Tectonics

■ **Plate tectonics,** the slow, large-scale movement of Earth's lithospheric plates (uppermost mantle), is a fundamental process that shapes Earth's physical geography, also producing earthquakes and volcanoes along the various types of plate boundaries (divergent, transform, and convergent):

1) **Divergent plate boundaries,** where plates move apart, are responsible for the Mid-Atlantic Ridge, a large mountain range under the Atlantic Ocean.

2) **Transform plate boundaries,** where two plates slide past each other, produce earthquakes like those along California's San Andreas Fault.

3) **Convergent plate boundaries** occur where two plates come together, producing the possibility of mountain building (Andes Mountains), subduction zones (one plate slides beneath the other), or earthquake activity.

■ Tectonic movements build mountains, islands, and continents and shape ocean geography; therefore, they are highly influential in **biogeography** (geographic distribution of life).

■ Over geologic time, rocks and the minerals that comprise them are heated, melted, cooled, and reassembled in a very slow process called the **rock cycle,** which recycles all matter within the lithosphere.

Major types of geologic hazards and the approaches required to mitigate their impacts

■ By driving plate tectonics, Earth's geothermal heating gives rise to the creative forces shaping our planet, some of which pose hazards to humans.

■ Earthquakes result from movement at transform and convergent plate boundaries that occur around the Pacific "ring of fire." The 2011 Tohoku earthquake resulted from movement along two converging plates (the Pacific and Eurasian plates).

■ Increased extraction of crude oil and natural gas from conventional wells and hydraulic fracturing has resulted in the increased injection of wastewater into porous rock layers wherever this extraction has occurred.

■ In the last decade, the south central United States, particularly Oklahoma, has experienced a rapid increase in earthquake activity near the injection sites of fracking operations. Previously, Oklahoma had experienced about 1.5 earthquakes per year, but in 2009 the number rose to 20, and by 2016 it had increased to 641.

■ Scientific studies have now confirmed the link between wastewater injection and increased seismic activity in this region and in the American Southwest where hydraulic fracturing operations are concentrated.

■ Although governments now monitor many wastewater injection wells for pressure and mandate slower injection rates and volumes, studies indicate a possible two-decade-long lasting effect for increased seismic activity.

■ **Volcanoes** arise from rifts (divergent plate boundaries), subduction zones (convergent plate boundaries), or hotspots. The Hawaiian Islands are an example of a series of islands resulting from a tectonic plate moving across a volcanic hotspot.

■ **Tsunamis** (caused by earthquakes displacing large amounts of ocean water) can cause immense human and environmental damage when this powerful surge of seawater displaces large volumes of ocean-bottom sediment, pushing water upward into waves that spread outward from the earthquake site. In the 2011 tsunami, waves overtopped the 19-foot seawall protecting the Fukushima Daiichi nuclear power plant. This led to a meltdown of the core reactors at the power plant and the subsequent displacement of approximately 340,000 people due to the radioactive contamination of large areas of land and nearby marine food resources.

■ Humans can minimize the impact of geologic hazards by making informed decisions about where and how to build (establishing strict zoning regulations and engineering codes) and by ensuring that public officials make sound policy decisions when global climate change is a factor.

Chapter 9: Soil Science and Agriculture

YOU MUST KNOW

- The major developments in the history of agriculture.
- The importance of soils to agriculture and the fundamentals of soil science.
- The major causes of soil erosion and land degradation.
- The principles of soil conservation and specific solutions to modern agriculture's overuse of water and fertilizer.
- The importance of pollinators to crop success.
- The major policy approaches for pursuing soil conservation and sustainable agriculture.

The major developments in the history of agriculture

- ▪ Approximately 10,000 years ago, as glaciers retreated and the climate warmed, people in some cultures began to raise plants from seed, to domesticate animals, and to practice selective breeding (choosing the best/hardiest versions of wild plants) by intentionally planting the most desirable seeds.

- ▪ The Middle East's "Fertile Crescent," China, Africa, and the Americas each began traditional agricultural practices independently. Initially, these farming practices were **subsistence agriculture,** producing only enough food for the family farming the land.

- ▪ The industrial revolution introduced large-scale mechanization and fossil fuel combustion to agriculture in the 19th century, boosting crop yields and also intensifying irrigation demands. Synthetic fertilizers and pesticides were introduced in the 1940s, along with the practice of **monoculture** (large-scale, uniform planting of a single crop). This approach was quite distinct from the **polyculture** ("many types") practices of traditional agriculture that mixed maize, beans, and squash in the same fields.

- ▪ Beginning in the 1950s, the **Green Revolution** spread industrial agriculture techniques, as practiced in developed nations, to developing countries. These new mechanized technologies and seed varieties increased crop yields, helping to avoid mass starvation in many developing countries; however, much soil degradation has resulted from the intensive use of synthetic fertilizers, pesticides, and the monoculture approaches of the Green Revolution.

- ▪ Today, **industrial agriculture** dominates Earth and has many negative consequences, including degradation of soil and water, and the decline of pollinators that are essential for a sustainable food supply.

- **Sustainable agriculture** has characteristics that maintain healthy soil, clean water, pollinators, and the ecosystem services that are necessary for *long-term,* sustainable crop and livestock production.

The importance of soils to agriculture and the fundamentals of soil science

- **Soil** is a complex system of inorganic, weathered parent material (rock), organic matter, water, gases, nutrients, and microorganisms. Soil is a renewable resource; however, if soil is degraded or lost to erosion, this renewal process can become unsustainable. Although it is derived from rock, soil is shaped by living organisms, and this natural process occurs very slowly.
- By volume, soil consists of approximately 50% mineral matter and up to 5% organic matter. The remainder consists of pore space taken up by air or water. The organic matter includes living and dead microorganisms as well as decaying material derived from plants and animals.
- Because of the complex interactions between its living and nonliving components, soil meets the definition of an ecosystem. Healthy soil is vital for agriculture, for forests, and for the functioning of Earth's natural ecosystems. It is especially important as the foundation for sustainable agriculture.
- Today, we use 38% of Earth's land surface to produce food and fiber—far more land area than for any other human activity. The percentages are even greater in the United States, where nearly half the land is devoted to agriculture.
- Soil formation is the slow physical, chemical, and biological **weathering** of **parent material** (the base geologic material, rock, or sediment of a particular location) and the accumulation and transformation of organic matter.
- The main factors influencing soil formation are climate, parent material composition, organisms, topography, and time.
- **Soil horizons,** or distinct layers of soil, eventually develop as wind, water, and organisms move and sort the fine particles weathering creates, producing a soil profile. The simplest way to categorize horizons is to recognize the A (topsoil), B (subsoil), and C (parent material) horizons. However, soil scientists often add at least three additional horizons (O, E, and R).

  - **O horizon**—the litter layer, consisting mostly of organic matter.
  - **A horizon**—the topsoil, consisting of some organic material mixed with mineral components.
  - **E horizon**—the zone of leaching (eluviation), where minerals and organic matter tend to leave this horizon and move into the next lower layer, or enter groundwater. Minerals commonly leached are iron, aluminum, and silicate clay.

■ **B horizon**—the subsoil, where minerals and organic matter accumulate from above.

■ **C horizon**—consists largely of weathered parent material.

■ **R horizon**—the rock or sediment of pure parent material.

O Horizon	**O**rganic (litter layer)	Organic matter deposited by organisms
A Horizon	Topsoil	Some organic material mixed with mineral components
E Horizon	**E**luviated (leaching layer)	Minerals and organic matter tend to leach out of this horizon
B Horizon	Subsoil	Minerals and organic matter accumulate here
C Horizon	Weathered parent material	Initial step in soil formation
R Horizon	**R**ock (parent material)	Bedrock, lava, etc.

Figure 9.4 The Major Soil Horizons

■ The A horizon, or **topsoil,** is the crucial horizon for agriculture and ecosystems. It is the most nutritive, taking its texture, coloration, and water-holding capacity from the **humus** (partially decomposed organic matter) content. Generally, the degree of weathering and the concentration of organic matter decrease as one moves downward in a soil profile. Minerals are transported downward by **leaching,** the process whereby solid particles, dissolved or suspended in liquid, are transported to another location.

■ Soil scientists classify soils based largely on properties of color, texture, structure, and pH.

■ **Soil texture** is determined by the size of its particles, ranging from **clay** (the smallest) to **silt** (intermediate) to **sand** (the largest). **Loam** is soil with an even mixture of clay, silt, and sand.

■ Soils with more than 20% clay have high water retention potential, the soil can become waterlogged, and plant roots are deprived of vital oxygen. Acid soils promote nutrient leaching, resulting in poor plant growth and development.

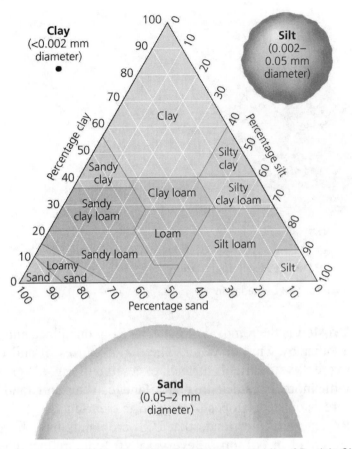

Figure 9.5   The Texture of Soil Depends on Its Mix of Particle Sizes

The major causes of soil erosion and land degradation

- **Land degradation** refers to deterioration that diminishes land's productivity and biodiversity, impairs the functioning of its ecosystems, and reduces the ecosystem services the land can offer.
- Land degradation is caused by intensive/unsustainable agriculture, deforestation, and urban development. It is manifested in processes such as soil erosion, nutrient depletion, water scarcity, salinization, waterlogging, changes in soil structure and pH, and loss of organic matter from the soil.

(b) Causes of soil degradation

Figure 9.17b   Causes of Soil Degradation

- **Erosion** is the removal of material from one place and its transport to another by wind or water. The major causes of soil erosion are (1) overcultivating fields through excessive tilling, (2) grazing rangeland with more livestock than the land can support, and (3) removing forests on steep slopes or with large clear-cuts.
- Recent studies estimate that U.S. croplands have been losing about 2.5 cm (1 in.) of topsoil every 15–20 years, reducing corn and wheat yields by approximately 5–10%.
- **Desertification** is a form of land degradation affecting arid lands in which more than 10% of productivity is lost as a result of erosion, soil compaction, forest removal, overgrazing, drought, salinization, water depletion, or other factors. China and Northern Africa are experiencing increasing levels of desertification with gigantic dust storms from denuded land, sometimes blowing across the Pacific Ocean to North America.
- In the early 1930s, a major drought occurred along with the already large-scale cultivation and overgrazing of native grasses in North America's Great Plains. The resulting **Dust Bowl** forced thousands of farmers off their unproductive land as millions of tons of topsoil eroded and were lost forever.
- **Overgrazing** by cattle, sheep, goats, or other livestock can contribute to soil degradation, especially when native grasses are removed. Worldwide, overgrazing causes as much soil degradation as conventional cropland agriculture does, and it is an *even greater* cause of desertification.
- Grazing now exceeds the sustainable supply of grass in India by 30% and in parts of China by up to 50%.

The principles of soil conservation and specific solutions to modern agriculture's overuse of water and fertilizer

- **The Soil Conservation Act** (1935) established the Soil Conservation Service (SCS) in response to the devastation caused in the Dust Bowl. In 1994 it was renamed the **Natural Resources Conservation Service (NRCS)**, and its responsibilities were expanded to include water quality protection and pollution control.
- Soil conservation efforts are thriving internationally, often utilizing a variety of approaches. Farming methods making use of the general principle of *maximizing vegetative cover to protect soils against erosion* are increasing, as are more sound methods for the use of water.

    - **Conservation tillage** describes approaches that reduce the amount of plowing relative to conventional farming. It is any method of limited tilling that leaves more than 30% of crop residue covering the soil after harvest. Critics have noted that this approach often requires substantial chemical herbicide and synthetic fertilizer use because weeds are not physically removed from fields after crop harvest.
    - **No-till agriculture** is the most extreme form of conservation tillage and does not involve tilling (plowing or disking) the soil. A "no-till drill" cuts furrows through the O horizon of dead weeds, crop residue, and the upper levels of the A horizon, dropping seeds and fertilizer into the furrow. By not removing the previous year's crop residue, the increased organic matter also helps to improve soil's fertility.

        - Researchers today are debating just how much impact no-till farming and conservation tillage can have on carbon sequestration and global climate change mitigation. Studies seem to have determined that these methods capture and store carbon that would otherwise make its way to the atmosphere.
        - Nearly 25% of American farmland is under no-till cultivation, and over 40% of American farmland is using some form of conservation tillage. Although pioneered in the United States and the United Kingdom, no-till and conservation tillage methods are now most widespread in subtropical and temperate South America (Brazil, Argentina, and Paraguay).

    - **Crop rotation** methods involve alternating the type of crop grown in a given field from one season to the next. This returns nutrients to the soil (legume planting), breaks plant disease cycles, and minimizes erosion.
    - **Contour farming** consists of plowing furrows sideways across a hillside, perpendicular to its slope and following the natural contours of the land, to prevent runoff and erosion.
    - **Terracing** is the most effective method for preventing soil erosion on extremely steep terrain. Terraces are level platforms, or steps, that are cut into steep hillsides to contain irrigation water.

- **Intercropping** minimizes erosion by planting different types of crops in alternating bands or other spatially mixed arrangements. The additional ground cover slows erosion much more readily than a single crop.
- **Shelterbelts,** or windbreaks, are a widespread technique used to reduce erosion caused by wind. These consist of rows of trees or tall shrubs that are planted along the edges of fields to slow the wind.

- While water is essential for maximum agricultural productivity, **irrigation,** the artificial provision of water beyond what crops receive from rainfall, can also damage soil (70% of all fresh water used on Earth is for irrigation). Irrigation efficiency worldwide is low, with plants using about 40% of all the water that is applied. In many cases, withdrawing water for irrigation has dried up rivers and lakes and has depleted groundwater in important aquifers like the Ogallala Aquifer and the groundwater under California's San Joaquin Valley.

  - **Salinization** occurs most frequently in arid agricultural areas when the small amounts of salts in irrigation water become highly concentrated on the soil surface through high evaporation rates. Salinization now inhibits production on one-fifth of all irrigated cropland globally, costing more than $11 billion each year. Irrigating efficiently, planting crops requiring less water, and irrigating with water low in salt help to prevent salinization.
  - **Waterlogging,** another water-use issue, occurs when overirrigation saturates the soil and causes the water table to rise to the level that plant roots are drowned, essentially suffocating the plants.
  - **Water-use solutions that increase efficiency** include:

    1) better matching of crops to climate (e.g., not growing rice and cotton in deserts),
    2) using **drip-irrigation** systems that target water directly toward plants (hoses drip water directly into soil near the plant's roots), and
    3) lining irrigation canals to prevent leakage, covering them to reduce evaporation, and adapting farming methods overall that reduce water loss (conservation tillage).

- Nutrients for plants are also essential, along with adequate water and a healthy soil. However, **fertilizers,** especially when overapplied, can chemically damage soils. Inorganic (mined or synthetically manufactured mineral supplements of N, P, or K) fertilizers are more susceptible to leaching and runoff, causing significant effects in waterways (eutrophication leading to hypoxia and "dead zones"). Organic (remains or wastes of organisms, manure, crop residues, and compost) fertilizers can improve soil structure, nutrient retention, and water-holding capacity, helping to prevent erosion.

- **Fertilizer/nutrient-use solutions** that increase sustainability include

    1) targeting the delivery of nutrients to plant roots to avoid the overapplication of fertilizer,
    2) planting buffer strips of vegetation along field edges and along rivers/streams on farmland property to help capture nutrient runoff along with any eroded soil, and
    3) using organic fertilizers because they not only provide nutrients, but also improve soil structure that helps to retain water and nutrients.

The importance of pollinators to crop success

- Although our grain crops (wheat and corn) are wind-pollinated, many fruit, vegetable, and nut crops depend on a variety of insects for pollination. In contributing to global food production success, insects provide more than $577 billion in ecosystem services each year.
- At least 800 types of cultivated plants rely on bees and other insects for pollination, with an estimated 73% relying directly on honeybees.
- The European honeybee, *Apis mellifera,* forms the foundation of modern agriculture, pollinating more than 100 crops that make up one-third of the U.S. diet and providing an estimated $17 billion in annual ecosystem services.
- Today, as a result of increased pesticide use, pesticide drift, habitat loss, and novel parasites and pathogens, many populations of native pollinators are decreasing and completely disappearing. This recent phenomenon, known as **colony collapse disorder,** has become a great concern for global agriculture. An additional new threat in the form of neonicotinoid pesticides, designed to be systemic in plants (killing the insects that consume plant parts), is also killing bees and butterflies.
- **Solutions to pollinator threats** include the following:

    1) establishing wildflower belts and flowering shrubs near cropland,
    2) eliminating or reducing chemical pesticide and herbicide use,
    3) planting pollinator gardens in suburban yards and urban parks, and
    4) ensuring genetic diversity in crops.

The major policy approaches for pursuing soil conservation and sustainable agriculture

- Today's industrial agriculture exerts tremendous impacts (often negative) on Earth's terrestrial lands and ecosystems. Some existing government policies often *worsen* land degradation.

    - **Subsidies** (government incentives of cash or tax breaks) can encourage people to cultivate land that would otherwise not be farmed. Approximately one-fifth of the income of the average U.S. farmer comes from subsidies.

- American ranchers currently benefit from subsidies, paying substantially **low grazing fees** to graze livestock on Bureau of Land Management (BLM) lands. In 2019, a grazing permit was just $1.35 per month per "animal unit." Such low fees can encourage overgrazing and land degradation through a "tragedy of the commons" scenario.

- The **Conservation Reserve Program,** established in the 1985 Farm Bill, pays farmers to stop cultivating highly erodible cropland and instead places it in conservation reserves planted with grasses and trees. Each year the federal government pays farmers about $2 billion for conservation of farmland accepted into the program. Besides reducing soil erosion, the program generates income for farmers, improves water quality, and provides increased wildlife habitat—a prime example of a program of "payment for ecological services."

- Financial incentives (the *Wetlands Reserve Program*) are being used as a means to protect the valuable ecosystem services of wetlands by offering payments to landowners who restore or enhance wetland areas on their property.

- Conservation measures for pollinators were included in the 2018 Farm Bill amendments and Environmental Incentive program.

Chapter 10: Making Agriculture Sustainable

> ## YOU MUST KNOW
>
> - The challenge of feeding a growing human population.
> - The goals, methods, and consequences of the Green Revolution.
> - The environmental issues involved in raising animals for food.
> - The strategies for pest and weed management.
> - The characteristics and potential of organic agriculture.
> - The science behind genetic engineering and debate over genetically modified food.
> - The environmental imperative of sustainable agriculture.

The challenge of feeding a growing human population

- Global food production has risen more quickly than world population growth over the past half-century.
- This steady rise in food production has resulted from the increased use of fossil fuels; a highly intensified use of irrigation, pesticides, and fertilizers; the cultivation of more land; and the development (through selective breeding and genetic engineering) of more productive crop and livestock varieties.
- Despite rising food production, more than 800 million people experience **undernutrition** (receiving fewer calories than the minimum dietary energy requirement); over 1 billion people are overweight as a result of **overnutrition,** and millions of children experience **malnutrition** (a shortage of essential nutrients, such as protein).

The goals, methods, and consequences of the Green Revolution

- In the 1940s, the desire for a greater quantity and quality of food and increased food security for the world's growing population led **Norman Borlaug** (who later won the Nobel Peace Prize for this work) to develop improved varieties of wheat through selective breeding. This technology was quickly transferred to developing countries such as Mexico, India, and Pakistan. Within two decades, Mexico tripled its wheat production and began exporting wheat.

- Although the yields of wheat, rice, and corn were boosted worldwide, these **Green Revolution** methods required synthetic fertilizer and pesticides, increased water and fossil fuel consumption, and resulted in pollution of soil, air, and water, worsened topsoil erosion, and increased salinization and desertification.
- In today's industrial agriculture, **monocultures,** large expanses of single crop types, have replaced the traditional, small-scale polycultures, as these monocultures were found to be more efficient for planting and harvesting. However, the risk of catastrophic failure of an entire crop due to disease increased, especially without large applications of pesticides.
- Between 1961 and 2013, global food production more than tripled and per-person food production rose 48%, while land area converted for agriculture increased only 11%.
- As industrial agriculture practices and the planting of monocultures increased worldwide, **seed banks** (institutions preserving genetic diversity as a kind of living museum) were initiated, storing millions of seeds from around the world as a safeguard against global agricultural collapse.
- The **Svalbard Global Seed Vault** (Spitsbergen, Norway) is the most renowned; however, the Royal Botanic Gardens Millennium Seed Bank in Britain, the U.S. National Seed Storage at Colorado State University, and the Wheat and Maize Improvement Center in Mexico are also major storehouses of seed diversity.

The environmental issues involved in raising animals for food

- Global meat production has increased more than fivefold since 1950, and per capita meat consumption has doubled.
- Food choices have significant implications for energy, land, and water usage; therefore, what we eat can significantly affect environmental quality. For instance, livestock in the United States account for 55% of the nation's soil erosion, 37% of pesticide application, 50% of antibiotics consumed, and one-third of the nitrogen and phosphorus pollution in U.S. waterways. Most experts believe that in order to sustain our growing population, we will need to begin raising livestock in ways that are less polluting and less resource-intensive and to reduce global meat consumption.
- Different animal food products (beef, pork, chickens, eggs, and milk) require different amounts of energy input (animal feed). The energy input per calorie of food produced is called the **energy subsidy.** For example, it takes 20 kg of grain to feed to cattle to produce 1 kg of beef (an energy subsidy of 20), whereas it takes only 2.8 kg of grain to produce 1 kg of chicken (an energy subsidy of 2.8).

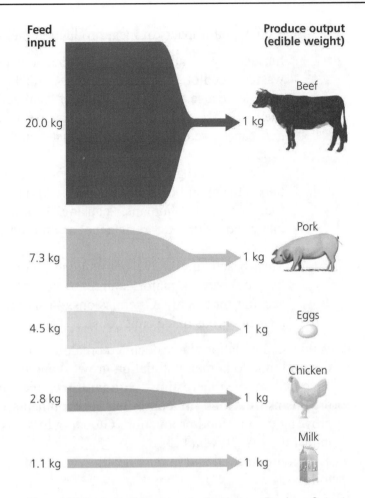

Figure 10.8 Animal Feed Inputs for Various Produce Outputs

- **Feedlots,** an industrial agriculture practice also known as **factory farms** or **concentrated animal feeding operations (CAFOs),** are huge warehouses or pens designed to deliver energy-rich food to confined animals living at extremely high densities. Farmers minimize land costs, improve feeding efficiency, and increase the fraction of food energy that goes into production of animal body mass. Heavy use of antibiotics (to control disease) and hormones (given to encourage fast weight gain) are standard feedlot practices.

- One-third of the world's cropland is devoted to growing feed for animals, and 45% of the global grain production goes to livestock and poultry. Therefore, as the world population continues to grow, plant-based diets have the potential of feeding many more people.

- Another potential approach currently occupying researchers and investors and driven by climate change concerns is to grow meat in a lab using *in vitro* tissue culture techniques or to produce plant-based "meat." As of 2019, a number of start-up companies are beginning large-scale commercial production of these new "meat" alternatives (such as the Impossible Burger and the Beyond Burger).

■ Environmental impacts of meat production include the following:

1) Surface water and groundwater become polluted from animal wastes (feedlot runoff). Rich in N and P, livestock waste is a common cause of eutrophication of localized waters.

2) Many disease-causing microorganisms such as *Salmonella* and *E. coli* can be released in animal wastes and also end up in water supplies.

3) Antibiotics and growth hormones, much of which are excreted by the animals, end up in wastewater and may be transferred up the food chain to humans, causing health problems including increased antibiotic resistance of microorganisms and human cancers.

4) Meat-based diets have consequences for climate change since livestock are a major source of greenhouse gases (livestock account for 5% of CO_2 emissions, 44% of methane emissions, and 53% of nitrous oxide emissions).

■ Wild fish populations have declined precipitously worldwide as increased demand (due to human population growth) and new fishing technologies have led to overharvesting. **Aquaculture,** the cultivation of aquatic organisms for food in controlled environments, is now the fastest-growing type of food production: Global output has increased eight-fold in just the past 30 years.

■ The environmental and human health *benefits* of aquaculture include the following:

1) Ensures a reliable protein source for human consumption.

2) Helps to reduce fishing pressure on overharvested and declining wild fish stocks, as well as lessens the **bycatch** (unintended catch of nontarget species).

3) Uses much less fossil fuel than does commercial fishing.

■ The environmental *disadvantages* of aquaculture include the following:

1) Aquaculture wastewater may contain bacteria, viruses, and pests that thrive in these high-density habitats and can then infect wild fish and shellfish populations.

2) Aquaculture wastewater contains much organic matter that can lead to eutrophication of local waters.

3) Fish that escape from aquaculture facilities may harm wild fish populations by outcompeting native species or by interbreeding with them (a significant concern if the escapees are GM-farmed fish).

The strategies for pest and weed management

- **Pesticides** are synthetic chemicals used to kill insects (insecticides), plants (herbicides), and fungi (fungicides), which humans consider damaging to valuable crops. An additional problem is that pesticides commonly kill nontarget organisms, including the predators and parasites of the pests that they are meant to target. Moreover, chemical pesticides affect bees and other beneficial pollinators of our food crops.

- Since 1990, pesticide use has risen nearly 80% worldwide. This widespread use of pesticides often kills nontarget organisms in addition to the targeted species.

- **Neonicotinoids,** a new class of chemical insecticides, have become common in treating crop seeds. The neonicotinoids become systemic in the plant, ending up in leaves, stems, fruits, and pollen. These "nionics" ultimately make the plant toxic to insects, killing them as they feed on or pollinate the plant.

- Pests can evolve resistance to chemical pesticides, requiring humans to design increasingly toxic poisons in order to kill the genetically resistant individuals, a phenomenon known as the "**pesticide treadmill.**"

- **Biological control** (biocontrol) is the use of living species (rather than pesticides) that are the natural enemy of or prey upon or parasitize the targeted pest.

  - Parasitoid wasps are frequently used as biocontrol agents of many caterpillars.

  - *Bacillus thuringiensis* **(Bt)** is a naturally occurring soil bacterium that produces a toxin that kills many caterpillars and some fly and beetle larvae. Bt can be sprayed on crops to protect against these insect attacks.

  - Occasionally the biocontrol agent itself can become a pest or have unintended effects if used in an area where it is not native and no natural predators exist. For example, the cactus moth's introduction to the Caribbean islands and its subsequent spread to Florida is of concern to Mexico and the American Southwest, where it could decimate native prickly pear cactus.

- **Integrated pest management (IPM)** incorporates numerous techniques, including biocontrol, use of limited chemicals when essential, crop rotation, transgenic crops, alternative tillage methods, and mechanical pest removal. IPM works especially well in landscapes at small to moderate scales such as small farms and university campuses. On a nationwide scale, success in countries such as Indonesia has led to the wide adoption of IPM in many parts of the developing world.

The characteristics and potential of organic agriculture

- **Organic agriculture** uses no synthetic fertilizers, insecticides, fungicides, or herbicides, but instead relies on biological approaches such as biocontrol and composting.
- Worldwide sales of organic food grew five times between 2000 and 2016, when sales neared $90 billion, as consumers are favoring organic food out of concern about health risks posed by the pesticides, hormones, and antibiotics used in conventional agriculture.
- Organic agriculture takes up less than 1% of agricultural land worldwide. This area is rapidly expanding, with Mexico the leader among developing nations. Europe has 33.3 million acres under organic management and the United States has 5 million acres.
- On average, crop yields on organic farms are about 80% of the yield on conventional industrial farms; however, greenhouse gas emissions and energy input are noticeably less with organic farming methods than with conventional farming.
- The world's two longest-running field experiments in organic farming (in Switzerland and at Rodale Institute, Pennsylvania) have produced soils with more microbial life, earthworm activity, water-holding capacity, topsoil depth, and naturally occurring nutrients than found with conventional farming.

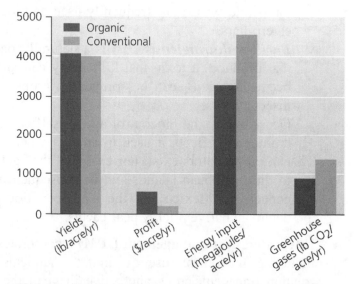

Figure 2 Organic Versus Conventional Farming Comparisons

The science behind genetic engineering and debate over genetically modified food

- **Genetic engineering** is any process whereby scientists directly manipulate an organism's genetic material in the laboratory by adding, deleting, or changing segments of its DNA.

- **Genetically modified organisms (GMOs)** are organisms that have been genetically engineered using **recombinant DNA,** which is DNA that has been spliced together from multiple organisms. The goal is to place genes that code for certain desirable traits (such as rapid growth, disease resistance, or high nutritional content) into the genomes of organisms lacking those traits. Roundup Ready soybeans are currently the most abundant GM crop in the world.

- **Transgenic organisms** are those that contain DNA from another species. All GM organisms are also transgenic species. In the last several years, researchers have brought genetic engineering to a new level with gene editing, the ability to make targeted changes to genomes. One popular approach, called CRISPR, was recently employed to produce the world's first gene-edited food for sale in the United States, the white-button mushroom. CRISPR techniques allow researchers to disable the mushroom's enzyme that turns its flesh brown, thereby extending its shelf life.

- The techniques geneticists use to create GM organisms differ from traditional selective breeding in several ways.

  - Traditional selective breeding mixes genes from individuals of the *same* species, whereas recombinant DNA techniques routinely mix genes of *different* species.
  - Selective breeding deals with *whole* organisms in nature, whereas genetic engineering works with *genetic material* in the lab.
  - Selective/traditional breeding selects from genes that come together on their own, whereas genetic engineering creates combinations that did not previously exist in nature and otherwise would not come together on their own.

- Today, most GM crops are engineered to resist herbicides and/or to resist insect attack. Examples include **Roundup Ready crops** (originally patented by Monsanto Chemical and containing genes to resist their widely used herbicide Roundup), **Bt crops** (which have the ability to produce their own toxic effects on insects), and golden rice (a nutritionally enhanced rice with GM genes producing vitamin A).

- In the United States, 95% of corn, soybeans, and cotton, and 100% of sugar beets and canola are GM varieties. It is conservatively estimated that over 70% of processed foods in U.S. stores contain GM ingredients. Thus, it is extremely likely that you consume GM foods on a daily basis.

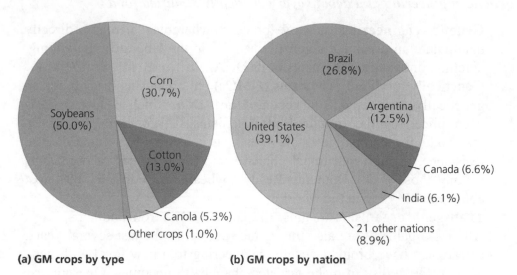

(a) GM crops by type   **(b) GM crops by nation**

Figure 10.24 a and b   GM Crops by Type and GM Crops by Nation

- **Critics of GM crops** cite environmental, health, and ethical concerns.
  - Currently, most scientists feel that *ecological impacts* of GM foods are a greater issue than potential health impacts. It is also known that much of the research into GM food safety is funded and/or conducted by the same corporations that stand to profit from transgenic crop approval.
  - Transgenes from GM crops might escape into nature, harming nontarget organisms. There is widespread concern today that the growing organic food market will be hindered if organic farms are contaminated with pollen or seed from GM plants.
  - Pests might evolve resistance to the GM crops and become "super pests." Also, genes for herbicide resistance can be transferred to other plants accidently—the result might be the creation of "superweeds."
  - Herbicide-tolerant crops tend to result in *more herbicide use* as farmers may apply additional herbicide if their crops can withstand it. Weeds may even evolve resistance to herbicides, making heavier applications necessary. Scientists have recently confirmed glyphosate resistance (the active ingredient in the Roundup herbicide) in 40 species of weeds, supporting the environmental concern of superweed proliferation.
  - GM crops are genetically engineered for tolerance to herbicides that the same company manufactures and profits from (e.g., Monsanto's Roundup Ready crops).
  - There is concern that the global food supply is becoming dominated by a few large agrobiotech corporations that develop GM technologies (Monsanto, Syngenta, Bayer, CropScience, Dow, DuPont, and BASF).
  - The Green Revolution was a largely public venture, whereas the "gene revolution" is largely driven by financial interests of corporations selling these GM products that they patent.

- Crops with traits that might benefit poor farmers in developing countries (such as increased nutrition, as well as drought and salinity tolerance) have not been widely commercialized because of the lower economic incentive for the big GM companies.

- **Supporters of GM crops** cite a number of environmental and economic benefits.

  - Because farmers do not have to till to control weeds, herbicide-tolerant crops may enable more no-till farming, thus protecting soil from erosion.
  - Insect-resistant Bt crops appear to reduce the use of chemical pesticides; however, herbicide use has increased with GM crops.
  - Drought-tolerant GM crops save on water needed for irrigation.
  - High-yield GM crops help to reduce the need for increased land clearing.
  - A 2014 meta-analysis of GM crop production found that GM crops produce yields 22% higher than non-GM crops and boosted farmer's profits by 68%.

- However, many experts feel that with regard to GM foods, we should be employing the **precautionary principle:** One should not undertake a new action until the ramifications of that action are fully understood.

- More than 60 nations require labeling of GM foods, although the United States does not. Only a few states (CT, VT, ME) have currently passed GMO labeling laws.

The environmental imperative of sustainable agriculture

- Industrial agriculture has allowed food production to keep pace with our growing population. However, it has also led to many adverse environmental impacts such as soil degradation, heavy reliance on fossil fuels, and human health concerns over heavy pesticide use, genetic modification, and intensive feedlot operations.

- **Sustainable agriculture** is agriculture that does not deplete soils faster than they form and does not reduce the amount of clean water or genetic diversity essential to long-term crop and livestock production. Fossil fuel inputs are greatly reduced, as are pesticides, synthetic fertilizers, growth hormones, and antibiotics. Reliance on biological approaches mimicking natural ecosystem functioning is emphasized, including composting, biocontrol, and recycling of matter.

- **Organic agriculture** is the production of crops without the use of synthetic pesticides or fertilizers, using ecological principles and attempting to keep as much organic matter in the soil as possible. The crops cannot be genetically engineered.

- The **Organic Food Production Act (1990)** established the national standards for organic products (both crops and livestock) in the United States.

▪ Currently, organic agriculture takes up less than 1% of agricultural land worldwide, but it is growing rapidly. Mexico is a leader in organic agriculture among developing nations: Approximately 3% of Mexico's land is used for organic agriculture, and 30% of Mexico's coffee crop is now organic.

▪ **Locally grown agriculture** is another key component of the move toward sustainable agriculture, reducing fossil fuel use by avoiding long-distance transport. **Community-supported agriculture (CSA),** where consumers partner with local farmers and pay in advance for a share of their yield, and **farmers' markets** are also growing rapidly in most communities.

▪ Experts point out that overall food production is not what limits our ability to feed the world. Politics and the logistics of transport limit food distribution. In addition, one-third of all food intended for consumption ends up going to waste. Thus, by reducing waste, eating less meat, and dealing with food distribution problems, the world would be taking important steps toward a more sustainable global agriculture.

Chapter 23: Minerals and Mining

YOU MUST KNOW

- The main types of mineral resources and their uses.
- The major mining methods, including a specific mineral resource example for each.
- Specific examples of the environmental and social impacts of mining.
- Examples of specific reclamation efforts and U.S. mining policy.
- Examples of the sustainable use of mineral resources.

The main types of mineral resources and their uses

▪ **Minerals** are naturally occurring solid elements or inorganic compounds with a crystal structure, specific chemical composition, and distinct physical properties.

▪ **Mining,** in its broadest sense, describes the extraction of any resource that is nonrenewable on the timescale of our society. It is the systematic removal of rock, soil, or other material for the purpose of extracting minerals of economic interest.

  ▪ **Metals** are chemical elements that are typically lustrous, opaque, and malleable and that conduct heat and electricity.

  ▪ Most metals are not found in a pure state in Earth's crust but instead are present within **ore,** a grouping of minerals from which we extract metals.

Copper, iron, lead, gold, and aluminum are among the many economically valuable metals we extract from mined ore.

■ **Alloys** can be made when we mix, melt, and fuse a metal with another metal or a nonmetal, making a product that has the beneficial characteristics of each separate substance.

■ The minerals we use come from all over the world. Some of the most economically important minerals (mostly metals), together with their major use and main nation of origin, include the following:

■ *Titanium,* used for airplanes, from China
■ *Copper,* used for electrical wiring, from Chile
■ *Nickel,* used in alloys for stainless steel, from Cuba
■ *Tin,* used for steel plating, from China
■ *Tungsten,* used in metalworking, from China
■ *Indium,* used for LCDs and solar cells, from Canada
■ *Gold,* used as ingots for monetary value, from South Africa
■ *Uranium,* used in nuclear fuel, from Australia
■ *Tantalum,* extracted from coltan ore and used in capacitors and other electronic equipment, notably cell phones, from Australia and D.R. Congo

■ Processing minerals exerts environmental impacts that are water and energy intensive, and cause a wide variety of air pollution problems, including generating greenhouse gases that contribute to global climate change. In addition, soil and water commonly become polluted by **tailings,** the portion of ore left over after metals have been extracted.

■ **Surface impoundments** often store toxic slurries of tailings in large reservoirs. There have been 40 significant impoundment failures this past decade, with the toxic material killing aquatic life and affecting drinking water for many communities for weeks to months.

■ **Nonmetallic minerals** and fuels are also mined: sand, gravel, phosphates, limestone, gemstones, uranium ore, coal, and other fossil fuels (petroleum and natural gas).

■ According to 2018 estimates by the U.S. Mining Education Coalition, the average American consumes 17,440 kg (38,449 lb) of new minerals and fuels each year. The mining and processing of these metals and nonmetals have significant environmental impacts globally.

The major mining methods, including a specific mineral resource example for each

■ In 2018, raw materials from mining contributed $82 billion to the U.S. economy, and mining employed more than 1.3 million people.

■ **Strip mining** removes surface layers of soil and rock (the **overburden**) to expose the mineral resource below. Coal and oil sands are mined in this manner. By completely removing vegetative cover and nutrient-rich topsoil, strip mining obliterates natural biota over large areas and also produces **acid drainage.** Sulfide minerals in newly exposed rock surfaces react with oxygen and rainwater, producing sulfuric acid, which then proceeds to leach toxic metals from underlying rocks, further compromising aquatic life and drinking water supplies.

- **Subsurface mining** involves constructing deep shafts and tunnel systems when a resource occurs in concentrated pockets or seams deep underground. Zinc, lead, gold, copper, diamonds, and coal are mined in this manner. Subsurface mining is the most dangerous form of mining and produces a wide array of human health/respiratory hazards.
- **Open pit mining** is used when a mineral is spread widely and evenly throughout a rock formation or when the earth is unsuitable for tunneling. This involves digging a gigantic hole and removing the desired ore along with waste rock surrounding the ore, leaving it in massive heaps outside the pit. Copper, iron, gold, and diamonds are mined in this manner. The world's largest open pit mine is for copper, near Salt Lake City, Utah (2.5 miles across and 0.75 miles deep).
- **Placer mining** uses running water to isolate minerals. Coltan ore, which contains the mineral tantalum (highly heat resistant and readily conducts electricity, making it ideal for capacitors used in all cell phones), is mined in this manner.
- **Mountaintop removal mining** involves removing several hundred vertical feet of a mountaintop after forests are clear-cut, topsoil removed, and rock blasted away to expose the mineral resource. Low-sulfur coal in the Appalachian Mountains of the eastern United States is mined in this manner. Overburden is placed back onto the mountaintop, but the waste rock is unstable and typically is dumped into adjacent valleys.
- **Solution mining** dissolves and extracts resources in place and is often used for mining salts, some uranium, and copper.
- **Ocean mining** can involve the extraction of some minerals from seawater (magnesium) and/or mining the ocean floor for sand, gravel, and especially phosphate deposits used in fertilizers.

Specific examples of the environmental and social impacts of mining

- Many mining methods completely remove vegetation and topsoil, destroying the biological community and habitat for many species; strip mining, open pit mining, and mountaintop mining are the leading offenders.
- **Acid drainage** occurs when water leaches compounds (especially sulfide minerals) from freshly exposed waste rock, leading to water pollution that is highly toxic (due to its low pH) to aquatic organisms. The Berkeley Pit, a former open pit copper mine in Montana, is today one of the largest Superfund toxic waste cleanup sites because of the highly acidic groundwater pollution it caused.
- When overburden (from strip mining, open pit mining, and mountaintop mining) is replaced, it is highly unstable and often erodes because the

original vegetation has been removed. As a result, high levels of sediment are deposited in surrounding waterways.

- **Mountaintop removal** for coal destroys forests, mountaintop habitats, and adjacent valleys and streams because the waste rock is most often dumped in these areas. Loss of biodiversity and loss of ecosystem services are the most obvious impacts; however, loss of rare, endemic species and loss of the ecosystem's ability to cycle nutrients and produce organic matter for downstream systems are less apparent but just as vital.
- Some minerals exposed from the mining processes, such as selenium, are known to **bioaccumulate** in organisms, causing birth defects.
- Various studies have found that when over 5–10% of a watershed's area is disturbed by human alteration, the water quality and biodiversity in a stream decline. Mountaintop mining typically disturbs percentages ranging from 17% to 51%.
- Mining often has negative health impacts on miners, especially with regard to respiratory conditions (e.g., black lung and emphysema).
- Mining often causes adverse living conditions for people living near mines due to increased noise pollution, groundwater pollution, and the inhalation of air pollutants and dust. Increased flood damage, due to flash flooding potential (resulting from the removal of vegetation and topsoil, which alters the topography), is also a major concern.

Examples of specific reclamation efforts and U.S. mining policy

- Because of the environmental impacts of mining, the United States and many other developed nations now require that mining companies restore or reclaim surface-mined sites following mining. The **Surface Mining Control and Reclamation Act** (1977) mandates restoration efforts, requiring companies to post bonds to cover reclamation costs before mining can be approved.
- Mine reclamation efforts are challenging and often not able to restore the original ecology because of the toxic soil and water conditions left behind by the mining operation.
- Mining policy in the United States is still being dictated by the **General Mining Act of 1872**. This act encourages prospecting for minerals on federally owned land by allowing claims to be staked on any plot of public land open to mining. No payments back to the public are required, and only recently has restoration of the land after mining been mandated.

- A 2014 study found that there may be a potential for treating fracking wastewater with acid mine drainage water, resulting in the removal of some contaminants (barium, strontium, sulfate, and radioactive radium) as precipitates (strontium barite), producing wastewater less damaging to the environment. Additional research into this possible approach is ongoing.
- Superfund sites, like Montana's Berkeley Pit, are slowly being reclaimed; however, the number of designated Superfund sites far exceeds those being actively cleaned up.

Examples of the sustainable use of mineral resources

- By encouraging **recycling of mineral resources,** we can address the two major challenges (finite supply and environmental damage issues) caused by mining. For example, currently 35% of our copper and 80% of our lead come from recycled sources such as pipes and wires. Over 40% of the aluminum in the United States is recycled, which is positive because it takes over 20 times more energy to extract virgin aluminum from more than it does to obtain it from recycled sources. Overall, 35% of all metals are currently recycled in the United States.
- Several factors affect how long a given mineral resource will last: discovery of new reserves, development of new extraction technologies, changing consumption patterns, and the extent of recycling of a specific mineral.
- **Electronic waste,** or e-waste, from discarded cell phones, computers, and other electronic products is rising fast and contains many valuable minerals, such as tantalum. Recycling, refurbishing, and reusing these devices rather than discarding them is a more sustainable approach and will require more efforts and focus. Currently, only about 10% of old cell phones are recycled.

Table 23.1 Recycled minerals in the United States

Mineral	U.S. Recycling Rate
Gold	Slightly less is recycled than is consumed
Iron and steel scrap	Nearly 100% for vehicles, 88% for appliances, 71–98% for construction materials, 70% for cans
Lead	71% consumed comes from recycled post-consumer items
Nickel	52% consumed is from recycled nickel
Zinc	25% produced is recovered, mostly from recycled materials used in processing
Chromium	29% is recycled in stainless steel production
Copper	35% of U.S. supply comes from various recycled sources
Aluminum	28% produced comes from recycled post-consumer items

Tin	22% consumed is from recycled tin
Germanium	30% consumed worldwide is recycled. Optical device manufacturing recycles more than 60%
Molybdenum	About 30% gets recycled as part of steel scrap that is recycled
Cobalt	29% consumed comes from recycled scrap
Niobium (columbium)	Perhaps 20% gets recycled as part of steel scrap that is recycled
Silver	18% consumed is from recycled silver. U.S. recovers as much as it produces
Bismuth	All scrap metal containing bismuth is recycled, providing less than 5% of consumption
Diamond (industrial)	2% of production is from recycled diamond dust, grit, and stone

Data are for 2018, from U.S. Geological Survey, 2019. *Mineral commodity summaries 2019.* Reston, VA: USGS.

■ Minerals are nonrenewable resources, and many are currently limited in supply. In 2019, geologists calculated that the world's known reserves of tantalum (mined in Australia for cell phone electronic circuitry and for capacitors) would last about 110 more years at today's rate of consumption. The dwindling supplies of indium (mined in Canada and a previously obscure metal) are now widely used for LCD screens and solar cells and are projected to last only another 25 years. A lack of indium threatens the production of high-efficiency photovoltaic solar cells. Recycling old electronic devices will help conserve valuable minerals such as tantalum (from coltan ore mined in the Democratic Republic of Congo) and also keeps the growing volume of e-waste out of landfills.

Multiple-Choice Questions

1. The soil horizon commonly known as subsoil is the
   (A) A horizon.
   (B) O horizon.
   (C) B horizon.
   (D) C horizon.

2. Which of the following is the *primary* environmental advantage of no-till agriculture?
   (A) Nesting migratory songbird populations are undisturbed.
   (B) The crop residues reduce the O horizon.
   (C) The topsoil is less susceptible to loss.
   (D) Less herbicides are needed to improve the overall stability of the soil.

3. Genetically modified (GM) organisms are best described as those that
   (A) have genes of several different members of the same species.
   (B) have genes of several members of a different species.
   (C) have genes that have been artificially created in a laboratory.
   (D) have genes that have bacterial genes for increased resistance, plus the most desirable genes of the species.

4. Which of the following best explains how a pest develops resistance to a chemical pesticide?
   (A) The pest develops adaptations to deal with adverse effects in its environment.
   (B) Mutation and genetic recombination occur naturally.
   (C) Genetically modified organisms are usually best adapted to be resistant.
   (D) Natural selection takes place.

Use the graph below to answer questions 5 and 6.

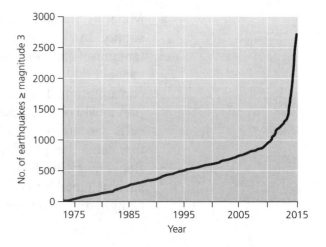

Earthquake frequency in west Texas and Oklahoma, 1973–2015.

5. The hypothesis that scientists proposed for the results shown in the above earthquake frequency graph was
   (A) decreased fault stability.
   (B) increased groundwater removal.
   (C) decreased environmental protection.
   (D) increased wastewater well injection.

6. The approximate percent change in earthquake frequency from 1995 to 2015 was
   (A) 4.5%.
   (B) 22.5%.
   (C) 225%.
   (D) 450%.

7. Many types of mining, such as those used to mine coal and copper, produce a specific type of water pollution called
   (A) eutrophication.
   (B) suspended limestone particles.
   (C) sediment load.
   (D) acid drainage.

8. International seedbanks have been established for the *primary* purpose of
   (A) preserving declining crop diversity.
   (B) finding more available substitutes for scarce agricultural crops for developing countries.
   (C) increasing productivity in developed countries.
   (D) international cooperation.

9. The environmental consequence of overfertilization of agricultural lands includes
   (A) sustained fertile soils in years to come.
   (B) rapid spread of crops into nearby areas.
   (C) large crop yields per acre.
   (D) eutrophication in nearby waters.

Use the following figure to answer questions 10 and 11.

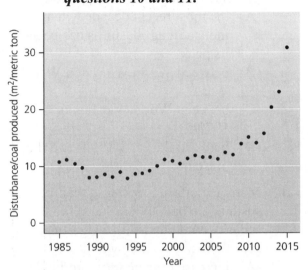

10. From 2010 to 2015, the amount of land that has been disturbed to secure a metric ton of coal has increased by approximately
    (A) 200%.
    (B) 100%.
    (C) 30%.
    (D) 15%.

11. Given the above results, the most probable method of mining employed was
    (A) strip mining.
    (B) belowground mining.
    (C) mountaintop removal mining.
    (D) open-pit mining.

12. Which of the following is an important feature of integrated pest management?
    (A) It requires subsistence agricultural practices, including composting.
    (B) It makes use of the natural enemies of pests.
    (C) It makes effective use of GMO-developed plants.
    (D) It involves relocating pests back to their native habitat, where they will do minimal damage.

13. The Green Revolution is most closely associated with which time period?
    (A) the most recent decade, when industrial agribusiness has been at its peak
    (B) between World War I and World War II
    (C) between World War II and the 1970s
    (D) between the early 1990s and the present

14. Many experts are reporting that the most sustainable path to long-term food security combined with a significant greenhouse reduction would
    (A) increase organic farm production.
    (B) dramatically decrease livestock as a food source.
    (C) increase grass-fed and free-range livestock.
    (D) increase genetically modified food production.

15. The U.S Surface Mining Control and Reclamation Act of 1977 requires
    (A) all mined minerals to be processed and sold within the United States.
    (B) minimal remediation of water pollution, except in the case of toxic uranium mining.
    (C) restoration of the identical ecosystem and biodiversity present prior to the mining activity.
    (D) mining companies to post bonds to cover restoration of the mined area before permits are granted.

16. IPM is the agricultural approach involving
    (A) biocontrol and alternative tillage methods.
    (B) treatment with chlorine and/or ozone.
    (C) pollinators, transgenic crops, and CAFOs.
    (D) Roundup Ready crops.

17. Leaching
    (A) can help plant growth if done sustainably.
    (B) is caused by movement of water upward through soil from the water table.
    (C) adds nutrients to soil naturally from weathered parent material.
    (D) removes water-soluble nutrients from soil.

18. Plate tectonics is a process that can affect
    (A) the normal ecosystem structure and function.
    (B) the shape of Earth's landscapes, including building mountains.
    (C) the frequency of volcanic eruptions resulting from tsunami events.
    (D) the essential flow of matter and recycling of energy.

19. Crops genetically engineered to fix nitrogen would have which of the following advantages?
    (A) increased disease resistance
    (B) increased tolerance of nitrous oxides in the air
    (C) decreased absorption of toxic chemicals
    (D) decreased need for chemical fertilizer

20. Critics of the Green Revolution most often cite
    (A) the overabundance of food produced, leading to unusually low food prices.
    (B) the necessity for seed banks, now that we are using so many varied seeds to grow crops worldwide.
    (C) the increased practice of monocropping, leading to increased risk of overall crop failure without the widespread use of pesticides.
    (D) new strains of GMO seeds that have transgenes, which may escape into nature, causing unknown and possibly harmful effects.

Use the graph below to answer questions 21 and 22.

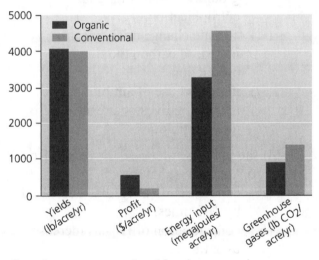

Organic versus conventional farming comparisons

21. A major conclusion that could be reached from the above data is that
    (A) greenhouse gas emission is improved with conventional farming methods.
    (B) energy input is reduced with organic farming methods.
    (C) profit comparisons are negligible between these two farming methods.
    (D) yields of conventional farming are high compared to organic farming methods.

22. When comparing greenhouse gas emissions, conventional farming
    (A) produces less emissions than organic farming.
    (B) produces approximately 1000 lb CO_2/acre/yr more.
    (C) produces approximately 1000 lb CO_2/acre/yr less.
    (D) produces approximately 500 lb CO_2/acre/yr more.

Use the figure below to answer questions 23 and 24.

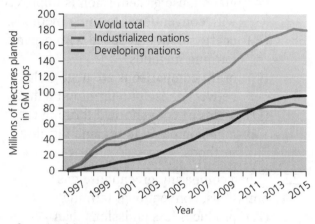

Growth of GM crops, 1997–2015

23. The percent change in the growth of the world's total GM crops between 2009 and 2012 is approximately
    (A) 170%.
    (B) 80%.
    (C) 40%.
    (D) 20%.

24. The graph evidence provides support for the conclusion that in the last 5 years, GM crops have been
    (A) growing faster in industrialized nations.
    (B) growing faster in developing nations.
    (C) positively influencing world food supply.
    (D) negatively influencing world food supply.

25. Conservation tillage is an agricultural practice that
    (A) maximizes intact ground cover to prevent soil erosion.
    (B) conserves all native grasses in order to promote intact ecosystems.
    (C) removes all weeds and competing plants in order to maximize crop yields.
    (D) promotes polyculture, including cattle grazing, to naturally fertilize fields.

26. The major environmental problem arising from feedlots is
    (A) damaged soil that will never be able to grow food crops.
    (B) pollution of surface and groundwater, resulting in eutrophication.
    (C) climate change arising from increased carbon dioxide production.
    (D) increased use of antibiotics and increasing livestock resistance to these antibiotics.

27. If the pH of a solution is increased from 7 to 9, it means that the
    (A) concentration of H^+ has decreased by 100 times.
    (B) concentration of H^+ has increased by 2 times.
    (C) concentration of OH^- has increased by 2 times.
    (D) concentration of H^+ has increased by 100 times.

Free-Response Question

The *Kansas Star Chronicler* recently published an article—***"Beyond Meatless Monday: Eliminating the American Hamburger"***—that received much attention across the United States. Read the following brief excerpt and answer the questions below.

> On average, Americans eat three hamburgers a week—a higher level of meat consumption than any other developed nation. For thousands of years, through selective breeding, humans have been influencing the genetic makeup of our livestock and crops to increase food production. Now plant genes are being altered in new ways to make crops more pest-, drought-, and cold-resistant, resulting in genetically modified organisms (GMOs). Even more recently, experts are suggesting the elimination of livestock as significant progress toward reducing climate change. According to one scientist, "Growing animal protein in the laboratory or developing plant-based meat is the climate solution, as the current use of animals in food production is an environmentally destructive technology that must be eliminated."

a) i. Identify two important GMOs on the market today.
    ii. For each of your GMO choices above, explain one *environmental* or one *health benefit*.
    iii. Describe an *ecological concern* for GMOs expressed by the scientific community.
b) Explain two significant *environmental* consequences of raising beef today. Use specific evidence to support each environmental consequence.
c) Critics of a meat-based diet say that eating meat is "wildly inefficient." Explain what is meant by this statement, and provide a solution for this criticism.

The Urban Environment

Chapter 13: The Urban Environment: Creating Sustainable Cities

---

YOU MUST KNOW

- The current trends and scale of urbanization.
- The causes and effects of urban sprawl.
- How to analyze environmental impacts and advantages of urban centers.
- How to assess urban ecology and the pursuit of sustainable cities.
- How to evaluate transportation options, urban parks, and green buildings.

The current trends and scale of urbanization

- **Urbanization,** the shift from living in rural areas to cities and suburbs, may be the single greatest change our society has undergone since its transition from a nomadic hunter-gatherer to a sedentary agricultural lifestyle. In 2009, for the first time ever, more people were living in urban areas than in rural areas.

- In 2019, the percentage of those living in urban areas in the United States stood at 82%, with approximately 50% in the suburbs. United Nations demographers project that in 2050, more than two of every three people will live in urban areas.

- In developing countries, most of the population still resides on farms; however, most of the fast-growing cities today are in the developing world (Delhi, India; Lagos, Nigeria; and Karachi, Pakistan), where population growth exceeds economic growth, producing conditions of overcrowding, pollution, and poverty as these countries continue to industrialize.

- U.S. cities grew rapidly throughout the 19th and early 20th centuries as a result of immigration and increased industrialization. By the 1950s, the rise in the number of automobiles, expanding road networks/interstate highways, and inexpensive and abundant oil were factors enabling people to move to suburbs and away from inner cities. Twenty-first century technology (cell phones and the Internet) has reinforced the spread of urban populations to suburban areas as they allow people to communicate more easily from locations away from major urban centers.

▪ Today, powerful technologies and cheap transportation have allowed cities to thrive and grow in resource-poor regions of the United States. Currently, southwestern cities such as Los Angeles, Las Vegas, and Phoenix flourish in desert regions by appropriating water from distant sources. Between 1990 and 2018, the population of Las Vegas grew by 112%.

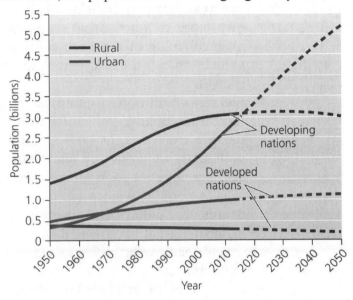

Figure 13.1 Urban growth in developing vs. developed nations today

The causes and effects of urban sprawl

▪ **Urban sprawl** is the spread of low-density urban or suburban development outward from an urban center, removing clear boundaries between the two. The landscape is often characterized by "strip malls," cluster housing, office parks, and "big box" retail stores separated by miles of roads.

▪ Many urban researchers define *sprawl* as the physical spread of development at a rate that exceeds the rate of population growth.

▪ The two main causes of sprawl are increased human population growth (there are simply more people alive each year) and per capita land consumption (each person taking up more land than in the past).

▪ The main causes of urban sprawl in the United States include increased human population and the following important factors.

  ▪ The development of federal and state **interstate highway systems** in the 1950s and 1960s promoted living in suburbs while continuing to work in cities. Also, **telecommunications** and the **Internet** have fostered movement away from urban centers.

  ▪ **Living costs** are often less in suburban and rural areas, as one can obtain more land and a larger house for much less money.

- **Urban blight** results when people move away from a city to the suburbs, causing the city's tax revenue to decline, which in turn forces city services to decline, encouraging even further flight from cities.

- Since sprawl means different things to different people (some positive, some negative), findings by urban researchers on the effects of sprawl are an important tool. Most studies show that urban sprawl

  - **constrains transportation options,** essentially forcing people to own more cars and drive more miles each day. Since 1980, the average length of the work commute has risen by 24%, and total vehicle miles driven has risen three times faster than population growth.

  - **increases pollution by compromising air and water quality.** With increased reliance on automobile use comes increased carbon dioxide emissions, as well as nitrogen and sulfur-containing air pollutants, which in turn lead to tropospheric ozone, urban smog, acid precipitation, and global climate change. Motor oil and road salts can pollute waterways.

  - **drains tax dollars** by diverting money that could be spent on maintaining and improving downtown centers because of the need to extend road, water, sewage, and communications systems outward into suburbs.

  - **contributes to increased land conversion** from existing forests, fields, and farmland. These forested and agricultural lands provide vital resources (food, recreation, wildlife habitat) and ecosystem services (water purification, climate modification, etc.).

  - **compromises human health,** in addition to the air and water pollution issues. People rely on cars to do their daily errands instead of walking, and the result is a decrease in physical activity.

How to analyze environmental impacts and advantages of urban centers

- **Urban planning** involves designing cities to maximize their efficiency, functionality, and beauty. One key tool that planners use is **zoning,** the practice of classifying areas for different types of development and land use. Zoning is a tool often used to separate industry and business from residential neighborhoods. Governments that use zoning can classify land areas into zones in which certain land uses are prohibited, such as the building of a factory in a residential area, sometimes restricting the use of private land for the greater good of the community.

- Cities and towns are **resource sinks.** High per capita resource consumption creates substantial waste and pollution in the long-distance transportation of these resources. However, if all the world's 4.3 billion urban residents were instead spread evenly across the landscape, there would likely be *more transportation required* to provide people the same access to resources and goods.

- Cities minimize per capita consumption costs through the efficient delivery of goods and services because people are densely concentrated.
- Urban citizens often suffer **noise and light pollution** (undesired ambient sound and light), a constant aspect of city life.
- **Urban heat island** effects result from the concentration of heat-generating buildings, vehicles, and factories, causing thermal pollution. Also, the dark surfaces of asphalt pavement and heat-absorbing buildings disrupt the normal convective cooling that would otherwise occur.
- By establishing **urban growth boundaries (UGBs)** in the late 1970s, urban planners in Oregon sought to curb sprawl by containing growth largely within existing urbanized areas. Urbanization preserves land, the important idea behind urban growth boundaries. For example, Oregon's law requires every city and county to draw up a comprehensive land use plan, incorporating UGBs, with an intent to revitalize city centers, prevent suburban sprawl, and protect farmland, forests, and open landscapes.
- Many other regions have now adopted UGBs, including the states of Washington, Tennessee, and California, along with a number of cities, including Boulder, Colorado; Honolulu, Hawaii; and Minneapolis-St. Paul, Minnesota.
- **Urban ecology** supports the central idea that cities should be viewed as ecosystems and that the fundamentals of ecosystem ecology and systems science apply to the urban environment. Major urban ecology projects are ongoing in Baltimore, MD, and Phoenix, AZ, as researchers are studying these cities with a view toward their potential as ecological systems. Using this approach, urban sustainability advocates suggest that cities should strive to

    - maximize efficient use of resources,
    - recycle as much as possible,
    - account for external costs,
    - use locally produced resources,
    - encourage urban agriculture, and
    - offer tax incentives to encourage sustainable practices.

How to assess urban ecology and the pursuit of sustainable cities

- **Sustainable cities** are cities that can function effectively and prosperously over the long term, providing generations of residents a good quality of life far into the future. Portland, Oregon, is a good example of a sustainable city that is enhancing the quality of life for its citizens and protecting environmental quality at the same time.
- **Urban sustainability** entails viewing the city as an ecological system. The extent and nature of positive and negative environmental impacts depend on how resources are used, how goods are produced, how materials are transported, and how wastes are dealt with.

- **Smart growth** focuses on strategies that encourage the development of sustainable, healthy communities.

  - This approach includes use of urban growth boundaries (UGBs).
  - Smart growth means "building up, not out," focusing development and economic investment in existing urban centers and favoring multistory shop-houses and high-rises.
  - The EPA lists 10 basic principles of smart growth, with some of the more important features being mixed land uses (residential, recreation, and business lands together), walkable neighborhoods, an economic range of housing opportunities, and preserving open space.

TABLE 13.1 Ten Principles of "Smart Growth"

- ▶ Mix land uses
- ▶ Take advantage of compact building design
- ▶ Create a range of housing opportunities and choices
- ▶ Create walkable neighborhoods
- ▶ Foster distinctive, attractive communities with a strong sense of place
- ▶ Preserve open space, farmland, natural beauty, and critical environmental areas
- ▶ Strengthen existing communities, and direct development toward them
- ▶ Provide a variety of transportation choices
- ▶ Make development decisions predictable, fair, and cost-effective
- ▶ Encourage community and stakeholder collaboration in development decisions

Source: U.S. Environmental Protection Agency

How to evaluate transportation options, urban parks, and green buildings

- **Bicycle transportation** is a key option that Portland, Oregon has embraced like few other American cities. Today more than 6% of its commuters ride to work by bike (the national average is 0.5%). Like many other cities, Portland is also currently experimenting with the feasibility and safety of electric scooters (e-scooters).
- **Transit-oriented development** is critical to new urbanism approaches that seek to design neighborhoods on a walkable scale, with homes, businesses, and other amenities all close together for convenience.

  - Public buses, trains, subways (heavy rail), and light rail (smaller rail systems powered by electricity) are all options. Portland's light rail systems are currently carrying 100 million riders per year.
  - It has been calculated that rail systems can save taxpayers a total of $67.7 billion in costs for congestion, consumer transportation,

parking, and road maintenance—far more than the $12.5 billion that governments currently spend to subsidize rail systems per year. New York City's subways, Washington D.C.'s Metro, and San Francisco Bay Area's BART carry more than one-fourth of each city's daily commuters.

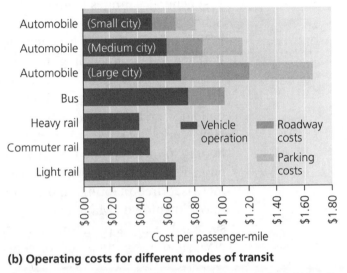

(b) Operating costs for different modes of transit

Figure 13.10b Operating costs for different modes of transit

- The United States lags behind most nations in mass transit, instead choosing to invest in road networks for cars and trucks. Japan, China, and many European nations have developed entire systems of modern high-speed "bullet" trains, whereas the United States has only one such train, Amtrak's *Acela Express,* connecting Boston and Washington, D.C.
- **Parks and open spaces** are key elements of sustainable cities. America's city parks began to arise in the late 19th century with the establishment of New York City's Central Park, designed by the leading American landscape architect, Frederick Law Olmsted. Boston, Philadelphia, and San Francisco subsequently developed major city parks.
- **Greenways,** strips of land that connect parks or neighborhoods, often run along rivers, streams, or canals and provide access to networks of walking trails. The newly developed High Line Park in New York City is used by more than 13,000 people per day.
- **Greenbelts** are long and wide corridors of parklands or open space, often encircling an entire urban area. The world's largest greenbelt surrounds the city of Toronto, Ontario.
- **Green buildings,** structures that incorporate various means of reducing the ecological footprint of a building's construction and operation, are a key approach toward sustainable cities. They are built from sustainable

materials, minimize their use of energy and water, minimize health impacts on their occupants, limit their pollution, and recycle their wastes.

- The **Leadership in Energy and Environmental Design (LEED)** program is a certification program for green buildings.
- Green building techniques add expense to construction, but the added cost generally ranges from 0–10%.
- Schools, colleges, and universities are leaders in sustainable building. LEED certification is booming throughout the United States, with Portland, Oregon leading the way. For example, the Rosa Parks Elementary School in Portland was built with locally sourced and nontoxic material, uses 25% less energy and water than comparable buildings, and diverted nearly all of its construction waste from landfills.
- New York City unveiled an extensive sustainability program in 2007, hoping to make it "the first environmentally sustainable 21st-century city." Reduction of greenhouse gas emissions, improved mass transit, increased tree planting, and a proposal to charge drivers for driving into downtown Manhattan are a few key approaches of this sustainable city's program. Recently, this program was renamed One NYC, and it is adding new dimensions to address economic equity.

TABLE 13.2 Green Building Approaches for LEED Certification

Approaches That Are Rewarded	Maximum Points
ENERGY: Monitor energy use; use efficient design, construction, appliances, systems, and lighting; use clean, renewable energy sources	37
THE SITE: Build on previously developed land; minimize erosion, runoff, and water pollution; use regionally appropriate landscaping; integrate with transportation options	21
INDOORS: Improve indoor air quality; provide natural daylight and views; improve acoustics	17
MATERIALS: Use local or sustainably grown, harvested, and produced products; reduce, reuse, and recycle waste	14
WATER USE: Use efficient appliances inside; landscape for water conservation outside	11
Points above may total up to 100. Then up to 10 bonus points may be awarded for:	
INNOVATION: New and innovative technologies and strategies to go beyond LEED requirements	6
THE REGION: Addressing environmental concerns most important for one's region	4

Out of 110 possible points, 40 are required for LEED certification, 50 for silver, 60 for gold, and 80 for platinum levels. Point allocation shown is for new construction. Allocation varies slightly for renovations and specific types of buildings.

Chapter 14: Environmental Health and Toxicology

> ## YOU MUST KNOW
>
> - The major goals of environmental health including the major environmental health hazards.
> - The major types of toxic substances in the environment and the factors affecting their toxicity.
> - How toxic substances move in the environment and how they affect organisms and ecosystems.
> - How toxic substances are studied in the laboratory and in the environment.
> - How to evaluate risk assessment and risk management, including different philosophical approaches to risk.
> - How environmental health hazards are regulated in the United States and in the international community.

The major goals of environmental health including the major environmental health hazards

- The study and practice of **environmental health** assesses environmental factors that influence our health and quality of life. Scientific studies can identify the steps needed to minimize the risks of encountering hazards and to mitigate the impacts of the hazards we do encounter.

- Environmental health hazards can be natural or **anthropogenic** (human-caused), can occur outdoors or indoors, and are categorized into four main types: biological, chemical, physical, and cultural.

  - **Biological hazards** cause the most human deaths. **Infectious diseases** (diseases caused by pathogens) result from viruses, bacteria, protists, fungi, parasitic worms, or other pathogens or vectors (a **vector** is an organism that transfers the pathogen to the host, for example, the mosquito that transmits the malaria-causing protist *Plasmodium*). The spread of infectious disease today is much faster than in the past because of the increased density of human populations, extensive travel, the emergence of new strains of diseases (Ebola in West Africa in 2014), and global climate change, which causes the movement of tropical diseases to new locations.
  - **Chemical hazards** include the many synthetic chemicals that society manufactures, such as pharmaceuticals, pesticides, plastics, and industrial chemicals.
  - **Physical hazards** arise from processes that occur naturally in our environment, such as ultraviolet (UV) radiation from sunlight.

- **Cultural hazards** result from our place of residence, socioeconomic status, occupation, or behavioral choices. Cigarette smoking, drug use, and nutritional choices are examples in this category.

■ **Indoor health hazards** are primarily due to chemicals and are important to consider because we spend approximately 90% of our lives indoors.

- **Cigarette smoke** and **radon** are both highly toxic. Radon is a colorless, odorless radioactive gas that seeps up from the ground in areas with certain types of bedrock, accumulating in basements and homes with poor air circulation.

- **Asbestos,** used in construction for its insulation, sound-proofing, and fire-retardant qualities, has been confirmed to cause lung cancer.

- **Lead poisoning** is a serious neurological health concern that can cause learning abnormalities; damage to the brain, liver, kidney, and stomach; and even death. Today, lead poisoning can come from lead-based paint exposure and drinking water that has passed through lead pipes. The 2014 drinking water crisis in Flint, Michigan was caused by lead in the city's water, at levels 1000 times higher than the allowable limit set by the Environmental Protection Agency.

- **Polybrominated diphenyl ethers (PBDEs)** are synthetically created compounds providing fire-retardant properties that are used in a wide array of products including computers, televisions, plastics, and furniture. These chemicals appear to act as hormone disruptors and neurological toxins.

- **Bisphenol A (BPA)** is a synthetically created compound used in the plastics industry to create polycarbonate, a hard, clear type of plastic that can be used in water bottles, food containers, eating utensils, eyeglass lenses, CDs and DVDs, laptops, and other electronics. Scientific studies have recently categorized BPA as an **endocrine disruptor** because it mimics the female sex hormone estrogen.

■ **Noninfectious disease** is a major focus of environmental health, given that the major killers (cancer, heart disease, and respiratory disorders) are noninfectious. These diseases develop without action from a foreign pathogen through a combination of genetics coupled with environmental factors (proximity to industrial centers, malnutrition, poverty, and poor hygiene caused by compromised water quality) and lifestyle.

■ **Infection diseases** spread when a pathogen enters a host through the skin, via the respiratory system, or by consumption of contaminated food. The plague (caused by a bacterium carried by fleas), malaria (caused by a protist in the genus *Plasmodium* and carried by mosquitoes), tuberculosis (caused by a bacterium affecting lungs), and diarrheal diseases are infectious diseases that have affected humans for centuries.

- **Emergent infectious diseases** are defined as diseases that were previously not described or have not been common for at least several prior decades. Acquired immunodeficiency syndrome (AIDS), severe acute respiratory syndrome (SARS), Ebola hemorrhagic fever, West Nile virus, and swine flu (H1N1 and H5N1) are in this growing category. Many of these new diseases have come from viruses that normally infect animal hosts but have unexpectedly jumped to human hosts through mutation.

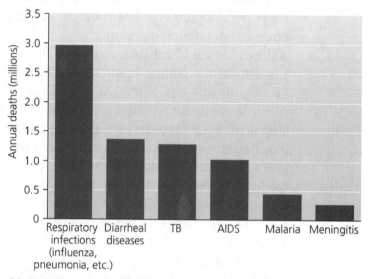

(b) Leading causes of death by infectious diseases

Figure 14.3b   Leading causes of death by infectious diseases

- It is thought that human-induced global warming and climate change are causing tropical diseases such as malaria, dengue, cholera, and yellow fever to begin expanding into temperate climate zones.
- Human land disturbance, which might create standing pools of water in formerly well-drained areas, can boost mosquito populations, causing renewed outbreaks of malaria that were formerly controlled by insecticides such as DDT.
- Improvements in **nutrition,** wider availability of **clean drinking water,** proper **sanitation,** and **education** are the four key approaches for lessening environmental health risks of both historical and emerging infectious diseases.

The major types of toxic substances in the environment and the factors affecting their toxicity

- **Toxicology** is the science that examines the effects of poisonous substances on humans and other organisms. Environmental toxicology deals specifically with toxic substances that come from or are discharged into the environment and uses organisms other than humans as test subjects.

- **Toxins** are natural toxic chemicals manufactured in the tissues of living organisms (for example, chemicals that plants use to ward off herbivores). In addition, we are exposed to many **synthetic** (artificial or human-made) chemicals.
- Rachel Carson's *Silent Spring* (1962) first brought the public's attention to the scientific studies and medical case histories regarding the insecticide DDT. Carson's message was that DDT and other artificial **pesticides** are hazardous to people, wildlife, and ecosystems. The chemical industry challenged Carson's book vigorously; however, the use of DDT was banned in the United States in 1973 and is now illegal in many nations.
- **Herbicides** (atrazine, acetochlor, and metolachlor) also pose a significant threat of toxicity, as they are applied in agriculture to kill undesirable plants and weeds.
- A **"circle of poison"** continues to exist. Although the United States has banned the use of DDT, it continues to manufacture and export the compound to developing nations. Thus, it is possible that pesticide-laden food can be imported back into the United States.
- Toxic chemicals are classified into five major groups based on their particular effects on living organisms.

  - **Carcinogens** are chemical substances or radiation that causes cancer. **Mutagens** are substances that cause mutations in the DNA of organisms. Some of the most well-known carcinogens include asbestos, radon, formaldehyde, and the chemicals (PAHs) found in cigarette smoke.
  - **Neurotoxins** are chemicals that disrupt the nervous systems of animals. Many pesticides, lead, and mercury are examples.
  - **Teratogens** are chemicals that interfere with the normal development of embryos. Thalidomide and alcohol are examples.
  - **Allergens** are chemicals that overactivate the immune system, causing an immune response when one is not necessary, often producing severe breathing difficulties. For a few individuals, peanuts and some drugs such as penicillin produce hyperallergic reactions.
  - **Pathway inhibitors** are toxicants that interrupt vital biochemical processes in organisms by blocking one or more essential steps of a biological pathway (rat poison, atrazine, cyanide). **Endocrine disruptors** have been recognized as toxicants that disrupt the normal functioning of human hormonal balance. These chemicals can affect an animal's endocrine system by blocking the action of hormones or accelerating their breakdown. Effective in very low concentrations, endocrine disruptors pose unusual challenges for toxicology. Bisphenol A (BPA), which mimics estrogen, and the phthalates contained in many plastics and cosmetics are examples of endocrine disruptors.

- Theo Colburn's *Our Stolen Future* (1996) was the first study to propose the concept of endocrine disruption; however, debate has been generated by the chemical industry as a result of the potential economic threat that the removal of BPA could present. Canada has banned BPA, and France has outlawed its use in food packaging. The United States has taken steps to regulate BPA and phthalates in products for babies and small children.

How toxic substances move in the environment and how they affect organisms and ecosystems

- Organisms possess enzymes to detoxify some harmful chemicals that enter the body, making them inert or water soluble so that they can be excreted. Some toxic substances cannot be effectively broken down and are instead sequestered in the animal's body (in fatty tissues and cell membranes).

- Toxic substances are released from agricultural, industrial, and domestic activities and may concentrate in and move through local surface water and groundwater, or they may travel long distances through the atmosphere. PCBs, for example, were a class of toxic industrial chemicals used in electrical equipment, paints, and plastics from 1929 to 1979, when they were banned in the United States. Yet arctic wildlife today is found to possess high levels of PCBs in their tissues, indicating long-distance transport through the atmosphere.

- When affected species become smaller in number, their decline can, in turn, affect other species. These **cascading impacts** can cause changes in the composition of the biological community.

- Some chemicals degrade quickly and become harmless (such as the Bt toxin used in biocontrol and in genetically modified crops); however, others may remain unaltered and persist for months, years, or decades (such as mercury, DDT, and PCBs).

- **Bioaccumulation** is the buildup of persistent chemicals in the tissues of an animal, producing a greater concentration of the substance than exists in the surrounding environment. Toxic substances that bioaccumulate (are persistent and fat soluble) may be transferred to other organisms when predators consume prey, a process known as **biomagnification.** Biomagnification means that the higher an organism is in the food web, the more toxicants it contains. A prime example is the high concentration of the pesticide DDT in top predators, such as birds of prey. Bald eagles, peregrine falcons, brown pelicans, and osprey have all suffered eggshell thinning because of high levels of DDT.

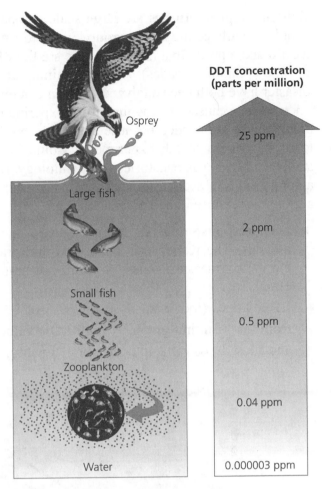

Figure 14.12 Effects of biomagnification

- Individuals vary in their responses to hazards. Fetuses, infants, and young tend to be much more sensitive to toxicants than adult organisms.
- Toxic substances can threaten ecosystem services. For example, pesticide exposure has been implicated as a factor in the recent decline of honeybee populations, affecting the ecosystem service of pollination of wild and agricultural crops.

How toxic substances are studied in the laboratory and in the environment

- **Field studies** of wildlife can inform scientists about potential human health effects. Louis Guillette's studies of Florida alligators showed bizarre reproductive problems that were later attributed to agricultural runoff containing DDT and the herbicide atrazine. Tyrone Hayes found similar reproductive problems in **lab studies** with frogs exposed to atrazine.

- **Epidemiological studies** are large-scale comparisons among groups of people, usually contrasting a group known to have been exposed to some hazard and a group that has not. These studies often last for long periods of time (years or decades). Asbestos mining and the Chernobyl nuclear disaster have both been analyzed from an epidemiological standpoint.
- To establish causation, manipulative experiments involving animal or plant studies are needed because subjecting humans to massive doses of toxic substances in lab experiments would be unethical. Thus human studies rely on case histories, epidemiology (large-scale comparisons among groups of people, some of whom were exposed to a hazard, against a group not exposed), and animal testing.
  - **Dose-response analysis** is the standard method of testing with lab animals. The response is quantified and graphed (a **dose-response curve**) by measuring the proportion of animals exhibiting negative effects.
  - **LD$_{50}$** values (the lethal dose for 50% of individuals) are calculated from the resulting graph. A high LD$_{50}$ value indicates low toxicity, and a low LD$_{50}$ value indicates high toxicity.

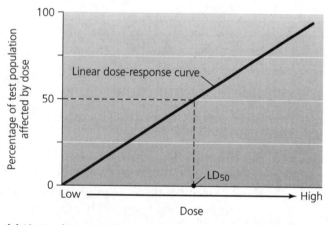

(a) Linear dose-response curve

Figure 14.15(a)   Linear dose-response curve

  - **ED$_{50}$** values (the effective dose for 50%) can be determined when the experimenter is interested in the sublethal effects, including teratogen, carcinogenic, and/or neurotoxic effects.
  - A **threshold dose** is that which elicits a response *only* above a certain dose or threshold.
- **Acute exposure** (high exposure for short periods of time) to an environmental toxicant differs from **chronic exposure** (low exposure over long periods of time). Lab tests and LD$_{50}$ values generally reflect acute exposure. Chronic exposure often affects organs gradually, as when smoking causes lung cancer.

- **Synergistic effects** are those in which the impact of mixing chemical toxicants becomes greater than the simple sum of their individual effects.

- Sometimes an organism's response may *decrease* as the dose of toxicant increases, contradicting the traditional assumption that "the dose makes the poison." This type of unconventional dose-response curve often occurs with endocrine disruptors such as BPA, likely because the hormone system is adapted to respond to minute concentrations (hormones in the bloodstream).

How to evaluate risk assessment and risk management, including different philosophical approaches to risk

- **Risk assessment** involves *quantifying* and comparing risks involved in different activities or hazardous substances. This process begins by *identifying* a potential hazard and assessing the risk that *specific concentrations* would have.

- Risk can be measured in terms of **probability,** a *quantitative* description of the likelihood of a certain outcome.

- Policy decisions made on whether to ban chemicals or restrict their use generally follow years of rigorous lab and environmental testing. Decisions also incorporate economics and ethics and are influenced by political pressure from powerful interests.

- Finally, comparing the costs and benefits of addressing the risk(s) is an essential part of **risk management** procedures. However, this can be challenging because the benefits are often economic, whereas the costs often pertain to human or environmental health, which are much harder to measure.

- For example, in the case of BPA and phthalates, eliminating food packaging in the name of safety could do more harm than good. Eliminating plastic BPA lining inside metal cans could cause metal corrosion and contamination of food by pathogens. On the other hand, keeping the plastic lining can release BPA into food, but finding a BPA alternative could also entail significant economic costs to industry.

- Because we cannot know a substance's toxicity until we measure and fully test it, endocrine disruptor effects are causing great uncertainty, and there remains so many untested chemicals and combinations, science may never be able to eliminate all the uncertainties that accompany risk assessment. Two philosophical and policy approaches exist for determining safety, and they differ mainly in where they place the burden of proof—whether product manufacturers are required to prove safety, or whether government, scientists, or citizens are required to prove danger.

  - The **innocent-until-proven-guilty approach** assumes that substances are harmless until shown to be harmful. This approach has the disadvantage of putting into wide use some substances that may later turn out to be dangerous. The burden of proof for harm is placed on the public.

- The **precautionary principle approach** assumes that substances are harmful until shown to be harmless. The burden of proof for safety is on the manufacturer.
- Many European countries have recently embarked upon a policy course that incorporates the precautionary principle, whereas the United States largely follows the innocent-until-proven-guilty approach.

How environmental health hazards are regulated in the United States and in the international community

- In the United States, the Food and Drug Administration (**FDA**) monitors safety of foods, food additives, cosmetics, drugs, and medical devices. The Occupational Safety and Health Administration (**OSHA,** 1970) regulates workplace hazards.
- The Environmental Protection Agency (EPA) regulates pesticides under the **Federal Insecticide, Fungicide, and Rodenticide Act (FIFRA),** 1947.
- The EPA regulates all synthetic chemicals not covered by other laws under the **Toxic Substances Control Act (TSCA),** 1976. The EPA is charged with "registering" each new pesticide that manufacturers propose to bring to market. This registration process involves risk assessment and risk management and takes economic considerations into account. This might allow hazardous chemicals to be approved if the economic benefits are judged to outweigh the hazards.
- The European Union is currently taking a precautionary principle approach toward testing and regulating manufactured chemicals with its **REACH** (2007) program, shifting the burden of proof for testing chemical safety to the industrial manufacturer.
- The **Stockholm Convention on Persistent Organic Pollutants (POPs)** came into force in 2004 and has been ratified by over 150 nations, demonstrating an increasing awareness of toxic chemicals that bioaccumulate and biomagnify up the food chain and the transboundary nature of the pollution that is occurring worldwide.

TABLE 14.2 The "Dirty Dozen" Persistent Organic Pollutants (POPs)

TOXICANT	DESCRIPTION	TOXICANT	DESCRIPTION
Aldrin	Insecticide to kill termites and crop pests	Furans	By-product of processes that release dioxins; also present in commercial mixtures of PCBs
Chlordane	Insecticide to kill termites and crop pests	Heptachlor	Broad-spectrum insecticide
DDT	Insecticide to protect against insect-spread disease; still applied in some countries to control malaria	Hexachlorobenzene	Fungicide for crops; released by chemical manufacture and processes that release dioxins and furans
Dieldrin	Insecticide to kill termites, textile pests, crop pests, and disease vectors	Mirex	Household insecticide; fire retardant in plastics, rubber, and electronics
Dioxins	By-product of incomplete combustion and chemical manufacturing; released in metal recycling, pulp and paper bleaching, auto exhaust, tobacco smoke, and wood and coal smoke	PCBs	Industrial chemical used in heat-exchange fluids, electrical transformers and capacitors, paints, sealants, and plastics
Endrin	Pesticide to kill rodents and crop insects	Toxaphene	Insecticide to kill crop insects and livestock parasites

Data from United Nations Environment Programme (UNEP), 2001.

Chapter 22: Managing Our Waste

> **YOU MUST KNOW**
>
> - The main types of waste generated.
> - The major approaches to managing waste.
> - Conventional waste disposal methods: sanitary landfills and incineration.
> - The major approaches for reducing waste: source reduction, reuse, recycling, and composting.
> - How industrial solid waste is managed.
> - The specific issues involved in managing hazardous waste.

The main types of waste generated

- **Waste** refers to any unwanted material or substance that results from a human activity or process.

    - **Municipal solid waste (MSW)** is nonliquid waste that comes from homes, institutions, and small businesses, commonly referred to as "trash" or "garbage." It includes everything from paper to food scraps to old appliances and furniture.
    - **Industrial solid waste** includes waste from production of consumer goods, mining, agriculture, and petroleum extraction/refining.
    - **Hazardous waste** refers to solid or liquid waste that is toxic, chemically reactive, flammable, or corrosive and can include everything from paint and household cleaners to medical waste and industrial solvents.

The major approaches to managing waste

- Because waste can degrade the water, soil, and air quality and is also a measure of inefficiency in the industrial process that created the waste, waste management has become a vital human pursuit.
- There are three main components of waste management.

    - **Source reduction**—minimizing waste at its source, thus reducing the amount of material entering the waste stream.
    - **Recycling**—the process of collecting used goods and sending them to facilities that extract and reprocess raw materials that can then be used to manufacture new goods.
    - **Safe waste disposal**—regardless of how effectively we reduce the waste stream through source reduction and recovery, there will likely always be some waste left to dispose. Disposal methods include burying waste in landfills and burning waste in incinerators.

- Paper products comprise the largest component of the municipal solid waste stream in the United States by weight.

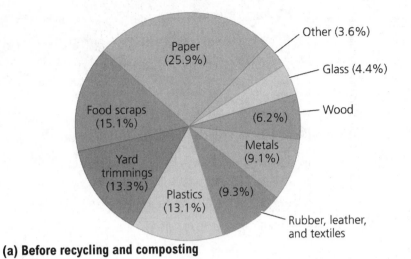

(a) Before recycling and composting

Figure 22.3a U.S. Municipal solid waste before recycling and composting

- The average American generates 2.0 kg (4.5 lb) of trash per day, considerably more than people in most other developed nations, primarily because of excess packaging and the use of nondurable goods ("the throwaway society"). In the United States, since 1960, waste generation has nearly tripled and per person waste generation has risen by 67%.
- In developing nations, consumption is less but is increasing steadily. As a result, trash is increasing and littering the landscapes of countries from Mexico to Kenya to Indonesia.

Conventional waste disposal methods: sanitary landfills and incineration

- Open dumping and waste burning were the acceptable approaches to dealing with **municipal solid waste (MSW)** until the human population and consumption rates increased dramatically in the late 20th century.
- As of 2015, United States waste managers were landfilling approximately 53% of MSW, incinerating 13%, and recovering 35% for composting and recycling.
- In 1988, the United States had nearly 8000 landfills, but today it has fewer than 1800. Waste managers have consolidated the waste stream into fewer landfills that are larger in size, with many older landfills reaching capacity and being closed.

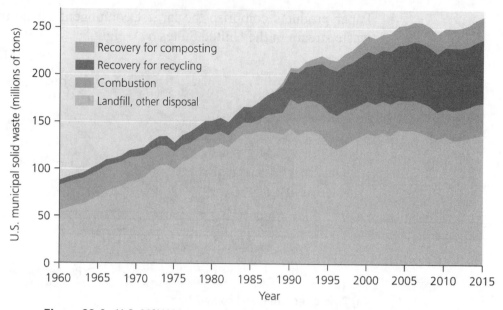

Figure 22.6 U.S. MSW Management and the decline of waste going to landfills

- **Sanitary landfills** are carefully engineered sites where waste is buried in the ground or piled up in large mounds away from wetlands and earthquake-prone sites and at least 6 m (20 ft) above the water table. Landfills are lined with impermeable surfaces (plastic or clay) to prevent aquifer/groundwater contamination by **leachate** (liquid that results when substances from the trash dissolve in water as it percolates downward). Soil is also layered along with the waste to speed bacterial decomposition, reduce odor, and lessen infestation by pests. Once at capacity, the landfill is closed and capped with an engineered cover that must be maintained as a barrier, preventing water from seeping down and gas from seeping up.

- **Landfill gas** (a mix of gases, mostly methane) can be collected, processed, and used as an energy resource in the same manner as natural gas. Today, hundreds of landfills are collecting landfill gas and selling it for energy to run municipalities and industries.

- The **Resource Conservation and Recovery Act (RCRA),** enacted in 1976 and amended in 1984, sets the standards to be met by all sanitary landfills in order to protect against environmental contamination.

- The drawbacks of landfills include the following:

  - The **"not-in-my-backyard" (NIMBY)** reaction causes challenges in finding suitable areas for their location.
  - The dry and anaerobic conditions of capped landfills are not conducive environments for bacterial decomposition of the enclosed/buried wastes. Decomposition rates are turning out to be much slower than originally predicted.

- **Incineration,** or combustion, is a controlled process in which mixed garbage is burned at very high temperatures, reducing the original weight by up to 75% and its volume by up to 90%.
- **Waste-to-energy (WTE)** facilities that use heat produced by waste combustion to boil water, creating steam that drives electricity generation, are a positive attribute of incineration. When burned, waste generates approximately 35% of the energy generated by burning coal. There are approximately 80 WTE facilities operating across the United States today.
- The drawbacks of incineration include the following:

  - The remaining ash contains toxic components that must be disposed of in hazardous waste landfills.
  - Hazardous chemicals, dioxins, heavy metals, and polychlorinated biphenyls (PCBs) can be created and released into the atmosphere.
  - Particulate matter needs to be physically removed from incinerator emissions and disposed of safely because it contains tiny particles of **fly ash.** This fly ash often contains some of the worst dioxin and heavy metal pollution.
  - The revenues from power generation are often not enough to offset the considerable financial cost of building and operating incinerators.

The major approaches for reducing waste: source reduction, reuse, recycling, and composting

- The **3 Rs ("Reduce, Reuse, Recycle")** and composting divert materials from the waste stream.
- **Source reduction** (reducing waste before it is generated) is the *best* waste management approach because it avoids the costs of safe disposal and recycling, helps conserve resources, minimizes pollution, and is economically sound for consumers.

  - Much of the waste stream consists of materials used to package goods and can be reduced with incentives.
  - In 2007, San Francisco became the first U.S. city to ban nonbiodegradable plastic bags. A number of cities, the states of Maine and Vermont, and more than 20 nations have now enacted bans or limits on the use of plastic bags.

- **Reuse** is a main strategy to reduce waste. Examples of reusable items include coffee cups and reusable cloth bags. More than 6000 reuse centers exist in the United States, including stores run by organizations such as Goodwill Industries and the Salvation Army.
- **Recycling** has grown significantly in recent years and now removes 25.8% of the U.S. waste stream. However, U.S. states vary greatly (2–43%) in the rates at which citizens recycle.
- The most recent survey of campus sustainability efforts indicates that the average recycling rate was only 29%, leaving definite room for growth. However, in 2019, 300 colleges and universities competed in the annual

RecycleMania competition, with Loyola Marymount University in Los Angeles taking top honors, recycling 89% of its campus waste.

- The economics of recycling are complex, as the expense required to collect, sort, and process recycled goods is often more than the recyclables are worth in the marketplace. Items collected are taken to **material recovery facilities (MRF),** where workers and machines sort items and prepare them for reprocessing into new goods. The low commodity prices of recent years have also posed a challenge to recycling programs (low oil prices worldwide lead to buying *new* plastic as opposed to the more expensive recycled plastic).

- In 2018, China's sharp cutback on its imports of recycled materials (particularly plastics) from other nations put recycling programs across the world in disarray. In particular, American waste managers have been struggling to deal with the consequences since so much recycled plastic and other recyclables had been previously exported to China. With China now demanding that imported recyclables not exceed a contamination rate of 0.5% (1 part in 200), it seems unlikely that China will begin accepting foreign materials for their MRFs anytime soon. In recent years, contamination in the U.S. recycling stream has surpassed 25%, with one out of every four items in the stream being a nonrecyclable.

- An even bigger challenge for recycling will be the expanding processing for plastics by energy companies looking to find an outlet for more of their fossil fuel by-products.

- Recycling advocates point out that market prices for recycled goods do not take into consideration external costs (the environmental and health costs of *not* recycling).

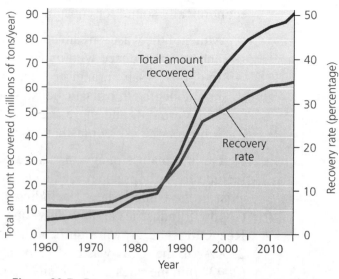

Figure 22.7   Recovery has risen sharply in the United States

- **Composting** recovers organic wastes and reduces landfill waste, enriches the soil, and reduces the need for chemical fertilizers.

- Financial incentives can help encourage waste reduction and recycling:

- The "pay-as-you-throw" approach to garbage collection encourages less waste generation.
- Bottle bills, which encourage consumers to return bottles and cans to stores after use in order to receive a refund, have reduced litter, and the per capita container recycling rates have risen 2.6-fold.
- We are just beginning to shift from an economy that moves *linearly* (from raw materials to products to waste) to a more sustainable economy that moves *circularly,* using waste products as the raw materials for new manufacturing.

How industrial solid waste is managed

- **Industrial solid waste** is defined as solid waste that is considered neither municipal solid waste nor hazardous waste under the U.S. Resource Conservation and Recovery Act (RCRA), and it is managed by state or local governments.
- **Industrial ecology** seeks to redesign industrial systems to reduce resource inputs and to maximize both physical and economic efficiency by functioning more like ecological systems and completing a product's **life cycle analysis.** The central idea is that industrial systems should function more like ecological systems in which organisms use most everything that is produced, a "cradle-to-grave" approach.
- The Swiss Zero Emissions Research and Initiatives (ZERI) Foundation sponsors dozens of innovative projects worldwide that attempt to create goods and services without generating waste.

The specific issues involved in managing hazardous waste

- In most developed nations, hazardous waste generation and disposal are highly regulated. Under RCRA, the EPA sets standards by which states are to manage hazardous waste, and industries are required to track hazardous materials "from cradle to grave."
- Two classes of chemicals are particularly hazardous because their toxicity persists over time and they can bioaccumulate: organic compounds and heavy metals.

  - **Synthetic organic compounds** and petroleum-derived compounds resist bacterial decomposition, can be readily absorbed through the skin, and can act as mutagens, carcinogens, teratogens, and endocrine disruptors.
  - **Heavy metals** such as lead, chromium, mercury, arsenic, cadmium, tin, and copper are fat soluble, break down slowly, and bioaccumulate/biomagnify in food chains.

- **Electronic waste (e-waste)** is a new and fast-growing source of waste due to today's proliferation of computers, printers, smartphones, tablets, and many other electronic technologies. E-waste currently comprises more than 1% of the U.S. solid waste stream, but due to the downsizing of many electronic products and the increased recycling of e-waste (40% of all e-waste is recycled), its generation appears to have recently leveled off. This recent trend also keeps toxic substances out of the waste stream and allows recovery of the rare and lucrative trace metals used in electronics. In terms of disposal, e-waste also contains heavy metals and toxic flame retardants, which easily classify them as hazardous waste; these materials should be kept out of conventional landfills and incinerators and instead be redirected to hazardous waste disposal sites.

- Hazardous waste from industrialized nations is also sometimes dumped illegally in developing nations—a major environmental justice issue.
- Disposal methods for hazardous waste include the following:

  - **Hazardous waste landfills**—require stricter standards and more impervious layers in order to keep hazardous material away from groundwater.
  - **Surface impoundments**—shallow depressions lined with impervious material serve as disposal sites for liquid hazardous waste.
  - **Deep-well injection**—wells are drilled deep beneath the water table into porous rock, where wastes are injected for long-term storage.

- The **Comprehensive Environmental Response Compensation and Liability Act (CERCLA)** was established in 1980 as a federal program to clean up U.S. sites polluted with hazardous waste from past activities. The EPA administers this cleanup program, called the **Superfund.** The original objective of CERCLA was to charge the polluting parties for cleanup of their sites, according to the polluter-pays principle; however, for many sites, the responsible parties have never been located.
- *Love Canal* (New York) and *Valley of the Drums* (Kentucky) were the two well-publicized locations of past large-scale toxic chemical disposal that eventually led to the passage of CERCLA and the creation of the Superfund.
- As of 2019, 1339 Superfund sites remained on the National Priorities List, and only 431 had been cleaned up or otherwise deleted from the list, primarily because of high expense and the lengthy cleanup time.

Multiple-Choice Questions

Use the figure below to answer questions 1 and 2.

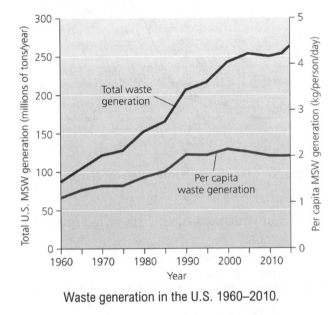

Waste generation in the U.S. 1960–2010.

1. The per capita waste generation in the United States in 2000 was approximately
    (A) 4 kg/person/day.
    (B) 250 kg/person/day.
    (C) 125 kg/person/day.
    (D) 2 kg/person/day.

2. Total waste generation in the United States has increased by approximately __% between 1990 and 2010.
    (A) 40
    (B) 25
    (C) 10
    (D) 5

3. Which of the following is *not* an environmental benefit of smart growth?
    (A) impervious surfaces
    (B) decreased fossil fuel consumption
    (C) decreased open space
    (D) decreased water pollution

4. An LD_{50} study indicates the
    (A) amount of toxicant it takes to kill half the population.
    (B) lowest dose that kills any member of the population.
    (C) lowest dose that kills 50 out of 1000 members of the population.
    (D) lowest survival dose of toxicant for 50% of the population.

5. In the United States, approximately how much of the municipal solid waste generated ends up being recovered in composting and recycling?
    (A) about 22%
    (B) about 34%
    (C) >45%
    (D) >50%

6. The federal legislation that imposes a tax on the chemical and petroleum industries to generate funds that pay for the cleanup of hazardous substances is
    (A) the Cradle-to-Grave Act.
    (B) the National Priorities List Act.
    (C) the CERCLA.
    (D) the EPA.

7. Which is the *most critical* environmental impact of urban sprawl?
    (A) increased air pollution
    (B) increased acid precipitation
    (C) increased consumption of locally grown produce
    (D) decreased loss of agriculture lands

8. A resource sink is
   (A) a resource that is desirable, is in high demand, and promotes competition between cities.
   (B) an area that produces almost none of the things that it needs.
   (C) an area that is able to trade for all of the resources it needs.
   (D) an area that produces a single resource and is therefore unable to control its price through competition.

9. Bisphenol A (BPA) is a chemical used in ___ and has the effect of _____.
   (A) herbicides; a neurotoxin
   (B) pesticides; a carcinogen
   (C) plastics; an endocrine disruptor
   (D) synthetic fuels; a carcinogen

10. Pesticides in the United States are registered for use through the
    (A) FDA.
    (B) BLM.
    (C) DOE.
    (D) EPA.

11. Currently, which of the following materials comprises the largest component of municipal solid waste (MSW) by weight?
    (A) e-waste
    (B) heavy metals
    (C) yard waste
    (D) paper

Use the figure below to answer questions 12 and 13.

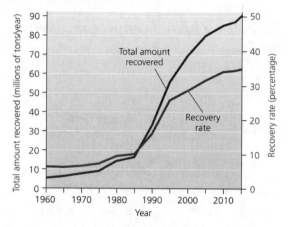

Figure 7 Material recovery rates for recycling and composting in the U.S.

12. In which decade did recycling grow the most?
    (A) the 1980s
    (B) the 1990s
    (C) the 2000s
    (D) the 2010s

13. The economics of recycling have become more complex for the United States recently because
    (A) importing recyclables has become very profitable.
    (B) more people are recycling.
    (C) finding an outlet for recycled products is harder.
    (D) exporting recyclables, particularly plastics, to foreign MRFs has become a limiting factor.

14. A LEED certification for an urban building indicates that
    (A) it has been built entirely of recyclable materials and is always less expensive than comparable modern buildings.
    (B) it meets all the requirements for smart growth.
    (C) it meets the requirements for being built in a sustainable greenway.
    (D) it has been built with consideration for minimum water and energy use.

15. Which of the following are naturally occurring chemicals, potentially toxic to people?
    (A) Bt and *Salmonella*
    (B) crude oil and radon gas
    (C) DDT and DDE
    (D) phthalates and bisphenol A

16. Which statement about dose-response studies is *false?*
    (A) Dose-response studies test chemicals across a range of concentrations.
    (B) Dose-response studies test only for lethal effects.
    (C) Dose-response studies can last for days or months.
    (D) LD_{50} values are divided by 10 to determine safe concentrations for wildlife.

17. Which of the following best represents criteria for classifying hazardous waste?
    (A) bioaccumulates, biomagnifies, fat soluble
    (B) municipal, industrial, agricultural
    (C) e-waste, toxic, gaseous
    (D) ignitable, corrosive, reactive

18. From an environmental waste perspective, which approach is the most effective and desirable?
    (A) reduce
    (B) reuse
    (C) recycle
    (D) compost

Use the figure below to answer questions 19 and 20.

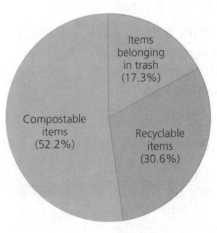

University of washington trashbin contents

19. The above pie chart shows the average contents of material thrown away from one floor of a building at the University of Washington. From these data, one can conclude that
    (A) most material is being disposed of properly.
    (B) over 50% of the disposed material could be reused in some form.
    (C) over 75% of the disposed material could be reused in some form.
    (D) recycling of plastics could be increased.

20. In an attempt to answer the question "Can campus research help reduce waste?" this University of Washington study could *best* be improved by which of the following?
    (A) more student participation
    (B) more universities being involved
    (C) including all classroom buildings in the study
    (D) including all faculty and staff offices in the study

21. Which of the following environmental hazards is most capable of biomagnification?
    (A) radon and Pu^{239}
    (B) lead
    (C) asbestos
    (D) PCB

22. Many chemical substances are very challenging for risk assessment studies because of their
    (A) hemorrhagic effects.
    (B) persistence in the environment.
    (C) quick disappearance and biological decay in the environment.
    (D) synergistic effects.

23. E-waste is a major source of
    (A) heavy metals.
    (B) radioactive materials.
    (C) combustible inorganic compounds.
    (D) ignitables.

24. Incineration is a contemporary method of handling municipal solid waste and contributes to all of the following except
    (A) generating electricity.
    (B) decreasing the life of sanitary landfills.
    (C) reducing volume.
    (D) extracting energy.

Free-Response Question

The Jones family lives in urban Boston, MA, in a 100-year-old historic house. This family of four is planning on adding more sustainable solutions to their daily living. Initially, they plan to focus on their municipal solid waste (MSW) stream, followed by reducing their daily exposure to environmental toxins. Currently, they generate 1.8 kg (4 lb) of MSW per day per person. The disposal fee in their city is $100 per ton (2000 lb).

The table below describes the percentage composition of the typical municipal solid waste (MSW) generated by the Jones family.

Material	Percentage (%)
Yard waste/grass clippings	13
Food scraps	13
Paper and cardboard	33
Plastic	12
Metals	8
Glass	5

Use the preceding table and information to answer the following questions. Show all work and provide complete explanations.

a) What is the annual cost to dispose of the MSW generated by the Jones household?
b) Recently, the Jones family became aware of the potential problem of plastic as an environmental toxicant in their municipal waste stream. Explain one specific problem that plastic presents for the environment and one specific problem for human health.
c) Recent research has demonstrated that a potential toxic substance "X" has been found in one of the plastics consumed by the Jones family. Describe an *experimental design* for determining its potential toxicity.
d) The Jones family would like to receive a LEED certification for their historic home; however, they realize that they will have to make several changes. *Propose two solutions,* along with the reason for each, that will allow them to receive a LEED certificate.

Water Resources: Use and Pollution

Chapter 15: Freshwater Systems and Resources

YOU MUST KNOW

- Water's importance and the distribution of freshwater resources on Earth.
- The major types of freshwater systems.
- The various categories of water use by humans and the problems associated with the current utilization of this resource.
- The solutions that can effectively address freshwater depletion issues.
- The main categories of water pollutants and how they affect water quality.
- The main procedures involved in drinking water and human wastewater treatment.

Water's importance and the distribution of freshwater resources on Earth

- A total of 97.5% of Earth's water resides in the oceans. Only 2.5% of Earth's water is considered fresh water, with most of this scarce resource tied up in glaciers, ice caps, and underground aquifers.
- Only 1% of fresh water is easily accessible on Earth's surface. Water is unevenly distributed across the planet's surface, with precipitation from 470 inches per year (on the tropical Hawaiian island of Kauai) to virtually zero (in Chile's Atacama Desert).
- Humans are *not* distributed across the globe in accordance with water availability. Moreover, there is a growing number of heavily populated countries located in arid lands where fresh water is scarce.

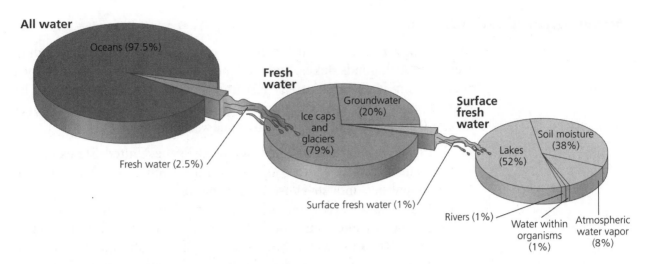

Figure 15.3 Distribution of Earth's 2.5% Fresh Water

- Water is essential and maintains all life and ecosystems. It regulates the temperature of the planet, redistributing heat, and cycles essential nutrients through land, air, and all living things.
- Fresh water is a renewable resource because of the hydrologic cycle, which returns water to both surface and groundwater sources from the atmosphere. However, *only if* water is used and managed sustainably can water be realized as a renewable resource. Currently, in many industrial nations, concerns over water *quantity* dominate, whereas in developing countries, concerns over both water *quantity* and *quality* persist.
- The decade-long drought in the American West and Southwest, notably in California and Texas, is an example of the water shortages also faced by many parts of the world today due to climate change. California has experienced record-low levels of precipitation combined with record-high heat since 2012, with devastating effects on its agricultural sector, including a reduction of hydroelectric power capacity, and extensive damage to its forests.
- The west Texas area, a location of extensive Permian shale deposits, is currently experiencing record levels of water demand for hydraulic fracturing operations. Three-fourths of the 40,000 U.S. fracturing wells drilled have been in water-scarce areas already stressed by drought.
- It is expected that global climate change will further worsen the disparity between water availability and human needs by altering precipitation patterns, melting glaciers, and intensifying droughts and flooding, producing a great need for sustainable, long-term water conservation programs.

The major types of freshwater systems

- **Surface water** is the fresh water that exists above ground, including streams, rivers, ponds, lakes, and wetlands. The area of land drained by a river system is referred to as a **watershed,** or drainage basin. The Mississippi watershed is the largest in the United States, draining over 40% of the land area of the lower 48 states.

  - Nearly three-quarters of all water used in the United States comes from surface water sources and is used for electric power generation, municipalities, industrial use, and irrigation.
  - Bodies of water are often classified according to their productivity. **Oligotrophic** lakes and ponds have low nutrients and high oxygen levels; **eutrophic** water bodies are high in nutrients and low in oxygen. Changes in a body of water can occur naturally; however, eutrophication now usually results from human-caused excessive nutrient pollution.
  - Excessive surface water withdrawals can drain rivers and lakes. The Colorado River is a prime example, as it often fails to reach the Gulf of Mexico because of overextraction by both Mexican and U.S. farmers.

- **Wetlands** are surface water systems in which the soil is saturated with water and which generally feature shallow standing water with noticeable vegetation. Marshes, swamps, and bogs are types of wetlands, all of which are enormously rich and productive. **Vernal pools** are seasonal wetlands containing water only at a specific time of the year (springtime, in the Northern Hemisphere).

  - Wetlands are extremely valuable as habitat for wildlife, providing important ecosystem services by slowing runoff, reducing flooding, recharging aquifers, and filtering pollutants.
  - Extensive drainage of wetlands for agricultural and urban development has occurred throughout the United States; less than half of all wetlands remain.
  - Wetlands can also be lost when water is withdrawn or diverted, rivers are channelized, and dams are built. A prime example of extensive wetlands loss includes the Louisiana delta region near New Orleans.
  - The Ramsar Convention on Wetlands of International Importance (1971) seeks to protect the many ecological, social, and economic benefits of wetlands worldwide within the context of sustainable development.

- **Groundwater** is water beneath Earth's surface held within the pores of soil and/or rock. Although groundwater sources account for only one-quarter of all water used in the United States, they supply almost half of all drinking water and are an important source of irrigation for Midwest cropland.

■ An **aquifer** is an underground reservoir contained in porous, spongelike formations of rock, sand, or gravel. The largest known aquifer is the Ogallala Aquifer, located under eight U.S. Great Plains states.

FIGURE 15.6 The Ogallala Aquifer is the world's largest aquifer.

■ As aquifers are withdrawn, they recharge *very* slowly; average rates of groundwater flow are only about 1 m per day. Therefore, groundwater is often more easily depleted than surface water because of this slow recharge.

■ The major Midland-Odessa, TX area, the fastest growing metropolitan region in the United States. from 2010 to 2015, is located at the southern end of the Ogallala Aquifer. Fracking, agriculture, and drinking water demands have contributed to a 100-foot drop in the water level of the Ogallala Aquifer in just the last 30 years.

■ **Water tables** (the upper limit of groundwater held in an aquifer) drop when aquifers are overdrawn; as a result, groundwater becomes more difficult and expensive to extract. In parts of Mexico, India, China, and many Asian and Middle Eastern nations, water tables are falling 3–10 feet per year.

■ In coastal areas, where extraction of groundwater is high, **saltwater intrusion** can affect an aquifer, making water undrinkable, with land subsiding and the creation of **sinkholes.**

The various categories of water use by humans and the problems associated with the current utilization of this resource

■ **Agriculture** accounts for approximately 70% of Earth's annual fresh water use.

  ■ The amount of land currently being irrigated has doubled in the last 50 years to meet the increased demand for human food.

  ■ Most irrigation remains highly inefficient, and crops end up using only 40% of the water applied by "flood and furrow" irrigation methods.

  ■ Overirrigation leads to the **salinization** of agricultural lands, reducing crop production.

  ■ Worldwide, about 15–35% of water withdrawals for irrigation are thought to be unsustainable. Often, the Colorado River and Rio Grande no longer flow to the Gulf of California as a result of the extensive diversions and current consumption rates these rivers have undergone.

■ **Industry** accounts for approximately 20% of Earth's annual fresh water use.

■ **Residential use** accounts for about 10% of Earth's fresh water use.

  ■ Bottled drinking water production now is a significant groundwater extraction and depletion problem, representing a $14 billion bottled water industry.

  ■ Americans now drink more bottled water than beer or milk and pay more per gallon for it than for gasoline.

  ■ Bottled water exerts substantial *ecological* impact because of heavy packaging, transportation over long distances using fossil fuels, and, in the United States, failure to recycle roughly 30–40 billion plastic containers per year.

    ■ Major U.S. cities including New York City, San Francisco, and Seattle now prohibit using government funds to purchase bottled water. Dozens of colleges and universities in the United States have banned the sale of plastic water bottles.

  ■ Bottled water is not demonstrably safer or healthier than tap water. In fact, its source is often unknown, unlike municipal tap water, which is strictly regulated by the U.S. Environmental Protection Agency (EPA).

- **Water diversion projects** have long been a part of human history, bringing surface water to farm fields, homes, and cities through the use of dams, aqueducts, pipes, and open-air canals.

  - California has one of the most extensive freshwater diversion schemes in the world. The Colorado River is a prime example of the use of dams (13 major dams store water in enormous reservoirs), open-air canals, and aqueducts (approximately 1200 miles), which have altered the once wild Colorado River for diversion. The result is that the diverted water is used mostly to irrigate crops in desert regions and to sustain the growth of Los Angeles, San Diego, Phoenix, Tucson, and Las Vegas.
  - California's arid Imperial Valley is the nation's largest irrigation district. The source of this federally subsidized water is the extensively diverted Colorado River.
  - The world's largest water diversion project is currently underway in China, where three sets of aqueducts totaling 1550 miles in length will move trillions of gallons of water from the Yangtze River in southern China to the more dry climate in the north and the populous capital, Beijing.
  - **Channelization** (straightening, deepening, widening, or lining existing stream channels) is an engineering technique that has been extensively used to transport water, as well as for flood control and drainage improvement. This process has caused extensive habitat destruction and fragmentation in many parts of the world.

- To protect urban and residential areas against floods, governments have built **dikes** and **levees** (long raised mounds of earth) along riverbanks to hold water in the main channels. However, in the long term and in rural agricultural areas, floods are immensely beneficial because floodwaters build and enrich floodplain soil by spreading nutrient-rich sediments over large areas. Overall, human development tends to worsen flooding because pavement and compacted soils speed runoff, sending intense pulses of water into rivers during storm events.
- The diverse costs and benefits of damming rivers and streams are currently being reevaluated in the United States. The largest U.S. dams are on the Colorado River (Hoover Dam and Glen Canyon Dam), each holding back a reservoir (Lake Mead and Lake Powell), which can be utilized for hydroelectric energy generation. Habitat alteration is one of the main negative impacts of a dam's construction and presence.

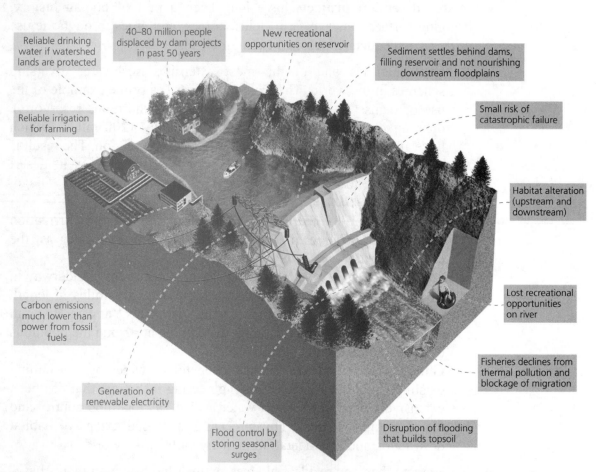

Figure 15.15 The Diverse Consequences of Damming Rivers for People and the Environment

- The world's largest dam project is the Three Gorges Dam on China's Yangtze River, completed in 2008 at a cost of $39 billion. Its reservoir flooded 22 cities, requiring the largest human resettlement project in China's history. The unexpected consequences of a severely degraded downstream environment and build-up of toxic pollutants behind the Three Gorges Dam have yet to be dealt with. Recently, the potential for earthquake damage to the dam, perhaps even leading to its collapse, has also been discussed.

- Some dams are being removed in areas where it appears, in retrospect, that the costs outweigh the benefits. By removing a dam, riparian ecosystems can be restored, economically valuable fisheries can be reestablished, and river recreation such as fly-fishing and rafting can be increased. The Edwards Dam on Maine's Kennebec River was one of the first to be removed (1999) in the United States. In 2014, the world's largest dam removal project was completed for the Glines Canyon Dam in Washington state. Within a year, 10 native species of migratory fish returned to their upstream habitat.

- Although strongly opposed by San Francisco because of its drinking water needs, a movement is now underway to remove the O'Shaughnessy Dam in Yosemite National Park, a removal that would drain and restore the scenic Hetch Hetchy Valley.

- Political tensions over water may heighten in the future as depletion of fresh water continues to lead to shortages and resource scarcity.

  - Many predict that water's role in regional conflicts will increase as the human population continues to grow and as climate change continues to alter precipitation patterns. Political and economic instability issues due to unequal access to freshwater supplies and current global water shortages are thought to make fresh water availability one of the greatest concerns to future U.S. national security.

  - "Water promises to be to the 21st century what oil was to the 20th century: the precious commodity that determines the wealth of nations" (*Fortune* magazine, May 2000).

  - **Water mining,** withdrawing water faster than it can be replenished, is now taking place in California's central agricultural regions, an area of important food production for the United States. In parts of Mexico, India, China, and many Asian and Middle Eastern nations, water tables are falling 1–3 meters per year.

The solutions that can effectively address freshwater depletion issues

- The most effective solutions to water depletion issues involve *reducing demand,* that is, focusing on *conserving* water and *increasing efficiency* of water use.

  - For *agriculture:* **efficient irrigation methods** (drip irrigation and low-pressure spray irrigation) and lining irrigation canals to prevent leaks result in a dramatic decrease of water lost to evaporation. Drip irrigation improves efficiency by delivering smaller volumes of water directly to crop roots for absorption.

  - Choosing **crops to match the land and climate** in which they are farmed can save huge amounts of water.

  - **Selective breeding and genetic modification** can produce crop varieties that require less water.

  - **Recycling treated municipal wastewater** for irrigation purposes conserves water. From 1980 to 2010, the United States decreased its water consumption by 16% through conservation efforts, even while its population grew 36%.

  - For the *residential* sector: households can reduce water use by installing **low-flow faucets, showerheads, toilets,** and **washing machines.**

- Repairing leaks in pipes and water mains conserves a considerable amount of water.
- Automatic dishwashers use less water than washing dishes by hand.
- Using **gray water** (the wastewater from showers and sinks) to water lawns and **xeriscaping** (landscaping using plants adapted to arid conditions) are effective in reducing water demand.

- Attempts to *increase the supply* (through temporarily increasing extraction or new diversion projects) may solve water shortages in one area, but they often cause new shortages in distant areas and have not proved to be sustainable in the long term. Desalination approaches are increasing supplies in some locations, with over 20,000 facilities operating worldwide.

  - **Desalination,** or desalinization, is the removal of salt from seawater or other water of marginal quality. Although increasing a local fresh water supply, desalination is expensive, requires large inputs of fossil fuel, kills aquatic life at water intakes, and generates a very concentrated salty waste.
  - **Reverse osmosis** (microfiltration) and **distillation** are the two methods used in desalination.
  - In late 2015, a San Diego County desalination plant, the largest in the United States, began supplying this southern California region with 190 million L/day of fresh water.

- **Market-based approaches** to water conservation are being debated. Will ending government subsidies of inefficient practices and allowing water to become a commodity (so that the price reflects the true costs of extraction) become solutions of the future? Market-based approaches support the idea that waste, inefficiency, and environmental degradation often result when prices do not reflect the scarcity of water.
- The **privatization of water** supplies, especially in developing countries, has also become an area of debate. In a private system, individuals buy, sell, and trade water rights rather than governments controlling all access to water. However, critics charge that private water markets will undersupply consumers, leading to inequitable distribution because private firms often have little incentive to allow equal access to water for rich and poor alike.

The main categories of water pollutants and how they affect water quality

- **Water pollution** is the release into the environment of matter or energy that causes undesirable impacts on the health or well-being of humans or other organisms. In 2013, the EPA reported that 55% of the 2000 U.S. streams and rivers sampled were in a too degraded condition to support aquatic life. Most forms of water pollution are not easily seen, but still result in diverse changes of the chemical, physical, or biological properties of water, resulting in negative and expensive impacts on aquatic life and human health.

- **Point sources** of water pollution come from discrete locations or specific spots, such as a factory or sewer pipe. In contrast, **non-point sources (NPS)** of pollution are cumulative, coming from multiple inputs over larger areas, such as runoff from farms, city streets, or residential neighborhoods. The U.S. Clean Water Act (1972, 1977) has addressed point-source pollution with some success; however, non-point-source pollution continues to be more problematic to control from such common activities as applying fertilizers and pesticides to lawns and applying salt to roads in winter.

- **Groundwater pollution** is a significant and growing global problem. Groundwater pollution resulting from industrial, agricultural, and urban wastes leaches through soil and enters aquifers where these pollutants can reside for decades. For example, nitrate from fertilizers has leached into aquifers across the United States and has been linked to cancers, miscarriages, and "blue baby" syndrome. Fracking wastewater has also been implicated in contamination of groundwater supplies.

- The main categories of water pollution are the following:

  1) **Toxic and endocrine-disrupting chemicals**

     - *Organic chemicals:* Pesticides (e.g., DDT), herbicides (e.g., atrazine), and petroleum products (e.g., oil) can directly poison plants and animals; some have been known to be human carcinogens. Some have produced a wide variety of adverse effects in the natural world. For example, DDT has caused thinning of bald eagle and brown pelican eggshells. Other adverse effects have resulted from ocean oil spills including the 1989 *Exxon Valdez* spill in Alaska's Prince William Sound and the 2010 British Petroleum's *Deepwater Horizon* oil contamination of the Gulf of Mexico.

     - **Endocrine disrupters** are chemicals that mimic the hormones that regulate physiology and stimulate growth, development, and sexual maturity. Some pesticides, herbicides, pharmaceuticals, and wastewater from livestock facilities (where animals are administered hormones to encourage rapid growth) are the primary sources of these problematic chemicals.

     - *Heavy metals:* Lead, mercury, and arsenic most often enter the water supply from industrial discharges and some household chemicals. These have been linked with cancer, disruption of the immune/endocrine systems, and nervous system disorders.

     - *Inorganic chemicals:* Acids, bases, and salts can enter the water supply as a result of the activities of industry, households, and mining. Acid precipitation damage to aquatic ecosystems (acid rain) has been highly documented, and acid mine drainage (water with a high concentration of sulfuric acid) from coal and metal mines causes significant water pollution.

♦ Leakage of these toxic chemicals from underground oil and gasoline storage tanks is a current focus of major EPA cleanup efforts across the United States. Wastewater from fracking wells is a growing concern to groundwater sources that are used for drinking water.

2) **Sediments:** When poor farming or forestry practices cause large-scale disturbance of vegetation, large sediment loads may damage aquatic systems by blocking out sunlight, impairing the normal photosynthetic processes and food chain relationships.

3) **Thermal pollution:** Water is often used to cool industrial processes, and when this warm water is returned to the environment its ability to hold oxygen is greatly reduced. Cold water can carry more dissolved oxygen than warm water, and aquatic life (fish and aquatic invertebrates) is very sensitive to changes that lower oxygen levels.

4) **Biodegradable wastes:** Organic matter (human sewage or animal wastes) nourishes the growth of microbes that are decomposers, and as the decomposition process proceeds, dissolved oxygen is consumed. This is referred to as **biochemical oxygen demand,** or **BOD** (the amount of oxygen required to break down organic matter over a specific period of time). High BOD values indicate that a water body is more polluted by organic wastes than one with a lower BOD value.

5) **Nutrient pollution:** Nitrates and phosphates contained in agricultural runoff of synthetic fertilizers from Midwest farms annually leads to eutrophication and hypoxia in both coastal marine waters (the Gulf of Mexico's "dead zone") and inland lakes and ponds. Research has indicated that in order to alleviate these "dead zones" characterized by low dissolved oxygen levels, it will be necessary to further reduce phosphorus pollution from industry and sewage treatment. Although phytoplankton needs both N and P, phosphorus has become the primary limiting factor in most freshwater environments.

6) **Pathogens and waterborne diseases:** Disease-causing organisms can enter any body of water that is contaminated with human waste from inadequately treated sewage or with animal wastes from feedlot runoff.

♦ Pathogenic viruses, protists, and bacteria cause more human health problems than any other type of water pollution.

♦ Drinking water treatment facilities are designed to reduce these pathogenic risks by treatment using chemicals and other disinfectant (UV) processes.

■ Scientists who monitor water quality use a variety of biological, chemical, and physical indicators/tests.

- **Biological indicators** include testing for the presence or absence of **fecal coliform** bacteria, which is the criterion used by the EPA to establish safe drinking water standards (0 fecal coliform/100 ml sample). **Aquatic invertebrate biodiversity** measurements are also used as biological indicators of water quality and ecosystem/stream health.
- **Chemical testing** includes determining pH, nitrate and phosphate content, and, most important, dissolved oxygen content.
- **Physical properties** of water that can reveal water quality are color, turbidity, and water temperature.

The main procedures involved in drinking water and human wastewater treatment

- Drinking water treatment is widespread in developed nations today; however, in developing countries the lack of safe drinking water is often the most serious water quality issue and the one causing the most deaths. Many developing countries also lack any type of formal sewage treatment, especially in rural areas. Urban wastewater treatment in most developed countries relies on primary and secondary treatment of sewage.
- **Drinking water treatment** consists of the following.

  - Reservoir or aquifer water is pumped to the facility, where it is first treated with chemicals to remove any particulate matter.
  - Water is then passed through filters of sand, gravel, and charcoal to further remove impurities.
  - Finally, the water is treated with chlorine and/or undergoes UV treatment for its final disinfection.

- **Wastewater** refers to water that people have used in some way. It includes water carrying sewage; water from showers, sinks, washing machines, and dishwashers; water used in manufacturing or industrial cleaning processes; and storm water runoff.
- **Septic systems** are methods of wastewater disposal in rural areas. The septic tank is designed to separate solids from liquid and to digest (biochemically change) and store organic matter for a while, allowing the clarified liquid to discharge into an underground drain/leach field and into the surrounding soil. The combination of pipes and soil makes up the leach field, where the decomposing septage is further degraded by soil microorganisms.

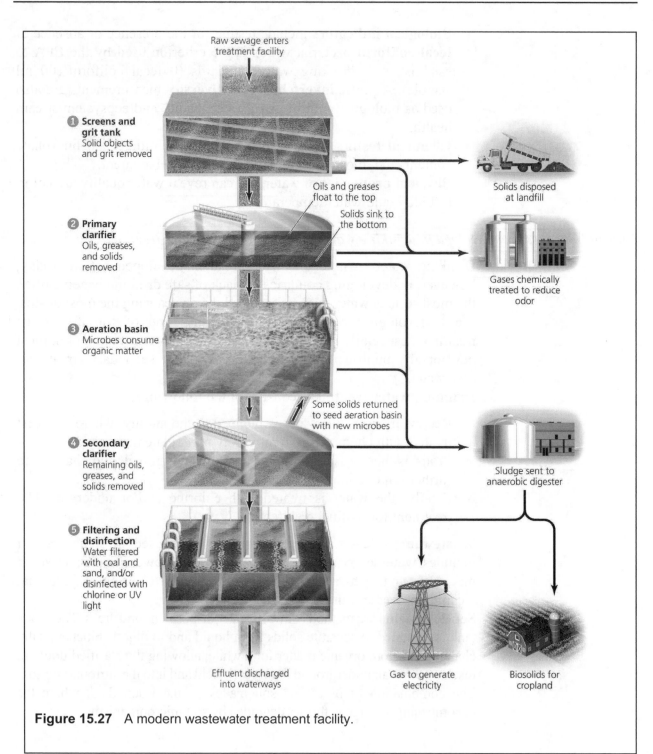

Figure 15.27 A modern wastewater treatment facility.

- **Municipal wastewater treatment** is routine in urban, densely populated areas in developed countries. Primary and secondary treatment is required by U.S. federal law and consists of the following.

  - **Primary treatment:** the physical removal of contaminants in settling tanks or clarifiers. Approximately 60% of suspended solids are removed.
  - **Secondary treatment:** a biological process that involves the wastewater proceeding to aeration basins where it is stirred and oxygenated so that aerobic bacteria can degrade the organic pollutants. Roughly 90% of the suspended organic solids are removed.
  - **Tertiary or advanced treatment:** a physical and chemical process removing specific pollutants left in the water after primary and secondary treatment. For example, this process could remove a specific toxic chemical (heavy metal) resulting from a local industrial plant or excess nitrates from water contaminated with excess fertilizers. This is an expensive process and exists in only a few urban locations.
  - Finally, the water is treated with chlorine, ozone, or ultraviolet light to kill infectious agents before the effluent is piped into the receiving river or the ocean.
  - **Sludge** is the solid material that is removed during the wastewater treatment process. It is partially dried on site and then either taken to the local municipal incinerator or disposed of in a landfill. Occasionally, some sludge is used as fertilizer on cropland in local areas where toxic industrial and manufacturing by-products are not present in wastewater.

- In summary, *preventing* water pollution is easier, much more economic, and more effective than mitigating it later. Water quality issues continue to take a toll on the health, economies, and societies of both developed and developing nations. Water depletion issues are becoming a critical concern in many areas of the developing world, as well as in arid regions of all developed nations.

- The emerging technology of hydraulic fracking, while comprising a small amount of the total water used in the United States, is part of a larger challenge faced by all nations—how to best manage increasingly scarce water supplies while still conserving some water for vital aquatic systems that supply invaluable ecosystem services.

Chapter 16: Marine and Coastal Systems and Resources

> ## YOU MUST KNOW
>
> - The ocean's role in climate regulation and how this is accomplished.
> - The major types of marine ecosystems.
> - The various categories and effects of the major marine pollutants.
> - The current state of marine fisheries and the reasons for their decline.
> - How to evaluate the effectiveness of marine conservation efforts as solutions to the major marine environmental concerns.

The ocean's role in climate regulation and how this is accomplished

- The world's oceans cover 71% of Earth's surface and contain 97.5% of its water. The salinity of ocean water ranges from 33 to 37 parts per thousand (~3.5% salt by mass).

- By absorbing heat and releasing it to the atmosphere, the oceans help regulate Earth's climate. They also influence climate by moving heat from place to place by surface currents flowing horizontally from equatorial regions to Europe (e.g., the Gulf Stream), moderating these higher latitudes. Ocean temperatures are much more stable than land temperatures because water has a high **heat capacity** (a measure of the heat required to increase the temperature by a given amount).

- Surface winds and heating also create vertical currents. **Upwellings,** the upward flow of cold, nutrient-rich deep water toward the surface, create biologically rich regions (upwelling zones off Peru's coastline), producing highly productive fisheries.

- **Thermohaline circulation,** also known as meridional overturning circulation (MOC), is a worldwide current system in which warmer, lower salinity water moves along the surface, and colder, saltier water (which is more dense) moves deep beneath the ocean's surface. Scientists hypothesize that interrupting the thermohaline circulation could trigger rapid climate change. For example, if global warming causes much of Greenland's ice sheet to melt, the resulting freshwater runoff into the Atlantic Ocean could stop the dense, salty **North Atlantic Deep Water (NADW)** formation to completely break down, resulting in a rapid and drastic drop in temperature for Europe and parts of North America.

Figure 16.7 Thermohaline Ocean Currents and the North Atlantic Deep Water (NADW) Circulation

- **El Niño–Southern Oscillation (ENSO)** is the exceptionally strong warming of the eastern Pacific Ocean that occurs every 2 to 7 years, depressing local fish and bird populations and significantly altering the marine food web. It is caused by a systematic shift in atmospheric pressure (from high to low), causing warm surface water from the western Pacific to flow eastward. This *suppresses upwelling* along the Pacific Coast of the Americas, shutting down the delivery of nutrients that support marine life and coastal industries such as Peru's anchovy fishery.

- **La Niña** events are the opposite of El Niño events. Scientists are currently exploring whether warming air and sea temperatures due to climate change may be increasing the strength and frequency of the El Niño/La Niña cycles.

- Since the Industrial Revolution, the oceans have sequestered roughly a third of the excess carbon dioxide that we've added to the atmosphere (through burning fossil fuels and forest clearing), slowing the onset of global climate change. The oceans may soon be reaching carbon dioxide saturation, with climate change accelerating. Ocean temperature increases, which in turn affect ocean chemistry and global current flow, are major environmental concerns today.

The major types of marine ecosystems

- The **open ocean,** far from the influence of land ecosystems, varies in its biodiversity and productivity, with most of this environment having significantly lower primary productivity than the many types of coastal marine ecosystems found around its vast perimeter. All of the following marine ecosystems are currently experiencing human development pressures and climate change effects.

  - **Coastal/intertidal** areas are often some of the most productive as a result of upwellings and/or their daily nutrient exchange with land. **Salt marshes** line temperate shorelines, have extremely high primary productivity, and provide critical habitat for shorebirds and many commercially important fish and shellfish. They also filter pollution and stabilize shorelines against the storm surges associated with hurricanes. When salt marshes are altered or removed to make way for coastal development, these valuable ecosystem services are lost.

■ **Mangroves** (salt-tolerant trees) line coasts in the tropics and subtropics and, with their partially aerial roots, provide essential habitat and nurseries for fish, shellfish, and many invertebrate species. Mangroves also protect vulnerable tropical coastlines from the destructive forces of annual hurricanes.

■ **Estuaries** are bodies of water where rivers flow into the ocean, mixing fresh water with saltwater and producing biologically productive ecosystems. Globally, estuaries have been affected by coastal development, water pollution, habitat alteration, and overfishing. The Chesapeake Bay, San Francisco Bay, and Washington's Puget Sound are all estuaries that have experienced significant development and human impact.

■ **Coral reefs** are composed of the calcium carbonate skeletons of tiny marine animals (corals and their symbiotic zooxanthellae) living in shallow subtropical and tropical waters. They are experiencing alarming declines worldwide due to "coral bleaching" (thought to be caused by increased sea surface temperatures associated with global climate change), nutrient pollution (which promotes algal growth, smothering the corals), and ocean acidification.

■ **Kelp forests** consisting of large brown algae, or kelp, grow along many temperate coasts, supplying shelter and food for many invertebrates and other marine organisms (the keystone species, sea otters, live in kelp forests). Kelp forests also absorb wave energy and protect shorelines from erosion, both essential ecosystem services.

The various categories and effects of the major marine pollutants

■ The oceans have been a sink for human sewage, municipal trash, and industrial wastes for centuries as a result of the misconception that oceans have an infinite capacity to absorb and dilute these toxic pollutants. The major marine pollutants are as follows:

■ **Oil** is often the first category of marine pollutant that comes to mind because about 30% of our crude oil and nearly half of our natural gas comes from seafloor deposits in regions such as the North Sea and Gulf of Mexico. Of the 1.3 million metric tons of petroleum entering the world's oceans each year, nearly 50% is from natural marine seeps and 38% from non-point sources originating on land. The majority does *not* come from tanker spills or offshore platform failures.

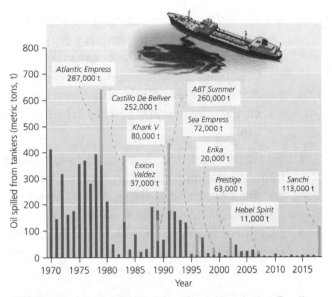

Figure 16.16 Oil Spills from Tankers on the Decline

- Fishing industries and tourism industries are economically devastated when oil is spilled, as in the 2010 British Petroleum's *Deepwater Horizon* offshore drilling platform explosion in the Gulf of Mexico.

- The **U.S. Oil Pollution Act of 1990** created a $1 billion oil pollution prevention and cleanup fund. It also required that all oil tankers in U.S. waters be equipped with double hulls by 2015.

- Sea turtles, dolphins, and birds die when they swallow oil, when oil interferes with breathing, or when oil coats birds' feathers, leading to hypothermia.

- **Plastic debris** and **discarded fishing nets** that are lost or intentionally discarded can snare and drown both fish and marine mammals or be mistaken as food, poisoning marine life by the toxic chemicals (bisphenol A and phthalates) in the plastics. Plastics are long-lived in marine environments, with up to 30% entering the oceans by rivers. A 2017 study concluded that 90% of these plastics come from 10 major rivers. A few examples of rivers contributing plastics are located in East Asia (Yangtze), Southeast Asia (Indus and Ganges), and Africa (Nile). Large numbers of people living without sanitation facilities along these rivers contribute to this massive plastic pollution problem.

  - **The North Pacific Gyre,** the region ringed by the clockwise flow of currents in the northern Pacific Ocean, is now often referred to as the **Great Pacific Garbage Patch (GPGP)** because of the density of plastic trash in the water, a 617,000-mi^2 aggregation of floating debris and plastics. The slow degradation of plastics in seawater, under the influence of sunlight and microbial action, has resulted in tiny **microplastics** becoming more and more numerous. The mass of these microplastics has recently been found to be 180 times the mass of plankton and tiny marine creatures.

- *Reducing* our use of plastics and *preventing their entry* into the ocean are thought to be the primary ways of meeting the great challenge of plastic pollution in the oceans today.
- Computer modeling is currently following plastic and other marine ocean debris and was able to predict the 2014 arrival of the Tohoku earthquake/tsunami (2011) debris on the western coast of the United States.

- **Toxic pollutants** such as mercury can make fish and shellfish unsafe for human consumption. Mercury, a toxic heavy metal emitted from coal combustion, mine tailings, and other sources, settles on land and water, *bioaccumulates* and then *biomagnifies* in animals' tissues. As a result, fish (swordfish and tuna) and shellfish at high trophic levels can contain substantial levels of mercury, making them particularly dangerous for children and pregnant women to consume.

- **Excess nutrients** from fertilizer runoff or other nutrient inputs can create dead zones (hypoxic conditions) in coastal marine ecosystems (e.g., the Gulf of Mexico's dead zone extending from the mouth of the Mississippi River). In addition, sometimes these excessive nutrient concentrations cause population explosions of harmful algal blooms, producing powerful neurotoxins that affect the vertebrate nervous systems. *Red tides* is the name often given to these toxic algal blooms that cause death among zooplankton, birds, fish, marine mammals, and humans.

- **Climate change** is significantly altering ocean chemistry through ocean acidification. **Ocean acidification** is the process by which today's ocean is becoming more acidic (lowering the pH) as a result of increased carbon dioxide moving from the atmosphere into the oceans. When ocean water absorbs CO_2 from the air and forms carbonic acid and bicarbonate ions, the calcium carbonate shells of marine creatures, such as corals, begin dissolving.

  - The chemical reactions involved in ocean acidification begin with the excess carbon dioxide (now found in the atmosphere) reacting with water and forming carbonic acid: $CO_2 + H_2O \rightarrow H_2CO_3$
  - This carbonic acid dissociates into bicarbonate ions and hydrogen ions: $H_2CO_3 \rightarrow HCO_3^- + H^+$
  - The resulting hydrogen ions then combine with carbonate ions (CO_3^{2-}) to form additional bicarbonate ions: $H^+ + CO_3^{2-} \rightarrow HCO_3^-$
  - As the availability of carbonate ions in ocean water declines, it becomes more difficult to build calcium carbonate shells (the process known as calcification) by marine organisms. In fact, as carbonic acid and bicarbonate ions become more abundant in ocean water, the calcium carbonate shells of marine creatures begin dissolving.

■ Because coral reefs provide billions of dollars' worth of ecosystem services, the potential decline of coral reefs due to ocean acidification is now considered to be one of the more serious consequences of global climate change.

The current state of marine fisheries and the reasons for their decline

■ Over 60% of the global marine fish populations are fully exploited and cannot be harvested further without depleting them. An additional 30% of marine fish are overexploited and are already being driven toward extinction. Only about 10% of global marine fish populations can actually yield more than they are already yielding without being driven into decline.

■ Total global fisheries catch, after decades of increases, leveled off after about 1988 despite increased fishing effort. The U.N. Food and Agriculture Organization (FAO) then concluded that "the maximum wild capture fisheries potential from the worlds' oceans has probably been reached."

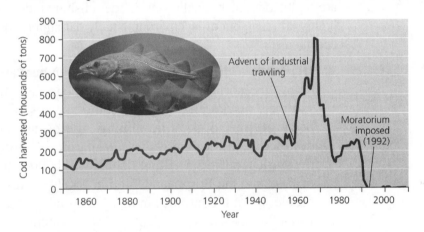

FIGURE 16.24 Cod harvested from Grand Banks

■ The collapse of the major cod fisheries on Canada's Grand Banks (off Newfoundland) and Georges Bank (off Massachusetts) resulted from overfishing and extensive bottom-trawling (fishing by dragging weighted nets across the seafloor, destroying underwater habitat).

   ■ By 1992, scientists reported that mature cod were at just 10% of their long-term abundance, and the Canadian Fisheries announced a two-year ban on commercial cod fishing off Labrador and Newfoundland. When cod stocks did not rebound by 1994, the moratorium was extended, and in 2003 the cod fisheries were closed indefinitely to recreational as well as all commercial fishing.

   ■ In 2009, a portion of the Great Banks off the southeastern coast of Newfoundland was reopened after data showed that the cod stocks were recovering slightly.

- In U.S. waters, cod stocks also collapsed, and in 1994 the National Marine Fisheries Service (NMFS) closed the prime fishing areas on Georges Bank. In 2008, managers announced that these stocks were only 12% of what they needed to be for sustainability, and today scientists continue to struggle to explain why cod have not completely recovered.
- In the absence of trawling on Georges Bank for over a decade, seafloor invertebrates like scallops have now begun to slowly increase in biomass.

- Today's **industrialized commercial fishing** fleets employ huge factory vessels using fossil fuels and use methods to capture fish that are highly efficient but also carry environmental consequences for marine biodiversity and habitat. Most of the current commercial fishing practices also capture nontarget organisms, referred to as **bycatch,** resulting in the deaths of millions of fish, sharks, marine mammals, and birds each year. A 2016 report from NOAA reports that 11% of all commercially harvested fish in U.S. fisheries are captured unintentionally. The modern fishing industry uses the following highly efficient, but often environmentally damaging, methods to harvest oceanic fish:

  - **Driftnets**—Miles-long transparent nylon nets are set out to drift just below the surface water to capture schooling fish such as herring, sardines, mackerel, and some squid species. This method has often been referred to as "strip-mining" the oceans because it is so very destructive in the removal of *all* marine life from large expanses of the worlds' oceans. Driftnet fishing was banned by the United Nations in 1992 and the European Union in 2002 because of the large bycatch problem, but it continues in many national waters today.
  - **Purse-seining** vessels deploy nets suspended in the upper water column by floating buoys around schools of fish. Dolphins, seals, and sea turtles have often been part of purse-seining bycatch.
  - **Long-lining**—Extremely long lines (up to 50 miles) with numerous baited hooks are set out in open ocean water. Tuna and swordfish are among the species targeted.
  - **Bottom-trawling**—Weighted nets are dragged along the floor of the continental shelf to catch groundfish (cod) and other benthic organisms such as scallops. Bycatch is a problem, but it is the benthic habitat destruction that often is the larger problem because the habitat can take decades to recover.

- The composition of nearly 50% of the plastics collected during 2018 research trawls in the Great Pacific Garbage Patch was discarded nylon nets, ropes, and lines from fishing vessels.

■ In just a decade after the arrival of industrialized fishing, catch rates often drop precipitously, with 90% of large-bodied fish and sharks eliminated. This means that the oceans today may contain only one-tenth of the fish they once did. Also, when animals at high trophic levels are removed from a food web, the proliferation of their prey can alter the nature of the entire community, and many scientists conclude that most marine environments may have been very different prior to the current industrial fishing practices.

■ Some of these environmental effects may be partially masked because fishing fleets are traveling longer distances, fishing in deeper waters, spending more time fishing, and setting out more nets and lines. However, as fishing pressures have increased, the size and age of fish caught have declined, and fleets have also been targeting fish species less desirable (changing from the popular cod to the less desirable "orange roughy" and the "Chilean sea bass"), a phenomenon referred to as "fishing down the food chain."

■ In summary, when fish biodiversity is reduced because of overfishing, many marine ecosystem services have been found to be threatened. The reduction in marine nurseries and reduced filtering and detoxification (ecosystem services provided by coastal, wetland vegetation) often lead to harmful algal blooms, dead zones, fish kills, and beach closures. Equally important, on a global scale, less marine biodiversity negatively influences the integrity and health of the entire ocean food web.

How to evaluate the effectiveness of marine conservation efforts as solutions to the major marine environmental concerns

■ **Maximum sustainable yield** (harvesting no more than half of any given population) approaches taken by fishery managers are not always working, as many fish stocks are continuing to plummet. Many now feel that **ecosystem-based management,** shifting the focus away from individual species and toward viewing marine resources as elements of larger, connected ecological systems, is the more appropriate approach.

■ **Marine protected areas (MPAs)** do not always protect marine species, as most allow commercial fishing and other extractive activities. Only 7.6% of the world's ocean areas are currently designated MPAs.

■ **Marine reserves** are protected areas that are "no take" in terms of harvesting marine species. These are designed to preserve ecosystems intact and to improve fisheries for the long term. Unlike terrestrial wilderness protection (4% of all land in the United States), far less than 1% of coastal waters in the United States is currently being protected in marine reserves.

■ Over the past two decades, data from marine reserves around the world have been indicating that reserves can benefit both fish species and fishing economies. On Georges Bank, once commercial trawling was halted in 1994, many marine species began to very slowly recover, including benthic invertebrates such as scallops and groundfish such as cod, haddock, and yellowtail flounder. Moreover, fish from protected areas also appear to spill over into adjacent waters, increasing the productivity and overall health of more extensive environments than the initial targeted areas. Important questions remain as to the best design for future marine reserves—their size, number, and placement—to take advantage of ocean currents and fishery protection.

- Scientific studies estimate that more of the ocean's area should be protected as no-take reserves. This approach would encourage sustainable fisheries and promote healthy fish stocks worldwide, support an increase in overall ocean biodiversity, and may well "seed" the seas and help lead us toward solutions for one of our most pressing environmental problems.

Multiple-Choice Questions

1. Which of the following would be the *best* indication that a lake was contaminated by human sewage from local septic systems?
   (A) lack of hypoxic zones
   (B) low BOD and a fecal coliform count of 2 colonies/100 ml of sample
   (C) high levels of nitrates and arsenic and a high BOD
   (D) a high BOD and a fecal coliform count of 5 colonies/100 ml of sample

2. Which of the following is *not* a non-point-source pollutant?
   (A) fertilizer runoff from golf courses
   (B) a sewage treatment plant effluent discharged into the local river
   (C) sediment loading of a branching tributary of the Mississippi River
   (D) stormwater runoff from a residential area

3. Ocean acidification is caused by
   (A) dissolving of the shells of marine invertebrates.
   (B) increased oxygen content around coral reefs.
   (C) increased carbonate ion concentration resulting from increased carbon dioxide concentration in oceans.
   (D) increased bicarbonate ion concentration resulting from increased carbon dioxide concentration in oceans.

Use the following graph to answer questions 4–6.

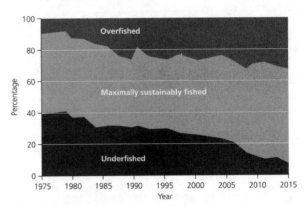

Figure 16.20 Global fish stocks that were overfished from 1975–2015

4. What percent of global fish stocks was overfished in 2015?
   (A) 25%
   (B) 50%
   (C) 75%
   (D) 90%

5. In 1995, the approximate percentage of underfished global fish stocks was
   (A) 50%.
   (B) 40%.
   (C) 30%.
   (D) 20%.

6. In 1975, the majority of fish stocks could be described as
   (A) overfished.
   (B) maximally sustainably fished.
   (C) underfished.
   (D) no category dominating.

7. Two *primary* reasons for the current drought conditions in California and in other parts of the American Southwest are
    (A) record-low precipitation and record-high temperatures.
    (B) global climate change and recent El Niño effects.
    (C) forest decline combined with increased agricultural productivity.
    (D) increased ocean temperatures and decreased precipitation.

8. Scientists are able to predict the possibility and length of *future droughts* and climate change by studying
    (A) rate of marine iceberg melting.
    (B) carbon dioxide levels in ocean waters.
    (C) temperature and precipitation data from the last 100 years in the American Southwest.
    (D) tree ring data from the United States, Canada, and Mexico.

9. ENSO, or El Niño Southern Oscillation, is characterized by
    (A) an increase in upwelling currents off South America.
    (B) a decrease in South American fisheries due to suppression of coastal upwelling.
    (C) an increase in precipitation worldwide.
    (D) an increase in air pressure over the western Pacific Ocean.

10. If you wanted to establish an oligotrophic pond at your school's outdoor environmental laboratory, you would want to
    (A) avoid increasing the oxygen saturation.
    (B) decrease the calcium available to the bottom-dwelling organisms.
    (C) avoid runoff from your school's football field maintained by the local lawn care provider.
    (D) provide carbon-based fertilizers to the entire pond in an effort to increase algal biodiversity.

11. *Bycatch* refers to
    (A) fishing for two species of fish concurrently.
    (B) the accidental harvesting of animals.
    (C) fishing only at the surface of the ocean.
    (D) fishing in both the surface and deep waters of the oceans.

Use the following graph to answer questions 12 and 13.

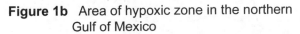

(b) Size of hypoxic zone in the northern Gulf of Mexico

Figure 1b   Area of hypoxic zone in the northern Gulf of Mexico

12. In the year that the nitrogen flux was the highest, what was the *value* of this flux?
    (A) 5000
    (B) 20,000
    (C) 22,000
    (D) 210,000

13. In what year was this area of the Gulf of Mexico the healthiest and able to support the widest biodiversity of fish and invertebrates?
    (A) 1989
    (B) 2000
    (C) 2002
    (D) 2008

14. The aquatic invertebrates in the lake at a local park are dying. A scientist from the Department of Environmental Protection is investigating the problem. She first measures the dissolved oxygen in order to check the
    (A) influence of local acid precipitation.
    (B) possible negative effects of sedimentation.
    (C) possibility of eutrophication effects.
    (D) possibility of bacterial parasitism of the aquatic invertebrates.

15. Red tides are most often caused by
    (A) coastal destruction of wetlands leaving red clays exposed to erosion.
    (B) increased ocean carbon dioxide content.
    (C) ocean acidification leading to red algal blooms.
    (D) coastal nutrient pollution from non-point sources.

16. During the important thermohaline circulation of global ocean current systems, surface currents are
    (A) saltier and colder.
    (B) cold and dense.
    (C) less salty, less dense, and warmer.
    (D) warm and dense.

17. The Great Pacific Garbage Patch (GPGP), discovered in 1997, is located in
    (A) the Pacific equatorial waters.
    (B) the South Pacific Gyre.
    (C) the Pacific upwelling region.
    (D) The North Pacific Gyre.

Free-Response Question

Commercial catches of Atlantic cod have been studied and well documented in the North Atlantic for the past 150 years, because this fish has represented such an important economic livelihood for Canadians. The graph below indicates exactly when industrial trawling began and when the Canadian government imposed the controversial moratorium. Where appropriate, use the graph to answer the following questions.

(a) Cod harvested from Grand Banks

a) Explain, with supporting detail, *two* specific reasons why industrial trawling would produce the change shown in the graph for the 5-year period *after* 1960.

b) Identify the 10-year period during which the greatest decline in the fish harvest took place. For that 10-year period, calculate the average *rate of decline* in the fish harvest, in thousands of tons (metric tons) per year. Clearly show how you determined your answer.

c) Compare and contrast the *environmental effects* of the commercial fishing practices of trawling versus the use of drift nets.

d) Of all the marine pollution effects currently being experienced by the world's oceans, which *two* specific pollutants would marine organisms off the coast of Canada's Grand Banks *most* likely experience? Justify your answers with evidence.

Atmospheric Science and Global Climate Change

Chapter 17: The Atmosphere, Air Quality, and Air Pollution Control

---

YOU MUST KNOW

- The composition, structure, and function of Earth's atmosphere.
- The major air pollutant categories.
- The major air pollution legislation including regulation of greenhouse gas emissions.
- The general status of global air quality.
- The processes involved in stratospheric ozone depletion and the steps taken to address this global problem.
- The processes and chemical reactions involved in acid deposition, including consequences and solutions.
- The scope of indoor air pollution and its potential solutions.

The composition, structure, and function of Earth's atmosphere

- Earth's atmosphere consists of 78% nitrogen (N_2) and 21% oxygen (O_2), with the remaining 1% composed of argon (Ar) and minute concentrations of several other permanent gases (remain at fixed concentrations) and variable gases (change in concentration as a result of natural processes or human activities).
- Today, human activity is altering the quantities of some of these variable gases, including carbon dioxide (CO_2), methane (CH_4), nitrous oxide (N_2O), ozone (O_3), and chlorofluorocarbons (CFCs).

Figure 17.1 Composition of the Earth's Atmosphere

■ Earth's atmosphere consists of four layers. The **troposphere** blankets the planet's surface (up to 7 miles high) and provides us with the air we need to live. The **stratosphere** extends from 7 to 31 miles above sea level and contains the **ozone layer,** which greatly reduces the amount of harmful UV radiation reaching Earth's surface. The ozone layer provides a protective layer for life on Earth. The **mesosphere,** extending from 31 to 51 miles above sea level, and the **thermosphere,** extending upward to an altitude of 300 miles, are the two top layers of our atmosphere. Temperature, atmospheric pressure, and relative humidity vary across all four layers.

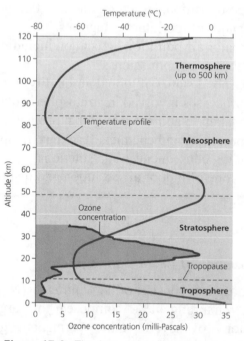

Figure 17.2 The Atmosphere Is Layered

■ Normally, temperature decreases as altitude increases in the troposphere. But sometimes a relatively warm layer of air at mid-altitude will cover a layer of cold, dense air below, producing a **thermal inversion.** This warm **inversion layer** traps emissions that then accumulate beneath it and is an air quality factor to consider in many cities.

- Cities encircled by mountains are often vulnerable to poor air quality. Los Angeles, Mexico City, Seoul, and Rio de Janeiro frequently experience thermal inversions, exacerbating already poor air quality due to dense populations and high automobile use.
- Energy from the sun heats the planetary surfaces *unequally* because of latitude differences and the tilt of Earth's axis, causing air and ocean circulation patterns that ultimately produce the seasons and influence weather and climate.
- **Weather** specifies atmospheric conditions over short time periods, typically hours or days, and within relatively small geographical areas. Weather is driven in part by the **convective circulation** of air being heated near Earth's surface. This air picks up moisture and rises. Once aloft, the air cools, moisture condenses to form clouds, and precipitation can result. The cooler and drier air descends, beginning the convective cycle anew.
- **Climate,** in contrast, describes the pattern of atmospheric conditions found across large geographic regions over long periods of time, typically seasons, years, or millennia.
- Large-scale circulation systems consisting of pairs of convective cells produce global climate patterns. Near the equator, intense solar radiation sets in motion the **Hadley convective cells,** resulting in warm air rising and expanding and ultimately releasing the moisture that becomes the heavy rainfall producing the tropical rainforests. The **Ferrel cells** and **polar cells,** two pairs of similar but less intense convective cells, lift air and create precipitation around 60 degrees latitude and dry conditions near the poles.

Figure 17.6 Large-Scale Convective Cells Determine Global Patterns of Humidity and Aridity

The major air pollutant categories

- **Natural sources of outdoor air pollution** (often called ambient air pollution) such as windblown dust, volcanic ash and particulates, and the soot and gases from naturally occurring forest and grassland fires are often made worse by human activity. Land use policies (e.g., "slash-and-burn" agricultural practices) and the buildup of fuel wood from fire suppression in U.S. national forests have increased the amounts of natural air pollutants in our atmosphere due to the increased frequency of fires.

- Today, climate change is leading to drought in many regions of the world, including California, where particulates from large-scale fires are greatly reducing air quality. Trade winds blow soil across the Atlantic Ocean from Africa to the Americas, harming Caribbean coral reefs with this sediment. Finally, strong westerlies lift soil from deserts in Mongolia and China, bringing it across the Pacific Ocean to North America, increasing atmospheric soil particulates and lowering air quality.

- **Anthropogenic (human-caused) air pollution** can emanate from **point sources** (a specific spot, such as a coal-fired power plant's smokestack) or **non-point sources** (diffuse sources, such as the millions of automobiles spread across a wide area).

- **Primary air pollutants** are those coming directly out of a smokestack, exhaust pipe, or natural emission source. They include carbon monoxide, carbon dioxide, sulfur dioxide, nitrous oxides, and most suspended particulate matter. **Secondary pollutants** are often primary pollutants that react with one another or with constituents of the atmosphere (water, O_2, sunlight), producing new compounds. Ozone and sulfuric acid are the most prevalent examples.

- The U.S. Environmental Protection Agency (EPA), as a result of **Clean Air Act** legislation, sets standards for **six "criteria pollutants,"** pollutants judged to pose especially great threats to human health.

- These six criteria pollutants are CO, SO_2, particulates, lead, NO_2, and tropospheric ozone. For each of these, the EPA has established **national ambient air quality standards** (NAAQS), which are the maximum concentrations allowable in ambient outdoor air. Across the United States, more than 4000 monitoring stations take hourly or daily samples of the following pollutants in order to assess ambient air quality.

  - **Carbon monoxide (CO)** is a colorless, odorless gas produced primarily by the incomplete combustion of fuel. CO poses a risk to humans and other animals because it can bind irreversibly to hemoglobin in red blood cells, preventing the essential binding of oxygen.

  - **Sulfur dioxide** (SO_2) is a colorless gas with a pungent odor. The vast majority of SO_2 results from the combustion of coal for electricity generation and industrial processes. Once in the atmosphere, SO_2

reacts with water to form sulfuric acid (H_2SO_4), which then returns to Earth as acid deposition.

■ **Nitrogen oxides (NO_x)** include both NO and nitrogen dioxide (NO_2). NO_2 is a highly reactive, foul-smelling reddish brown gas that contributes to smog and acid deposition. Most U.S. NO_x emissions result from combustion in vehicle engines.

■ **Volatile organic compounds (VOCs)** and mercury, though not officially listed in the Clean Air Act, are commonly monitored by state and local agencies. VOCs are carbon-containing compounds emitted by vehicle engines that are used in a wide variety of solvents and industrial processes.

   ♦ One group of VOCs comprises hydrocarbons, such as methane (CH_4), propane, butane, and octane.

   ♦ VOCs can react to produce secondary pollutants, as occurs in urban smog formation.

   ♦ The remainder of VOCs comes from natural sources. For example, plants produce isoprene and terpenes, compounds that produce a bluish haze that has given the Blue Ridge Mountains their name.

■ **Particulate matter** is composed of solid or liquid particles small enough to be suspended in the atmosphere, including primary pollutants (e.g., soot and dust) as well as secondary pollutants (e.g., sulfates and nitrates). Particulate matter can damage respiratory tissues when inhaled.

■ **Tropospheric ozone (O_3)**, also called **ground-level ozone,** is a colorless gas created by the reaction of NO_x and VOCs in the presence of sunlight. A major component of smog, O_3 is a secondary pollutant that poses human respiratory health problems.

■ **Lead** is a heavy metal that enters the atmosphere as a particulate pollutant. Exhaust from the combustion of leaded gasoline emits airborne lead that can be inhaled or deposited on land and water. Lead is a neurotoxin and can enter the food chain, bioaccumulate, and cause central nervous system malfunction.

■ **Ammonia (NH_3)** is a colorless gas with a sharp and pungent odor. The main sources of ammonia emissions are feedlots for cattle, hogs, chickens, and agricultural fertilizers.

The major air pollution legislation including regulation of greenhouse gas emissions

■ **The Clean Air Act of 1970** was a revision of prior congressional legislation to control air pollution. It set stricter standards for air quality, imposed limits on emissions from new sources, provided new funds for pollution control research, and enabled citizens to sue parties violating the standards.

- **The Clean Air Act of 1990** strengthened regulations pertaining to air quality standards, auto emissions, toxic air pollutants (mercury from coal-burning plants and VOCs), acid deposition, and stratospheric ozone depletion. In 1995, an emissions trading program for sulfur dioxide was also introduced.

  - This market-based incentive program has helped reduce SO_2 emissions nationally.
  - Similar cap-and-trade programs for other pollutants, including greenhouse gases, have been implemented.
  - California took the lead among U.S. states in adopting pollution control technology and setting strict emissions standards. Los Angeles adopted its own cap-and-trade program in 1994, decreasing SO_2 and NO_2 emissions by over 90% since 1960.
  - Total emissions of the six "criteria pollutants" have been reduced substantially since passage of the Clean Air Act of 1970. These dramatic reductions have occurred despite significant increases in the nation's energy consumption, miles traveled by vehicles, and the gross domestic product. Some of the policy changes and technological developments resulting in cleaner air include the following:

    1) **Catalytic converters** have been required in all new U.S. automobiles beginning in 1975. This required technology converts the hydrocarbons, NO_x, and CO emissions into CO_2, H_2O vapor, and NO_2 gas, resulting in cleaner-burning engines.
    2) **Scrubbers** use a combination of air and water that actually separates and removes particulates and SO_2 before they are emitted from smokestacks.
    3) Leaded gasoline phase out caused U.S. lead emissions to plummet by 93% in the 1980s alone.
    4) **Electrostatic precipitators** installed in smokestacks use an electrical charge to make particulates coalesce so that these small particles can be physically removed before entering the atmosphere.
    5) The **sulfur dioxide permit-trading program** and clean coal technologies have reduced SO_2 emissions.

- **Regulation of greenhouse gases** has been a concern since the 1990s, especially as it relates to global climate change.
- In 2007, the U.S. Supreme Court ruled that the EPA has legal authority under the Clean Air Act to regulate carbon dioxide (CO_2) and other greenhouse gases as air pollutants; however, this has been challenging to accomplish. In 2011, the EPA introduced moderate carbon emission standards for cars and light trucks. In 2012, it announced it will gradually phase in CO_2 limitations for *new* coal-fired power plants and cement factories (but not *existing* ones).
- U. S. CO_2 emissions rose by 51% from 1970 to 2005; however, they decreased by 11% from 2007 to 2018 as a result of shifting from coal to cleaner-burning natural gas and improved fuel efficiency in automobiles.

The general status of global air quality

- Currently, inhabitants of the vast, sprawling cities of India, China, Pakistan, Bangladesh, and other Asian nations suffer the world's worst air quality.

- Some pollutants are not declining, some new air pollutants are emerging, and greenhouse gas emissions continue to rise. Emissions of CO_2 and other greenhouse gases that warm the lower atmosphere are arguably today's biggest air pollution problem.

- The *Asian Brown Cloud*, or *Atmospheric Brown Cloud*, a massive and persistent 2-mile-thick layer of pollution that hangs over southern Asia throughout the dry season, is the result of air pollution primarily from industrialized technologies in China, India, and Iran. Industrializing and developing nations worldwide are suffering increasing urban air pollution problems.

- China, over the past several decades, has fueled its rapid industrial development with its abundant reserves of coal, the most-polluting fossil fuel.

- China's government is now starting to reduce pollution by closing down some heavily polluting industries, installing pollution controls in power plants, expanding mass transport, and developing wind, solar, and nuclear power more aggressively than any other nation in the world.

- Of all the world's cities, Mexico City is perhaps most celebrated for its success in reducing smog, even as its population, number of cars, and economic activity continue to grow. Catalytic converters, the removal of lead from gasoline, improved refineries, a mass transit system with a fleet of low-emission buses, and bike-sharing and car-sharing programs have been put in place. As a result, smog has been reduced since 1990 by more than half, particulates are down by 70%, CO by 74%, SO_2 by 86%, and lead by 95%.

- Currently, nine people out of ten in the world live in areas where air quality fails to meet the health guidelines of the World Health Organization (WHO).

- Air quality is also a rural issue worldwide, as a great deal of air pollution emanates from feedlots (dust and the gases of methane, hydrogen sulfide, and ammonia). Some of the worst air quality in the United States occurs in rural areas, including California's Central Valley (the nation's agricultural fruit basket) and areas near rural natural gas extraction and fracking sites.

- **Industrial smog,** or gray-air smog, is the most common air quality problem since the onset of the Industrial Revolution. When coal or oil is burned, some portion is completely combusted, forming CO_2, some is partially combusted, producing CO, and some remains unburned and is released as soot (particles of carbon). The sulfur in coal reacts with oxygen to form SO_2, which ultimately reacts with water in the atmosphere to also produce sulfuric acid.

- **Photochemical smog,** or brown-air smog, is formed when sunlight drives chemical reactions between the large amounts of NO and VOCs released from the exhaust of automobiles. Over 100 different chemicals are produced, with **tropospheric ozone** (O_3) often being the most abundant. Sunlight is essential for the production of this ground-level ozone, and the high levels of NO_2 cause photochemical smog to form a brownish haze over cities. This type of smog afflicts many urban areas, especially those with sunny climates and a topography that includes cities surrounded by mountains that trap the pollutants. Despite the progress in reducing lead and VOCs, Los Angeles county residents still breathe air that frequently violates national ambient air quality standards. As of 2017, over 100 million Americans lived in counties that regularly violated the tropospheric ozone air quality standard.

(a) Formation of photochemical smog

Figure 17.17a   Formation of Photochemical Smog

- Catalytic converter mandates on automobiles, removal of lead from gasoline, use of cleaner gasoline, and removing pollutants from the liquefied petroleum gas that city residents use for cooking and heating are being employed worldwide to reduce photochemical smog.
- Other methods employed include vehicle inspection programs, restricting traffic into city centers, and requiring older vehicles to be taken off the road, with the critical focus on the rising use of automobiles worldwide.
- **Toxic air pollutants,** substances known to cause cancer, reproductive defects, and immune or respiratory problems, are also regulated by the EPA. These pollutants include mercury (produced from coal-burning power plants), benzene (a component of gasoline), and methylene chloride (found in paint stripper).

The processes involved in stratospheric ozone depletion and the steps taken to address this global problem

- **Stratospheric ozone** molecules (O_3) are extremely effective at absorbing incoming ultraviolet (UV) radiation from the sun. Even in concentrations of 12 ppm (parts per million), this diffuse concentration of ozone helps to protect all life on Earth's surface from the penetrating and damaging effects of UV radiation.

- Stratospheric ozone and tropospheric (ground-level) ozone are easily confused, as they are the same gas, O_3. However, stratospheric ozone occurs in a *higher* atmospheric layer and performs a *completely different* function.

- Human-made compounds called halocarbons, in which hydrogen atoms are replaced by atoms of chlorine, bromine, or fluorine, have been found to destroy ozone by splitting its molecules apart. **Chlorofluorocarbons (CFCs)** are now known to be one of the specific halocarbons that are **ozone-depleting substances.** These CFCs were mass produced in the 1970s as refrigerants, fire extinguishers, and propellants for aerosol spray cans and for the manufacturing of polystyrene foams.

- In the stratosphere, intense UV radiation breaks the bond connecting chlorine to the CFC molecule.

- Then, in a two-step chemical reaction, each newly freed chlorine atom can split an ozone molecule and then ready itself to split another one. This depletion of ozone molecules results in greater UV penetration of the atmosphere, leading to more skin cancer and, scientists predict, crop damage and reduced productivity of ocean phytoplankton.

Figure 17.19 The Chemical Reactions Involved in Stratospheric Ozone Destruction

- In 1985, scientists discovered that ozone depletion was most severe over Antarctica, where an "ozone hole" appeared each spring. In response to these scientific concerns, international policy efforts to restrict production of CFCs came together in 1987 with the **Montreal Protocol.** This treaty, with 196 signatory nations, agreed to cut CFC production in half by 1998. Follow-up agreements deepened the cuts, advanced timetables for compliance, and added nearly 100 additional ozone-depleting substances as the industry ultimately shifted to safer alternative chemicals. Earth's ozone layer is not expected to recover completely until after 2060.

- Although the Antarctic ozone hole has been stopped from growing worse, it will be many decades before the stratospheric ozone layer is expected to recover completely because of the slow diffusion rate of CFCs into the stratosphere. This fact is one reason scientists often argue for a proactive policy guided by the precautionary principle, rather than reactive policy that risks responding too late.

- The Montreal Protocol and its follow-up amendments are widely considered the *biggest success story* so far in addressing *any* global environmental problem and are widely viewed as a model for international cooperation in addressing other global problems such as climate change, persistent organic pollutants (DDT, dioxins, PCBs, etc.), and biodiversity loss.

The processes and chemical reactions involved in acid deposition, including consequences and solutions

- All rain is naturally somewhat acidic because of the reaction between water and atmospheric carbon dioxide, which lowers the pH from a neutral 7.0 to 5.6 because of the presence of the carbonic acid that is produced.

- **Acid deposition** refers to the deposition of acidic or acid-forming pollutants that have a pH lower than 5.6 (acid rain, snow, sleet, or hail); it sometimes also consists of dry deposition of acid particulates.

- Acid deposition originates primarily with the emission of sulfur dioxide and nitrogen oxides, largely through fossil fuel combustion by automobiles, electric utilities, and industrial facilities. Once airborne, SO_2 and NO_x will combine with water to produce sulfuric and nitric acids that may travel days or weeks for hundreds of kilometers before falling in precipitation.

Figure 17.23 The Chemistry of Acid Deposition

- Acid deposition has wide-ranging, cumulative detrimental effects on ecosystems and on our built environment. These effects include those listed in Table 17.2 below.

TABLE 17.2 Ecological Impacts of Acid Deposition

ACID DEPOSITION IN NORTHEASTERN FORESTS HAS . . .

- Accelerated leaching of base cations (ions such as Ca^{2+}, Mg^{2+}, NA^+, and K^+, which counteract acid deposition) from soil
- Allowed sulfur and nitrogen to accumulate in soil, where excess N can over fertilize native plants and encourage weeds
- Increased dissolved inorganic aluminum in soil, hindering plant uptake of water and nutrients
- Leached calcium from needles of red spruce, causing trees to die from wintertime freezing
- Increased mortality of sugar maples due to leaching of base cations from soil and leaves
- Acidified 41% of Adirondack, New York, lakes and 15% of New England lakes
- Diminished lakes' capacity to neutralize further acids
- Elevated aluminum levels in surface waters
- Reduced species diversity and abundance of aquatic life, affecting entire food webs

Adapted from Driscoll, C.T., et al., 2001. *Acid rain revisited.* Hubbard Brook Research Foundation. © 2001 C.T. Driscoll. Used with permission.

- The severity of all these effects depends not only on the pH of the precipitation or the extent of deposition, but also on the *acid-neutralizing capacity* of the soil, rock, or water that receives the acid input. Precipitation is most acidic in the Northeast and Midwest, near and downwind from areas of heavy industry, with pH readings often ranging from 4.6 to lower than 4.0.

- At Dartmouth University's Hubbard Brook Research Forest in New Hampshire, long-term ecosystem studies have taken place since 1963, and the pH of individual rainstorms has been measured as low as 2.1—almost 10,000 times more acid than ordinary rainwater.

- The Acid Rain Program established under the Clean Air Act of 1990 set up an emission trading program for SO_2 that resulted in reducing these emissions. The economic incentives provided encouraged polluters to invest in technologies such as scrubbers, and as a result, the SO_2 emissions across the United States fell by 67%.

- In the industrializing world, acid deposition is becoming worse, especially in nations where coal is used widely. China currently has the world's *worst acid rain problem,* as a result of coal combustion in power plants and in factories that lack effective pollution control equipment.

The scope of indoor air pollution and its potential solutions

- Indoor air pollution causes far more deaths and health problems worldwide than outdoor air pollution. In the developing world, the indoor burning of fuelwood, charcoal, and animal dung is a major health risk for millions of people.

- Even in the developed world, recognizing indoor air pollution as a problem is still quite novel. **Tobacco smoke** and **radon** are the most dangerous pollutants in developed nations. After cigarette smoke, radon gas is the second-leading cause of lung cancer in the developed world, responsible for an estimated 21,000 deaths per year in the United States and 15% of lung cancer deaths worldwide.

- **E-cigarettes** were initially thought to be safer than traditional cigarettes; however, in 2019 there have been numerous illnesses and deaths linked with vaping products, resulting in bans by many states until further research is accomplished. When a person "vapes," or inhales aerosols from heated liquid, VOCs (including formaldehyde), fine particles, heavy metals, and flavored chemicals along with the nicotine are brought into contact with the sensitive membranes of the respiratory system.

- Many VOCs are released by everything from plastics to oils to furnishings, building materials, carpets, laser printers, and photocopying machines. With the exception of formaldehyde, the implications for human health of chronic exposure to VOCs are far from clear. However, formaldehyde is one of the most common synthetically produced chemicals, and it has been shown to irritate mucous membranes, induce skin allergies, and cause many other ailments.

- Microbes (molds, mildews, and fungi) that induce allergic responses are thought to be a major cause of building-related illness. **Sick-building syndrome** refers to a building-related illness whose cause is a mystery and whose symptoms are general and nonspecific.

- Limiting our use of plastics and treated wood as building materials and limiting our exposure to pesticides, cleaning fluids, and other known indoor toxicants are important practices. Most of all, keeping our indoor spaces well ventilated will minimize concentrations of the pollutants among which we live.

Chapter 18: Global Climate Change

YOU MUST KNOW

- Earth's climate system and the greenhouse gases that influence the global climate.
- How humans influence Earth's atmosphere and climate.
- How scientists study climate change.
- The current and future trends and impacts of global climate change.
- Specific actions we can take in response to climate change.
- The economic considerations and approaches involved in the reduction of greenhouse gas emissions.

Earth's climate system and the greenhouse gases that influence the global climate

- Earth's climate varies naturally over time and, to some extent, is always changing. However, these changes today are rapidly accelerating, and scientists agree that human activities, notably fossil fuel combustion and deforestation, are largely responsible.

- *Climate* describes an area's long-term atmospheric conditions, including temperature, moisture content, wind, precipitation, barometric pressure, and solar radiation.

- **Global climate change** describes trends in Earth's climate, involving parameters such as temperature, precipitation, and storm frequency and intensity. Global climate change is *not* synonymous with the term **global warming.** The latter refers specifically to an increase in Earth's average surface temperature, which is only one aspect of global climate change. Some researchers point out that the terms *warming* and *change* are so mild-sounding as to be misleading and that a more accurate term for what is happening today would be *climatic disruption.*

- The three factors exerting the most influence on Earth's climate are the sun, Earth's atmospheric gases that absorb and re-emit the sun's infrared radiation, and the oceans, which store and transport heat and moisture.

- **Greenhouse gases** in Earth's atmosphere include water vapor, ozone (O_3), carbon dioxide (CO_2), nitrous oxide (N_2O), methane (CH_4), and the synthetic halocarbons. After absorbing radiation emitted from Earth's surface, these gases subsequently re-emit infrared radiation back downward, warming the lower atmosphere (troposphere) in a phenomenon known as the greenhouse effect. Without these gases, our planet would be too cold to support life as we know it. However, it's the **anthropogenic** (human-generated) intensification of the greenhouse effect that concerns scientists. By adding novel greenhouse gases (certain halocarbons) and by increasing the concentrations of several natural greenhouse gases (CO_2 and CH_4)

over the past 250–300 years, humans are intensifying the greenhouse effect beyond what our species has ever experienced.

■ The **global warming potential** refers to the relative ability of one molecule of a given greenhouse gas to contribute to warming. Values are expressed in relation to CO_2, which is assigned a global warming potential of 1. For example, one molecule of methane is 84 times as potent as one molecule of carbon dioxide.

TABLE 18.1   Global Warming Potentials of Four Greenhouse Gases

GREENHOUSE GAS	RELATIVE HEAT-TRAPPING ABILITY (IN CO_2 EQUIVALENTS)	
	OVER 20 YEARS	OVER 100 YEARS
Carbon dioxide	1	1
Methane	84	28
Nitrous oxide	264	265
Hydrochlorofluorocarbon HFC-23	10,800	10,200

Data from IPCC, 2013. Fifth Assessment Report.

■ However, since CO_2 is the most abundant greenhouse gas in the atmosphere and resides in the atmosphere longer, it contributes more to the natural *and* to the anthropogenic greenhouse effect. According to the latest data, since the Industrial Revolution, CO_2 has caused nearly twice as much warming as have methane, nitrous oxide, and halocarbons combined.

How humans influence Earth's atmosphere and climate

■ Human activities have boosted Earth's atmospheric concentration of **carbon dioxide** from 278 parts per million (ppm) in the late 1700s to more than 410 ppm today, the highest level by far in over 800,000 years. Increased fossil fuel use (changing ancient terrestrial carbon reservoirs into atmospheric CO_2) and increased deforestation (eliminating the capacity of forests to remove current and future atmospheric CO_2 during photosynthesis) have both contributed significantly to increased concentrations of CO_2 in the atmosphere.

■ **Methane** concentrations are also rising—2.5 times higher than in 1750, primarily because of livestock metabolic wastes (more feedlots), disposing of more organic matter in landfills, and growing more crops such as rice to feed the world's increasing human population.

■ **Nitrous oxide** emissions and tropospheric ozone emissions from anthropogenic sources, specifically from increased automobile usage, have also increased 22% since 1750.

- **Ozone** concentrations in the troposphere have risen 40% since 1750 as a result of photochemical smog but have begun to slow because of the Montreal Protocol.
- In summary, emissions of all greenhouse gases combined are 42% higher than in 1990. Various factors, in addition to greenhouse gases, warm and cool the Earth's surface:

   1) **Aerosols,** microscopic droplets and particulates (from burning solid materials) can have either a warming or a cooling effect, depending on the color of these particles and whether they are located over land or water.

   2) Earth is currently experiencing **radiative forcing** (the amount of change in thermal energy that a given factor causes) of 2.3 watts/m^2 of thermal energy above what it was experiencing in the pre-industrial Earth of 1750. This means that today's planet is receiving and retaining 2.3 watts/m^2 more thermal energy than it is emitting back into space.

   3) **Milankovitch cycles** are types of variation in Earth's rotation and orbit that result in slight changes in the relative amount of solar radiation reaching Earth's surface. As the cycles proceed, heat distribution patterns are changed and both ice ages and other climate changes can be triggered.

   4) **Ocean absorption** of CO_2 is now *less than* the amount of CO_2 that humans are adding to the atmosphere. As ocean water warms, it absorbs less CO_2 because gases are less soluble in warmer water—a positive feedback effect that *further* accelerates warming of the atmosphere and the potential for climate change.

   5) **Ocean circulation patterns** are being actively studied as fresh water from Greenland's melting ice sheet may have the potential to affect the thermohaline circulation that moves warm tropical water northward to Europe. Disruption of this circulation would plunge Europe into much cooler conditions.

How scientists study climate change

- **Proxy indicators** are types of indirect evidence that serve as substitutes for direct measurement. To understand past climate, scientists can decipher clues from thousands or millions of years ago by using **paleoclimate** evidence (data from climate conditions in the geologic past). This evidence is a type of proxy indicator, or indirect evidence, and can shed light on past climate conditions. The following are examples:

   - **Ice core data**—By examining the trapped air bubbles in ice cores, scientists can determine the atmospheric composition, greenhouse gas concentration, temperature trends, snowfall, and even frequency of forest fires and volcanic eruptions at the time these bubbles of gas were trapped. Recently, researchers drilled down 3,270 m (10,728 ft) in Antarctica, pulling out more than 800,000 years' worth of ice, in the deepest ice core analysis so far accomplished.

FIGURE 1 Data from Antarctica Ice Core Reveal Changes Across 800,000 Years

- **Tree ring data**—By examining the width of each tree ring, scientists can determine the amount of precipitation available for plant growth.
- **Packrat middens** in the arid regions of the U.S. southwest are a valuable source of climate data. The seed collections that can be preserved for centuries in these middens allow researchers to study past flora and the climate that produced this vegetation.
- **Coral reef biochemistry**—Because living corals take in trace elements from ocean water as they grow, their growth bands give clues to ocean conditions at the time the bands were deposited in the coral skeleton.
- **Sediment core data** beneath bodies of water—Sediments often preserve pollen grains from plants that grew in the past. Because climate influences the types of plants that grow in an area, knowing what plants were present can tell us a great deal about the past climate at that place and time.

- **Direct measurements** of temperature, precipitation, and other conditions tell us about current climate and can be compared to the paleoclimate evidence. Direct measurement of CO_2 concentrations began in 1958 when **Charles Keeling,** at the Mauna Loa Observatory in Hawaii, began analyzing hourly air samples. These data show that atmospheric CO_2 concentrations have increased from 315 ppm in 1958 to more than 410 ppm today.

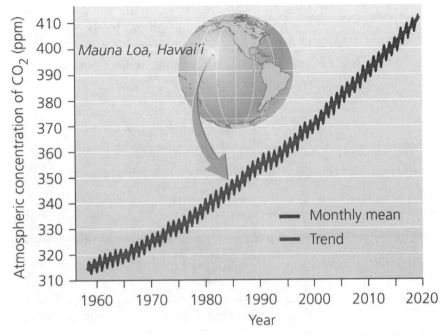

Figure 18.7 Atmospheric Concentrations of Carbon Dioxide are Rising Steeply

- **Climate models** (computer programs that combine what is known about atmospheric and oceanic circulation and feedback cycles to simulate climate processes) also serve to predict future changes in climate, in spite of the uncertainties. These models require manipulating vast amounts of data with complex mathematical equations—a task not possible until the advent of modern supercomputers.

The current and future trends and impacts of global climate change

- Virtually everyone is noticing changes in the climate these days; examples include flooding in Miami, the multi-year droughts in California, and the increased hurricane and storm surges for the entire Atlantic and Gulf coastlines.
- **The Intergovernmental Panel on Climate Change (IPCC),** an international panel of scientists, has compiled the massive climate research data produced since 1988. This thorough review and widely accepted synthesis of scientific information published from the IPCC has

documented observed trends in surface temperature, precipitation patterns, snow and ice cover, sea levels, and storm intensity patterns worldwide. The IPCC was awarded the Nobel Peace Prize in 2007 for its work in informing the world of the trends and impacts of climate change on wildlife, ecosystems, and society, including possible strategies we might pursue in response to climate change.

■ The 2017 IPCC report concluded that average surface temperatures on Earth increased by an estimated 1.1°C (2.0°F) in the past 100 years, with most of this increase occurring since 1975. At the end of the 21st century, the IPCC predicts that global temperature will be 1.0–3.7°C (1.8–6.7°F) higher than today's, depending on how well we control our CO_2 emissions. Polar regions will continue to experience the most intense warming effects.

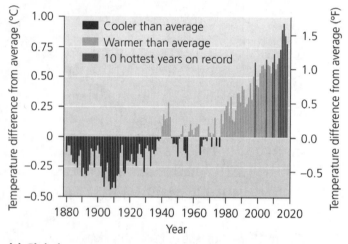

(a) Global temperature measured since 1880

Figure 18.10a Global Temperatures Have Risen Sharply in the Past Century

■ Future **changes in precipitation** are predicted to vary; however, in general, precipitation is expected to increase at high latitudes and decrease at low and middle latitudes, worsening water shortages in many developing countries of the arid subtropics. Precipitation has increased worldwide by 2% over the past century.

■ **Extreme weather** is now becoming "the new normal." The sheer number of extreme weather events since 2012—droughts, floods, hurricanes, snowstorms, cold snaps, heat waves—has caught everyone's attention. In the past several years, scientists have begun to focus on a general answer involving polar warming and weakened jet streams. With hurricanes, the explanation is now well understood: the oceans have absorbed more than 90% of the planet's excess energy from global warming, and warmer ocean temperatures impart more energy to hurricanes.

■ **Glaciers** are disappearing, **Arctic sea ice** and the **Greenland ice sheet** are melting, the coastal **ice shelves in Antarctica** are disintegrating as a result of contact with warmer ocean water, and the **Arctic's permafrost** (permanently frozen ground) is thawing. Earth's albedo (the capacity to reflect light) is decreasing with less ice, allowing the darker ice-free land to absorb more of the sun's rays, warming these surfaces. This leads to a positive feedback and further warming effects, causing even more snow and ice to melt.

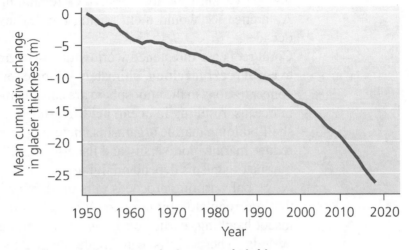

(a) The world's major glaciers are shrinking

Figure 18.16 Glaciers Are Melting Rapidly

■ As continental glaciers and ice sheets melt, increased runoff into the oceans causes **sea level rise.** Sea levels also are rising because warmer water has a higher thermal expansion than cooler water. Worldwide, average sea levels rose an estimated 26.0 cm (10.2 in.) since 1880. The IPCC predicts that by 2100, the mean sea level will be 10–32 inches higher than today's, depending on our future level of greenhouse gas emissions. However, recent research is finding that ice in Antarctica, and especially in Greenland, is melting much more quickly than originally predicted, which would also cause sea levels to rise more quickly—perhaps 1–2 m (3.3–6.5 ft) by 2100!

■ Sea level rise and climate change have many adverse effects:

1) Higher sea levels lead to **beach erosion, coastal flooding, intrusion of salt water into aquifers,** and the possibility that some low-lying island nations (the Maldives, Tuvalu, Bangladesh, and regions of South Florida and the U.S. Gulf Coast) will completely disappear, displacing hundreds of millions of people. A 1 meter or more rise in sea level by 2100 is a common prediction. At risk will be 180 U.S. cities, including those in South Florida (2.4 million people and 1.3 million homes).

2) In the United States, more than half of the population lives in coastal counties. A total of 3.2 million Americans live within 1 vertical meter of the high tide line, and vulnerability to **storm surges** as occurred when Hurricane Katrina struck New Orleans (2005) is an ongoing reality. Superstorm Sandy (2012) caused over $600 billion in damages, leaving 160 people dead and thousands homeless in New Jersey.

Hurricane Katrina killed more than 1800 people and inflicted $80 billion in damages.

3) Whether sea level rises 26 cm, 1 meter, or more, hundreds of millions of **people will be displaced** worldwide. A 2015 study has calculated that if we burn all the fossil fuel remaining in the world, *all* the Antarctica ice would melt, raising the sea level by about 1 foot per decade.

4) Coral reefs are threatened worldwide, as warming ocean waters leads to **coral reef bleaching,** ultimately killing corals. Also, enhanced CO_2 concentrations in the atmosphere are causing more CO_2 to be absorbed in oceans, resulting in **ocean acidification** and the potential loss of all shell-building marine organisms, including corals. These effects would reduce marine biodiversity and fisheries significantly because so many marine organisms depend on living coral reefs for food and shelter.

5) As global warming proceeds, it is **modifying biological phenomena** that are regulated by temperature, including spring leaf-out, earlier insect hatching, earlier bird migrations, and earlier animal breeding periods. These shifts can create mismatches between a species' seasonal location and the availability of its food source. **Spatial shifts in the ranges** of organisms, with plants and animals moving toward the poles or upward in elevation in response to warmer temperatures, are occurring. However, many species (for example, trees) may not be able to shift their distribution fast enough to avoid extinction. The IPCC has estimated that climate change could threaten 20–30% of all plant and animal species with extinction.

6) Climate change affects the lives and livelihoods of millions of people because of its **effects on agriculture** (shifting agricultural belts northward may result in lower crop production because of poorer soils at these new latitudes) and forestry.

7) Longer, warmer, drier conditions (along with decades of forest fire suppression) are promoting outbreaks of bark beetles that are destroying millions of trees, **threatening forests** worldwide.

8) Health, wealth, and national security are being affected by climate change. The expansion of tropical diseases and increased respiratory diseases due to photochemical smog are examples of health issues. The **social costs of carbon** (the cost of damages resulting from each ton of CO_2 we emit) have been estimated by the U.S. government to be roughly $40 per ton, and the government currently determines when and how to impose regulations based upon this estimate. The IPCC has estimated that climate change may cost 1–5% of gross domestic product (GDP), with poor nations paying proportionally more. Many costs and impacts of climate disruption are beginning to endanger the ability of nations to ensure stability for their citizens. For example, when environmental conditions worsen, crops may fail, and people may be forced to leave their homes and become refugees.

▪ Climate change and its impacts will vary regionally. For example, in the United States, winter and spring precipitation are projected to *decrease* across the South but *increase* across the North. Sea level rise may affect the East Coast more than the West Coast. The *Fourth National Climate Assessment* produced in 2017–18 is an excellent guide to the many impacts that Americans can expect.

TABLE 18.2 Some Predicted Impacts of Climate Change in the United States

- Average temperatures will rise 1.4°C (2.5°F) further by 2050 and likely more after that.
- Droughts, flooding, and wildfire will worsen; dry areas will get drier and wet areas wetter.
- Extreme weather events will become more frequent. The costs they impose on society will grow.
- Sea level will rise an additional 0.3–1.2 m (1–4 ft) by 2100. Sea level rise will be greater than this global average on the U.S. Atlantic and Gulf coasts.
- Daily tidal flooding is accelerating in 25 coastal cities. Storm surges will erode beaches and coastal wetlands, destroy real estate, and damage infrastructure.
- Health problems due to heat stress, disease, and pollution will rise. Some tropical diseases will spread north.
- Drought, fire, and pest outbreaks will continue to alter forests.
- Ocean acidification will affect marine ecosystems and fisheries.
- Although enhanced CO_2 and longer growing seasons favour crops, increased drought, heat stress, pests, and diseases will decrease most yields.
- Snowpack will decrease in the West; water shortages will worsen in many areas.
- Alpine ecosystems and barrier islands will begin to vanish.
- Melting permafrost will undermine Alaskan buildings and roads.
- Impacts to infrastructure, property, labor productivity, and natural resources may result in annual economic losses of hundreds of billions of dollars by 2100.

Adapted from U.S. Global Change Research Program, 2017. *Climate science special report: Fourth national climate assessment, Volume I*
(Wuebbles, D.J., et al., eds.). USGCRP, Washington, D.C.; and U.S. Global Change Research Program, 2018. *Impacts, risks, and adaptation in the United States: Fourth national climate assessment, Volume II*
(Reidmiller, D.R., et al., eds.). USGCRP, Washington, D.C.

▪ Scientists agree that most or all of today's global warming is due to the well-documented recent increase in *anthropogenic* greenhouse gases in our atmosphere. They also agree that the rise in greenhouse gases results from our combustion of fossil fuels for energy and secondarily from land use changes, including deforestation and agriculture.

Specific actions we can take in response to climate change

- In the United States, although many of the original naysayers of climate change now admit that the climate is changing, a few still doubt that humans are the cause. For years, public discussion remain mired in misleading debates fanned by corporate interests. For instance, the oil corporation ExxonMobil funded articles against climate change for decades, even though its own in-house scientists had done cutting-edge research back in the 1980s, *documenting climate change.*

- Today, we know exactly what is needed to bring down atmospheric greenhouse gas concentrations and reverse climate change: *We need to begin withdrawing more carbon from the atmosphere than we put into it.* Climate change action can take two fundamentally different approaches: mitigation and/or adaptation.

- **Mitigation** is the strategy aimed at alleviating the problem, that is, attempting to reduce greenhouse gas emissions so as to lessen the severity of climate change. Examples include energy conservation, improving energy efficiency, switching to clean and renewable energy sources, preserving and restoring forests, and encouraging practices that protect soil quality. All of the following are examples of mitigation that can lower an individual's **carbon footprint** (the amount of carbon each person is responsible for emitting):

  1) **Electricity generation** is the largest source (35%) of U.S. CO_2 emissions. Fossil fuel combustion generates two-thirds of U.S. electricity, and coal accounts for most of the resulting emissions. Encouraging conservation and improved efficiency, as well as making greater use of nuclear power and renewable energy, will reduce these CO_2 emissions.

  2) **Transportation** accounts for 35% of U.S. carbon dioxide emissions. Increasing fuel efficiency for American automobiles and developing technologies that bring alternative approaches (hybrid and fully electric vehicles) to the traditional combustion engine automobile are reducing greenhouse gas emissions. Development of and a greater reliance on mass transit will be necessary to further reduce transportation's contribution of greenhouse gases.

  3) In **agriculture,** sustainable land management on cropland and rangeland will enable soil to store more carbon. In forest management, the reforestation of cleared areas helps restore forests, which are then able to absorb additional carbon from the atmosphere.

  4) Making more **informed food choices** is also a significant way of lowering one's carbon footprint: vegetarian or vegan diets greatly reduce carbon emissions, as do eating locally grown foods and reducing food waste (40% of U.S. food currently goes to waste). Scientists estimate that animal agriculture currently accounts for 14.5% of the world's greenhouse gas emissions.

5) **Pressing for climate action now,** with the model of young Swedish activist Greta Thunberg, along with the estimated 4 million youth and adults who took to the streets of thousands of world cities in the global climate strike on Friday, September 20, 2019.

6) Finally, billions of dollars are being spent to develop **carbon capture and storage technologies.** Carbon capture removes carbon dioxide from power plant emissions and is a growing technology. **Carbon sequestration** or carbon storage, in which the carbon is stored underground under pressure in rock formations, is being researched; however, this technology is still a long way from being feasible.

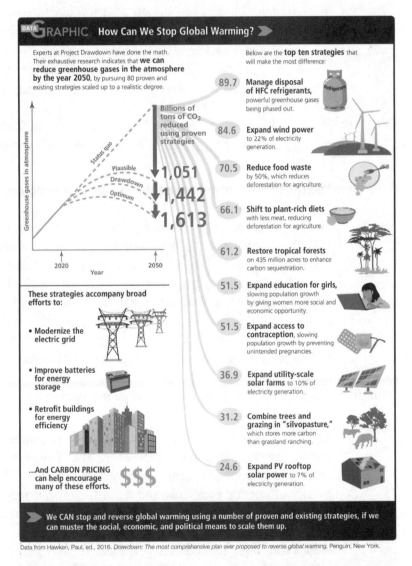

DATA GRAPHIC   How Can We Stop Global Warming?

Experts at Project Drawdown have done the math. Their exhaustive research indicates that **we can reduce greenhouse gases in the atmosphere by the year 2050,** by pursuing 80 proven and existing strategies scaled up to a realistic degree.

Billions of tons of CO₂ reduced using proven strategies

↓ **1,051**
↓ **1,442**
↓ **1,613**

Below are the **top ten strategies** that will make the most difference:

89.7 **Manage disposal of HFC refrigerants,** powerful greenhouse gases being phased out.

84.6 **Expand wind power** to 22% of electricity generation.

70.5 **Reduce food waste** by 50%, which reduces deforestation for agriculture.

66.1 **Shift to plant-rich diets** with less meat, reducing deforestation for agriculture.

61.2 **Restore tropical forests** on 435 million acres to enhance carbon sequestration.

51.5 **Expand education for girls,** slowing population growth by giving women more social and economic opportunity.

51.5 **Expand access to contraception,** slowing population growth by preventing unintended pregnancies.

36.9 **Expand utility-scale solar farms** to 10% of electricity generation.

31.2 **Combine trees and grazing in "silvopasture,"** which stores more carbon than grassland ranching.

24.6 **Expand PV rooftop solar power** to 7% of electricity generation.

These strategies accompany broad efforts to:

• **Modernize the electric grid**

• **Improve batteries for energy storage**

• **Retrofit buildings for energy efficiency**

...And CARBON PRICING can help encourage many of these efforts. **$$$**

➤ We CAN stop and reverse global warming using a number of proven and existing strategies, if we can muster the social, economic, and political means to scale them up.

Data from Hawken, Paul, ed., 2016. *Drawdown: The most comprehensive plan ever proposed to reverse global warming.* Penguin, New York.

■ **Adaptation** is the strategy aimed at minimizing the impacts of climate change by finding ways to cushion oneself from its effects. Examples include erecting seawalls, restricting coastal development, adjusting farming practices to cope with drought, and modifying water management practices to deal with reduced river flows and salt contamination of groundwater.

■ Both adaptation and mitigation approaches are necessary because even if we halt all global emissions today, global warming will continue. Mitigation is necessary because if we do nothing to diminish climate change, it will eventually overwhelm any efforts at adaptation we might make.

■ Because climate change is a global problem, the world's policymakers have tried to tackle it by means of international treaties. The 1997 **Kyoto Protocol** mandated signatory nations, by the period 2008–2012, to reduce emissions of six greenhouse gases to levels below those of 1990. The United States refused to ratify the Kyoto Protocol and remains the only developed nation not to join this international effort.

  ■ The United States emits 20% of the world's greenhouse gases, so its refusal to join international efforts to curb greenhouse emissions has generated widespread resentment.

  ■ As of 2016 (the most recent year with full international data), nations that signed the Kyoto Protocol had *decreased* their emissions by 13.0% from 1990 levels.

  ■ Nations not a part of the Kyoto Protocol, including China, India, and the United States, *increased* the overall emissions of greenhouse gases.

■ **In the Paris Agreement (2015),** nations declared a joint goal to limit global temperature rise to 2.0°C (3.6°F) above pre-industrial levels and to attempt to keep the rise below 1.5°C (2.7°F). In their joint announcement, U.S. President Obama pledged that the United States would reduce carbon emissions by 28% by 2025 and Chinese President Xi Jinping promised that China would halt its emission growth by 2030. In 2017, President Trump announced that his administration would withdraw the United States from the Paris Agreement. The unity that nations displayed in the face of Trump's announcement suggested that other nations might now redouble their commitment to fighting climate change.

The economic considerations and approaches involved in the reduction of greenhouse gas emissions

■ The U.S. Senate has consistently opposed emissions reductions out of fear that this would dampen the U.S. economy. However, the United States was able to reduce its CO_2 emissions by 11% from 2007 to 2018 as a result of energy efficiency measures and a shift from burning coal to natural gas in power plants. Industrializing nations such as China and India have so far resisted emissions cuts under the same assumption, given that so much of these economies depend on fossil fuels.

■ Germany, France, and the United Kingdom, all signatory nations of the Kyoto Protocol and with a standard of living comparable to that of the United States, have significantly lowered their per capita emissions.

■ Per person, the emission of greenhouse gases in wealthy countries such as Denmark, New Zealand, Hong Kong, Switzerland, and Sweden is less than half that in the United States.

- Many industrialized nations are positioning themselves to gain economically from major energy transitions in a post-fossil-fuel era. Germany and Japan are currently leading the world in production and deployment of solar energy technology.
- In 2015, China *surpassed* the United States to become the world's biggest greenhouse gas emitter, although it still emits far less per person than the United States. It is also embarking on initiatives to develop and sell renewable energy technologies on a scale beyond what any other nation has yet attempted.

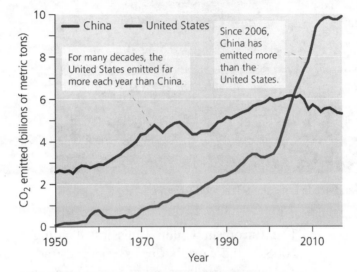

(a) Total CO_2 emissions each year since 1950

Figure 18.36a   United States and China Total CO_2 Emissions Since 1950

- If the United States does not act quickly to develop energy technologies for the future, then the future could belong to nations like China, Germany, and Japan.

- In the absence of action by the U.S. federal government to address climate change, state and local governments across the country are advancing policies to limit emissions.

  - In 2006, California passed the **Global Warming Solutions Act,** which aims to cut California's greenhouse gas emissions 25% by the year 2020.
  - In the wake of Trump's decision to withdraw from the Paris Agreement, state, regional, and local efforts went into overdrive. For example, New York City Mayor Michael Bloomberg brought together dozens of governors, university presidents, and corporate leaders who promised action to support the U.S. emissions pledge under the Paris Agreement.

- Market mechanisms are being used to address climate change. Supporters of **permit trading programs** (cap-and-trade programs) argue that they provide the fairest, least expensive, and most effective method of reducing emissions. For example, emission sources with too few permits to cover their emissions must find ways to reduce their emissions, buy permits from other sources, or pay for credits through a carbon offset project. Sources with excess permits may keep or sell them, and the price of a permit is meant to fluctuate freely in the market, creating the same kinds of financial incentives as any other commodity in a capitalist economy.

Figure 18.33   The Cap-and-Trade Emissions Trading System

- The European Union Emission Trading Scheme, operating since 2005, is the world's *largest* cap-and-trade program; however, it has had some problems with over-allocation of permits to industries, causing little incentive to reduce emissions. Europeans have now addressed these problems by making emitters pay for permits, and the market runs more efficiently today.

- The Chicago Climate Exchange (involving over 350 corporations) was the world's *first* emissions trading program for greenhouse gas reduction.

- Critics of cap-and-trade systems instead often prefer that governments enact a **carbon tax.** In this approach, governments charge polluters a fee for each unit of greenhouse gas they emit. This gives polluters a financial incentive to reduce emissions; however, many polluters simply pass the cost along to consumers by charging higher prices for their products or services.

- A **fee-and-dividend** approach has been put forth by proponents of carbon taxes. In this approach, funds from the tax or "fee" paid to government by polluters are transferred as a tax refund or "dividend" to taxpayers.

- **Carbon offsets** are also popular in that they allow participants to make voluntary payments intended to enable another entity to reduce emissions that one is unable to reduce oneself, thus offsetting one's own emissions. For example, a coal-burning power plant might pay a reforestation project to plant trees that will soak up as much carbon dioxide as the coal plant emits.

- Carbon offsets have become popular among utilities, businesses, universities, and governments trying to achieve **carbon neutrality,** a state in which no net carbon is emitted. These offsets are voluntary payments intended to enable another entity to help reduce the emissions that one is unable to reduce. The payment thus offsets one's own emissions.

- The most environmentally sound factor may be the collective decisions of millions of regular people taking steps to approach a **carbon-neutral lifestyle.** Determining one's individual **carbon footprint** and then taking the necessary steps to change behavior and consumption choices will be essential. Global climate change may be the biggest challenge we face, but reversing it would be our greatest environmental accomplishment for this century.

Multiple-Choice Questions

Use the following figure to answer questions 1 and 2.

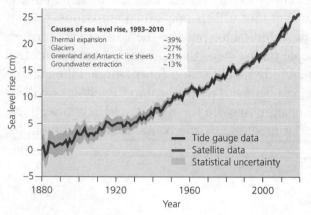

1. Since 1880, global sea level has risen approximately
   (A) 2.6 cm.
   (B) 26 mm.
   (C) 26 cm.
   (D) 260 cm.

2. The data indicate that the *main* contributing factor of sea level rise has been
   (A) Arctic ice melting.
   (B) the thermal expansion of warmer water.
   (C) Greenland and Antarctic ice sheets melting.
   (D) glacier melting throughout Europe.

3. Tropospheric carbon dioxide levels have been directly measured for more than 50 years. Scientists have recently measured these levels at slightly over ___ ppm.
   (A) 300
   (B) 350
   (C) 410
   (D) 450

4. Of the following greenhouse gases, ___ concentrations have increased the most since 1750, the beginning of the industrial revolution.
   (A) methane
   (B) carbon dioxide
   (C) nitrous oxide
   (D) ozone

5. The pollutant *least* likely to be emitted from an industrial factory's smokestack is
   (A) particulates.
   (B) carbon dioxide.
   (C) ozone.
   (D) sulfur dioxide.

6. Under natural, unpolluted conditions, the pH of rainfall is closest to
   (A) 8.0.
   (B) 7.1.
   (C) 5.6.
   (D) 4.5.

Use the following graph to answer questions 7–9.

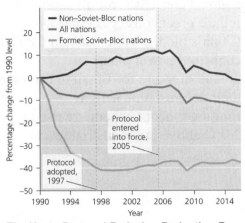

The Kyoto Protocol Emission Reduction Results

7. The global average reduction of emissions by 2016 for all nations ratifying the Kyoto Protocol was approximately ___%.
   (A) 2
   (B) 13
   (C) 20
   (D) 38

8. This overall reduction was largely due to the specific reductions by
   (A) the United States Clean Energy Plan.
   (B) the European Union nations.
   (C) China and India.
   (D) economic contractions by the former Soviet-bloc nations.

9. The Kyoto Protocol
   (A) increased federal funding for controlling greenhouse gas emissions from U.S. power plants.
   (B) required equal concessions from all countries involved in greenhouse gas emission.
   (C) required more concessions from developing countries because of their high dependence on fossil fuels.
   (D) was intended to reduce greenhouse gas emissions to levels lower than those of 1990.

10. Specific examples of the "criteria pollutants" regularly monitored by the EPA are
    (A) NO_2, NO_2, SO_2, and particulates.
    (B) NO_2, SO_2, and CO_2.
    (C) NO_2, CO_2,, and VOCs.
    (D) S_3, NO, and CO.

11. Which of the following is *not* yet regulated by the U.S. EPA?
    (A) lead
    (B) ozone
    (C) carbon dioxide
    (D) particulates

12. Which of the following is a major consequence of acidic deposition?
    (A) It washes toxic metals out of the soil, resulting in healthier soils for biodiversity.
    (B) It results in offshore eutrophication, contributing further to coral reef demise and ocean acidification.
    (C) It leaches out important minerals from soils, resulting in the loss of biodiversity.
    (D) It creates rainwater that can damage skin cells and cause cancer.

13. The greenhouse effect involves warming of Earth's surface and the
    (A) stratosphere.
    (B) thermosphere.
    (C) mesosphere.
    (D) troposphere.

14. The Montreal Protocol
    (A) is another example of the many failed attempts to reduce international air pollution.
    (B) is the successful international effort to reduce the effects of global acid deposition.
    (C) developed the much-needed international treaty for eliminating radon emissions from nuclear power plants.
    (D) resulted in significant reduction of CFCs by those countries signing the treaty.

15. The Intergovernmental Panel on Climate Change (IPCC) has synthesized several decades of data and documented observed trends in all of the areas below, *except*
    (A) Earth's surface temperature and its increase.
    (B) the ocean's contribution to photosynthesis and global productivity.
    (C) precipitation patterns and their regional differences.
    (D) storm intensity patterns.

16. The *primary* accomplishment of the 2015 Paris Agreement was the goal of
    (A) a global consensus for all nations to reduce greenhouse gas emissions.
    (B) China's pledge to cut back on their coal-fired power plants.
    (C) greater pressure for Brazil to decrease their deforestation activity.
    (D) limiting global temperature rise to 2.0°C above pre-industrial levels.

Free-Response Question

Personal Costs of Climate Change

Climate change studies are now the fastest-developing area of environmental research, with new scientific papers and findings refining our understanding of global climate change each month. The Intergovernmental Panel on Climate Change (IPCC) serves as the world's clearinghouse of scientific studies, and human activities have now been thoroughly documented to play the major role in causation.

Today, very few argue that we need "more proof" before we commit to substantial changes involving a new course of action toward a sustainable energy policy.

The U.S. government estimates the social costs of carbon emissions to be $40 per ton, and it is documented that each American citizen's impact currently produces an average of 20 tons of carbon per year.

---

a) The Intergovernmental Panel on Climate Change (IPCC) produced its *Fifth Assessment Report* in 2017, summarizing thousands of scientific studies with already *observed* trends. Describe and explain three different trends that the report has documented, including one planetary *physical change,* one *biological effect,* and an effect directly impacting *humans*.

b) Suppose that you would like to make your own lifestyle *carbon-neutral* and that you plan to begin by reducing your greenhouse gas emissions by 25%. What *two* specific actions would you take to achieve this reduction, and why?

c) If you are able to achieve a 25% reduction of greenhouse gas emissions, what would be your personal savings produced each year?

d) Currently, the average rate of increase in sea level is 3.4 mm/year. Calculate the expected increase in sea level, in meters, during the next 50 years.

Energy Resources and Consumption

Chapter 19: Fossil Fuels and Energy Efficiency

YOU MUST KNOW

- The origin of fossil fuels and the trends in global energy consumption.
- How to explain the extraction and use of the major types of fossil fuels.
- The nature and potential of unconventional fossil fuels.
- The ways in which we are extending our reach for fossil fuels.
- The major environmental impacts of fossil fuel use.
- Potential solutions involved with fossil fuel technologies.
- The political, social, and economic aspects of fossil fuel use.
- Specific strategies for conserving energy and enhancing efficiency.

The origin of fossil fuels and the trends in global energy consumption

■ Since the industrial revolution, nonrenewable **fossil fuels**—including coal, natural gas, and oil—have become our primary sources of energy to heat and light our homes; power our machinery; fuel our vehicles; and produce plastics, pharmaceuticals, synthetic fibers, and more. All fossil fuels are produced by the slow anaerobic (with little or no oxygen) decomposition and compression of organic matter from ancient plant material.

■ When plants die and are preserved in sediments under anaerobic conditions, they may impart their stored chemical energy (energy originally from the sun that was converted to chemical bond energy during photosynthesis) to coal, natural gas, or crude oil—each having a high energy content—making them efficient to burn, ship, and store.

■ Global consumption of the three main fossil fuels has risen steadily for years and is now at its highest level ever. Oil use rose steeply during the 1960s to overtake coal, and today it remains the leading global energy source, representing approximately 35% of the energy consumption market.

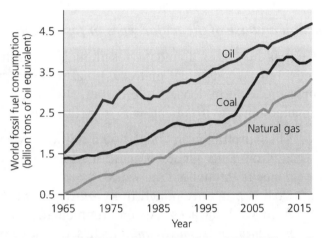

Figure 19.2 Global Consumption of Fossil Fuels Over the Past Fifty (50) Years

■ Fossil fuel deposits are unevenly distributed over Earth's surface, with nearly half of the world's proven reserves of crude oil in the Middle East. The Middle East and Russia hold more natural gas than any other country; however, the United States possesses the most coal of any nation.

■ Fossil fuels take such a long to form that, once depleted, they cannot be replaced within any time span useful to our civilization. For example, it takes a thousand years for the biosphere to generate the amount of organic matter that must be burned to produce a single day's worth of fossil fuels for our society.

■ Developed nations consume more energy than developing nations. For example, the United States has only 4.4% of the world's population; however, it consumes fully one-sixth of the world's energy resources.

■ To extract, process, and deliver the energy used, it is necessary to invest substantial inputs of energy. **Net energy** expresses the difference between energy returned and energy invested: *Net energy = Energy returned – Energy invested.*

■ The **energy returned on investment (EROI)** ratio is useful when assessing the value of energy sources: *EROI = Energy returned/Energy invested.* A higher ratio means that we receive more energy from each unit of energy than we invest. Fossil fuels are widely used because their EROI ratios have historically been high. EROI ratios for producing conventional oil and natural gas in the United States declined from roughly 24:1 in the 1950s to around 11:1 by 2010. For unconventional fossil fuel sources like the Alberta oil sands (the

Keystone XL Pipeline project), the EROI ratios are even lower, with estimates averaging around 4:1, because oil sands are typically a low-quality fuel that requires a great deal of energy to extract and process.

■ Because fossil fuel deposits are *finite* and *nonrenewable,* easily accessible supplies of these main fossil fuels have dwindled, and the EROI ratios have also fallen.

How to explain the extraction and use of the major types of fossil fuels

■ **Coal** is our most abundant fossil fuel. It results from organic matter (generally woody plant materials) that was compressed under very high pressure to form dense, solid carbon structures. Coal typically forms in an anaerobic environment, with very little decomposition taking place.

■ The proliferation 300–400 million years ago of swampy environments where organic material was buried has created coal deposits throughout the world.

■ Coal is primarily mined from *underground deposits* and *strip-mined* from land surfaces. An environmentally destructive process called *mountaintop removal mining* has recently become common in the Appalachian Mountains of the United States.

■ In 2019, coal provided 8.4% of the electrical generating capacity of the United States and was the main fuel source powering China's surging economy. China is now the world's primary producer (46.7%) and consumer (50.5%) of coal.

■ Electricity is generated in modern coal-fired power plants by burning coal in order to convert water to steam. The steam then turns a turbine, generating electricity by passing magnets past copper coils. The steam finally cools and condenses back to water and is returned to the boiler in a continuous loop to repeat the process.

Figure 19.10 Generating Electricity at a Coal-Fired Power Plant

- Coal varies in its water and carbon content and the amount of potential energy it contains, ranging from *peat* (least compressed and most water content) to *bituminous* and finally to *anthracite* coal, containing the highest potential energy.

- Scientists estimate that Earth holds enough coal to supply our society for roughly 132 years. This estimate for how long a remaining resource will last is based on the **reserves-to-production ratio (R/P ratio).** The R/P ratio for coal is far larger than that for oil or natural gas.

- **Natural gas** consists primarily of methane, CH_4, and typically includes varying amounts of other volatile hydrocarbons. It is increasingly favored as a "bridge fuel" because it is versatile and clean-burning, emitting just half as much CO_2 per unit of energy produced as coal and two-thirds as much as oil.

  - Most gas extracted commercially results from compression and heat at depths below 3 km (1.9 mi) and is found above deposits of crude oil or seams of coal. Its extraction often accompanies the extraction of those fossil fuels.

  - Today, natural gas extraction also makes use of **hydraulic fracturing** techniques to break into rock formations, as many of the most accessible natural gas reserves have already been exhausted.

- **Petroleum** is a fluid mixture of hydrocarbons, water, sulfur, and natural gas that occurs in underground deposits and forms from the remains of ocean-dwelling phytoplankton. **Crude oil** is liquid petroleum that is a thick, liquid mixture of hydrocarbons formed 1–2 miles underground under high temperature and pressure. All crude oil is a mixture of hundreds of different types of hydrocarbon molecules; therefore, the specific properties depend on the chemistry of the organic starting materials, the geologic environment of its location, and the details of the formation process.

  - Oil is the world's most-used fuel today, accounting for 35% of the world's commercial energy consumption.
  - Geologists estimate the *"technically recoverable"* versus the *"economically recoverable"* amount of oil based on seismic surveys. The **proven recoverable reserve** is the amount of a fossil fuel that is technologically and economically feasible to remove under current conditions.
  - **Oil refineries** separate the many types of hydrocarbon molecules present by using high heat to boil the crude oil, causing its many hydrocarbon constituents to volatilize and proceed through a distillation column. Based on differences in boiling points, the heavier fuels can be separated from the lighter fuels. Combining refining with other chemical processes, crude oil can also be transformed into lubricating oil, asphalts, and the precursors of plastics, synthetic fibers, and pharmaceuticals.
  - Some scientists have estimated that we have already extracted half the world's oil reserves. At current levels of production (34.6 billion barrels globally per year), the estimated remaining 1.7 trillion barrels will last about 50 years. Applying R/P ratios to natural gas reserves has resulted in estimates of a 51-year future.
  - **Peak oil** is the term used to describe the point of maximum production of petroleum in the world (or for a given nation), after which oil production declines. This is also expected to be roughly the midway point of extraction of the world's oil supplies. Once we pass the peak and production slows, the gap between rising demand and falling supply may pose immense economic and social challenges for our society.
  - Predicting an exact date for peak oil *globally* is more challenging because many companies and governments do not reveal their true data on oil reserves. Today, U.S. hydraulic fracking has enabled extraction of formerly inaccessible oil and also the pursuit of various unconventional petroleum sources. Since about 2005, production of conventional oil has been declining, and the United States has had to seek a variety of novel petroleum sources to compensate for this decline.

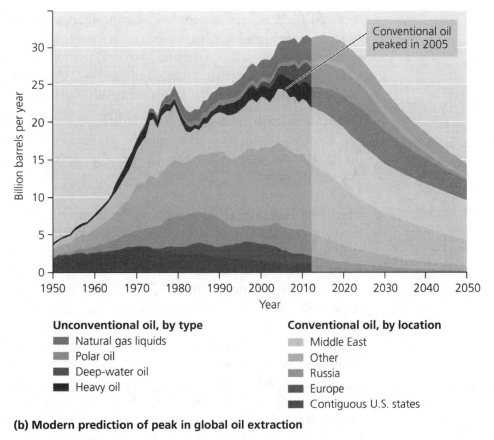

Unconventional oil, by type
- Natural gas liquids
- Polar oil
- Deep-water oil
- Heavy oil

Conventional oil, by location
- Middle East
- Other
- Russia
- Europe
- Contiguous U.S. states

(b) Modern prediction of peak in global oil extraction

Figure 19.12b   Modern Prediction of Peak in Global Oil Production

The nature and potential of unconventional fossil fuels

- As oil production declines, there will be more reliance on natural gas, coal, and the potential of unconventional fossil fuels and hydraulic fracturing. However, these sources are also in the process of peaking and declining because of their finite, nonrenewable nature.

- Three types of unconventional fossil fuels exist in large amounts: oil sands, oil shale, and methane hydrate.

  - **Oil sands** (also called **tar sands**) are deposits of moist sand and clay containing 1–20% bitumen, a thick and heavy form of petroleum that is rich in carbon and poor in hydrogen. Bitumen is too thick to extract by conventional oil drilling, so oil sands are generally removed by strip mining vast areas of land, resulting in mile-wide open pits.

    ♦ Canada's controversial **Keystone XL Pipeline** project focused on extracting these oil sands. In late 2015, President Obama decided against approving the pipeline, noting that it would not lower gas prices, would not enhance America's energy security, and would undercut U.S. leadership in the area of global climate negotiations.

    ♦ Once elected, President Donald Trump reversed Obama's decision; however, many legal obstacles have blocked further construction of the pipeline. Meanwhile, the broader debate over the role of fossil fuels in our economy has continued, especially as climate change impacts have increased

♦ Impacts from the extraction of oil sands surpass those of conventional fuel extraction, creating 14–21% more pollution and climate warming, without producing additional energy.

■ **Oil shale** is sedimentary rock filled with kerogen (organic matter) and can be processed to produce liquid petroleum. About 40% of global oil shale reserves are in the United States, mostly in Colorado, Wyoming, and Utah. The EROI is very low, with estimates ranging from 4:1 down to 1.1:1.

■ **Methane hydrate** is an ice-like solid consisting of molecules of methane embedded in a crystal lattice of water molecules. It is believed that there are immense amounts of this resource in sediments in the Arctic and ocean floor, possibly holding twice as much carbon as all known deposits of oil, coal, and natural gas combined. However, we do not yet know how to extract this energy source safely.

■ For all of the above alternatives, the net energy values are low because they are expensive to extract and process—resulting in low EROI ratios. Also, these fuels exert severe environmental impacts (for example, strip mining, habitat destruction, and increased air and water pollution). Finally, the combustion of these fuels would emit at least as much carbon dioxide and methane as conventional fossil fuels, increasing global climate change concerns.

The ways in which we are extending our reach for fossil fuels

■ We are investing more and more money, energy, and technology into locating and extracting new fossil fuel deposits, with the result of expanding our proven reserves.

■ Currently, the major ways of extending fossil fuel extraction and reserves are the following:

1) **Mountaintop mining for coal:** In this method, entire mountaintops are blasted away to access coal seams. Although it may be economically efficient, it can cause large amounts of rock and soil to slide downslope, resulting in polluting and burying of existing streams and disrupting life for people living nearby.

2) **Hydraulic fracturing for oil and natural gas:** Fracking is a process that injects large volumes of chemically treated water and sand under high pressure into deep deposits of shale in order to fracture them. After the water-chemical mixture is pumped out, the natural gas liberated flows into the well and can be pumped to the surface. Recent studies are showing that the contaminated "produced water" resulting from the fracking process is full of chemical residues that can easily compromise underground water quality and quantity.

- Hydraulic fracturing has been used to extract natural gas from the formation of Marcellus shale (in Pennsylvania and New York) and for oil in the Bakken formation (in North Dakota, Montana, and southern Canada). This new flow of oil reduced U.S. dependence on foreign imports and led to a glut on world markets, bringing oil prices down to less than one-fourth of its 2008 high.
- Yet despite the benefits, fracking has sparked controversy wherever it has occurred, affecting landscapes, economies, and human health issues.

3) **Secondary extraction:** Since a typical oil or gas well extraction facility may leave as much as two-thirds of a deposit in the ground after **primary extraction,** companies may return later to use new technologies involving solvents, steam, and water to force the remaining oil or gas out by pressure. Hydraulic fracturing is an example of secondary extraction.

4) **Offshore drilling in deep waters:** Roughly 35% of the oil and 10% of the natural gas extracted in the United States today comes from deposits located offshore, primarily in the Gulf of Mexico and off the southern California coastline. Drilling in shallow water has occurred for several decades; however, as oil and gas reserves have declined and technology has improved, the U.S. long-standing moratorium on offshore drilling was lifted in 2008. In 2010, after British Petroleum's *Deepwater Horizon* oil-drilling platform exploded and sank, causing the largest oil spill in world history, the Obama administration canceled all offshore drilling projects, only to backtrack in 2011 by issuing a five-year plan that opened access to 75% of the oil and gas reserves off Alaska and in the Gulf of Mexico.

5) **Exploiting new "unconventional" fossil fuel sources:** Although the three sources of "unconventional" fossil fuels—oil sands, oil shale, and methane hydrate—could theoretically supply the world for centuries, their net energy values and EROI ratios are very low, and these fuels will exert severe environmental impacts on land and water. However, the major concern is that in burning these fuels, the emission of greenhouse gases in excess of that resulting from our current burning of coal, oil, and natural gas would dramatically worsen air pollution and climate change.

The major environmental impacts of fossil fuel use

- **Climate change:** When we burn fossil fuels, we alter fluxes in Earth's carbon cycle by taking carbon that has been retired into a long-term reservoir underground and releasing it into the atmosphere as CO_2. Because CO_2 is a major greenhouse gas, its increased concentration warms our planet and drives many changes in our global climate. Carbon dioxide pollution is now becoming recognized as the biggest negative consequence of fossil fuel use.

■ The vast amounts of greenhouse gases emerging from U.S. hydraulic fracturing and Canada's oil sands create serious concerns about their potential impact on global climate change.

■ Any time natural gas leaks (during extraction, transport, and processing) into the atmosphere, the powerful greenhouse gas methane further impacts global warming and climate change.

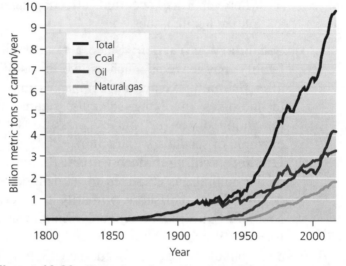

Figure 19.23 Emissions from Fossil Fuel Combustion Have Risen Dramatically

■ **Human health:** Fossil fuel emissions also affect human health directly, as respiratory irritants, and coal combustion emits mercury that can bioaccumulate in organisms. Some hydrocarbons, such as benzene and toluene, are also carcinogenic, and crude oil often contains trace amounts of known poisons such as lead and arsenic.

■ **Air pollution:** The combustion of oil in our vehicles and coal in our power plants releases sulfur dioxide and nitrogen oxides, which contribute to industrial and photochemical smog and to acid deposition, both major air pollution problems. Acid deposition exerts many adverse effects on freshwater ecosystems and their aquatic life. Hydraulic fracturing also gives rise to air pollution, as methane and the volatile toxic chemicals of fracking fluids seep up from fracking sites.

- **Marine oil spills:** The extracting of fossil fuels leads to many types of marine pollution, including the following:

  - Oil pollution of marine environments, such as occurred in the 2010 *Deepwater Horizon* offshore drilling platform explosion. Many bird species, shrimp and fish species, and coastal marsh plants were killed in the world's biggest-ever accidental oil spill.
  - The Taylor marine spill, first noticed in 2004 when Hurricane Ivan set off submarine landslides, destroyed a Gulf platform and is continuing to release 300–700 barrels of oil each day.
  - The Taylor and *Deepwater Horizon* spills have now eclipsed the 1989 *Exxon Valdez* spill in the amount of oil spilled.

- **Habitat destruction:** Coal mining devastates natural systems by destroying large swaths of habitat, especially with the mountaintop removal approach. It also can cause chemical runoff into waterways through the process of **acid drainage**—when sulfide minerals in newly exposed rock surfaces react with oxygen and rainwater to produce sulfuric acid that is toxic to organisms.

- Oil and gas extraction also modifies the environment, extensively **fragmenting habitat** with the construction of road networks, pipelines, housing for workers, and toxic sludge ponds. Other environmental concerns include the following:

  1) The Arctic National Wildlife Refuge (ANWR), on Alaska's North Slope, has been the focus of development debate for decades. Advocates of oil drilling have tried to open its lands for drilling, and proponents of wilderness have fought for its preservation.
  2) The proposed Keystone XL Pipeline route across the sensitive Sandhills region of Nebraska, a migration route to the world's Sandhill crane population, has been a major area of environmental concern.
  3) Large-scale boreal forests in Alberta, Canada and tropical forests in Venezuela are being destroyed in order to create the vast open pits necessary to mine the oil sands.

- **Groundwater contamination:** Hydrofracking presents risks of groundwater pollution that are not yet completely understood, including chemical contamination (by fracking fluids) and methane contamination of drinking water. Hydrofracking also produces immense volumes of wastewater laced with salts, radioactive elements, and other toxic chemicals that become a serious problem to dispose of.

- **Aquifer overuse and contamination:** The extraction and transport of oil from Alberta, Canada's oil sands/Keystone XL Pipeline project also have the potential of contaminating the continent's largest aquifer (the Ogallala Aquifer), which serves as the irrigation source for America's breadbasket and the drinking water for millions of people. Three barrels of water are required to produce each barrel of oil from oil sands operations. The toxic wastewater resulting from production is then discharged into huge surface reservoirs. When migratory waterfowl land on these contaminated reservoirs, bird feathers become oil-clogged, resulting in birds being unable to properly insulate themselves.

■ **Earthquakes:** Finally, fracking is now known to cause earthquakes, and although most have been minor, they do raise questions about whether all the economic and social costs of fracking have been considered.

Potential solutions involved with fossil fuel technologies

■ **Clean coal technologies** refers to a wide array of techniques, equipment, and approaches that aim to remove chemical contaminants during the process of generating electricity from coal. Among these technologies are scrubbers that remove SO_2 and/or NO_x from smokestack emissions or filtering devices used to capture tiny ash particles. **Gasification,** in which coal is converted into a cleaner synthetic gas (syngas) by reacting with oxygen at high temperatures, is also an approach being utilized.

■ Current research efforts focus on **carbon capture and storage (CCS),** or sequestration, as the burning of even the cleanest fossil fuel pumps huge amounts of CO_2 into the air, intensifying global climate change. The CCS approach consists of capturing CO_2 emissions, converting the gas to a liquid form, and then storing it in the ocean or underground in a geologically stable rock formation. The world's first coal-fired power plant to approach zero emissions, using carbon capture and storage technology, opened in 2008 in Germany. However, at this point the technology is too unproven to be the central focus of a clean energy strategy for any nation.

■ The costs of alleviating all environmental impacts from fossil fuels are high and are generally not internalized in market prices; however, we all pay these *external costs* through medical expenses, costs of environmental cleanup, and impacts on our quality of life. Equally important to understand is that U.S. fossil fuel prices have been kept inexpensive as a result of government subsidies to fossil fuel industries.

The political, social, and economic aspects of fossil fuel use

■ Today's societies are so reliant on fossil fuel energy that sudden restrictions on oil supplies can have major economic consequences.

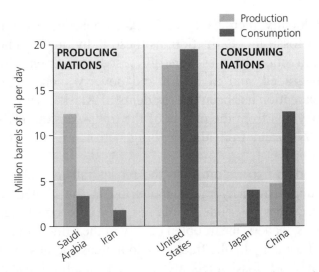

Figure 19.22 Comparison of Oil Consumption and Production Patterns

- Since its 1970 oil production peak, the United States relied more and more on foreign energy, but today imports just over 20% of its crude oil. This represents a significant reduction since 1970 as conservation measures, increased renewable energy research, secondary extraction, expansion of domestic offshore drilling, and hydraulic fracturing efforts have increased.

- In response to the 1973–1974 OPEC (Organization of Petroleum Exporting Countries) embargo, the U.S. government enacted a series of policies designed to reduce reliance on Middle Eastern oil and moved toward developing additional domestic sources (Alaska's North Slope). Concern over reliance on foreign oil has repeatedly driven the debate to open the Arctic National Wildlife Refuge (ANWR) to drilling, despite critics' charges that such drilling would do little to alleviate the nation's dependence. It is currently estimated that ANWR contains approximately 7.7 billion barrels of "technically recoverable" oil—just over 1 year's worth of U.S. consumption.

- Diversification of oil sources toward non–Middle Eastern nations (Canada, Mexico, and Colombia) is the current approach pursued by the United States. However, even with this approach, there is no guarantee that these nations will continue exporting to the United States over the long term.

- The U.S. government is currently urging oil companies to pursue secondary extraction at sites that have been closed down after primary extraction had ceased being cost-effective. U.S. leaders have also enacted conservation measures, funded research into renewables, and established an energy stockpile (which today stores one month's worth of oil), all in efforts to increase energy security.

- Globally, there have been mixed consequences for people living in areas of fossil fuel extraction, as these individuals do not always benefit from extraction of these energy resources. Often, local environments are degraded, and ill health and poverty increase for local residents. An exception has been the residents of Alaska, who are continuing to receive payouts from the profits of the trans-Alaska pipeline construction in the 1970s and from the ongoing petroleum extraction on Alaska's North Slope.
- Today, experts attribute the recent fall in global oil prices to increased supply from hydraulic fracturing in the United States, followed by the decisions of Saudi Arabia and OPEC to boost their own production. For U.S. leaders, the troubled history of the Middle East has enhanced the allure of using hydraulic fracturing to increase domestic oil and gas extraction.
- In short, fossil fuels are not a sustainable long-term solution to energy needs, since fossil fuels are all finite in supply and their use has concretely demonstrated adverse health, environmental, political, and socioeconomic consequences.

Specific strategies for conserving energy and enhancing efficiency

- Until our society transitions to renewable energy sources, we will need to find ways to minimize the expenditure of energy from our dwindling fossil fuel resources.
- **Energy efficiency** describes the ability to obtain a given result or amount of output while using less energy and is generally a result of technological improvements.
- **Energy conservation** describes the practice of reducing energy use and results from behavioral choices. Americans use far more energy per person than people in most other developed nations. European nations have a standard of living similar to those of Americans yet use less energy per capita.

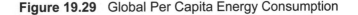

(a) **Per capita energy consumption**

Figure 19.29 Global Per Capita Energy Consumption

■ Immediately after the OPEC embargo of 1973–1974, the United States enacted a mandated reduction in the national speed limit to 55 mph and increased the mile-per-gallon (mpg) fuel efficiency for newly constructed automobiles. However, these initiatives were abandoned over the next three decades, and U.S. policymakers repeatedly failed to raise the *corporate average fuel efficiency (CAFE) standards,* which set benchmarks for auto manufacturers to meet.

■ Currently, more than two-thirds of the fossil fuel energy we use is simply lost (as waste heat) in power plants and in automobiles. **Cogeneration,** in which excess heat produced (during the generation of electricity) is captured and used to heat nearby workplaces and homes, can be employed to effectively reduce heating requirements.

■ The recent rise in U.S. fuel efficiency occurred after Congress passed legislation in 2007 mandating that automakers raise average fuel efficiency to 35 mpg by 2020. When automakers requested a government bailout during the 2008–2009 recession, President Obama persuaded automakers to boost average fuel economies to 54.5 mpg by 2025. However, the Trump administration has since moved to revoke these policies.

■ U.S. gasoline prices are extremely low, relative to other nations, and do not account for substantial *external costs* that oil extraction and consumption inflict on the environment in the form of land degradation, air and water pollution, and climate change.

- **Individual behavioral choices** can be made to conserve energy, including driving less, turning off lights when rooms are not being used, dialing down one's home thermostat, and cutting back on the use of energy-intensive machines and appliances. Specific personal actions that promote energy conservation and enhance efficiency include the following:

    1) Better home design (passive solar) and increased home insulation.
    2) Reduction of "vampire" power loss by powering off electrical appliances and not leaving appliances in standby mode.
    3) Use of energy-efficient lighting (compact fluorescent light bulbs initially replaced incandescent bulbs, reducing energy use by up to 80%). More recently, light-emitting diodes (LEDs) have become affordable and are being adopted quickly.

(a) Conversion to more efficient bulbs in the United States

Figure 19.31a Conversion to More Efficient Light Bulbs in the United States

4) Use of energy-efficient appliances (refrigerators, dishwashers, etc.) rated by the U.S. EPA Energy Star program.
5) Choosing public transportation whenever possible. Alternatively, one can choose electric cars, electric/hybrids, plug-in hybrids, or vehicles that use hydrogen fuel cells. The current U.S. fuel-efficient models obtain fuel economy ratings of up to about 50 mpg—twice that of the average American car.

- Although essential, effective energy conservation practices and using more efficient technology do not add to our supply of available fuel. Regardless of how much we conserve, we will still need energy, and the only sustainable way of guaranteeing a reliable long-term supply is to ensure sufficiently rapid development of renewable energy sources. The energy path that is chosen will have far-reaching consequences for human health, for Earth's climate, for our environment, and for the stability and future progress of our civilization.

Chapter 20: Conventional Energy Alternatives

> ## YOU MUST KNOW
>
> - The reasons for seeking energy alternatives to fossil fuels.
> - The contributions to world and U.S. energy production by conventional alternatives to fossil fuels.
> - The specifics of nuclear energy, including how it is generated.
> - The specifics of the debate over nuclear power.
> - The major sources and impacts of biomass.
> - The scale and impacts of hydroelectric power.

The reasons for seeking energy alternatives to fossil fuels

- The global economy is largely powered by fossil fuels, with over 80% of our energy coming from oil, coal, and natural gas.
- All of these fossil fuels are finite, nonrenewable energy sources, which contribute to many adverse human health and environmental impacts, the most important of which is the production of the greenhouse gases driving climate change.
- In addition to addressing the nonrenewability, adverse air pollution, and climate change issues, developing alternatives to fossil fuels has the added benefit of helping to diversify an economy's mix of energy, thus lessening price volatility and dependence on foreign fuel imports.

The contributions to world and U.S. energy production by conventional alternatives to fossil fuels

- The alternative energy sources that are currently the most developed and widely used are nuclear power, hydroelectric power, and energy from biomass. Each is generally considered to exert less environmental impact than fossil fuels, but more impact than the "new renewable" alternatives such as solar, wind, geothermal, and ocean power. In addition to having potential for renewability, all these alternatives are best viewed as intermediates along a continuum of renewability depending on how they are utilized.
- Although nuclear (10.4%), hydroelectric (16.3%), and biomass (8.0%) contribute substantially to the world's electricity generation, fossil fuels still power two-thirds of global electricity generation.

- Sweden has demonstrated that it is possible to replace fossil fuels gradually with alternative sources, having decreased its fossil fuel use from 81% to 26% since 1970. Today, nuclear power, bioenergy, and hydropower together provide Sweden with two-thirds of its total energy and 90% of its electricity.

- By comparison, in the United States these three fossil fuel alternatives only provide approximately 16% of our total energy consumption.

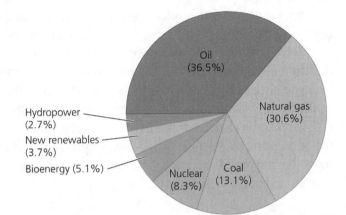

(a) U.S. energy consumption, by source

(b) U.S. energy consumption, 1950–2018

Figure 20.4a and b   U.S. Energy Consumption, 1950–2018

The specifics of nuclear energy, including how it is generated

- Nuclear power comes from converting the energy of an atom's nuclear bonds into thermal energy using radioactive elements as the fuel source. **Nuclear fission,** the splitting apart of atomic nuclei, is the reaction that drives the release of nuclear energy in power plants. Uranium-235 is the primary fuel for conventional nuclear reactors because this isotope is easily split using neutrons, resulting in the production of heat, light, radiation, and additional neutrons, which go on to split additional atoms in a chain reaction.

- **U-235** is found in uranium ore and represents a very small portion (1%) of the uranium mined. Ninety-nine percent of the uranium from nature occurs as the much less fissionable isotope U-238; therefore, mined uranium ore must be processed to enrich the U-235 concentration to at least 3% in order to sustain a fissionable chain reaction.

- The enriched uranium is formed into pellets of UO_2, which are incorporated into metallic tubes called *fuel rods* that are placed inside the nuclear power plant's *reactor core*. This reactor core is housed within a *reactor vessel,* and the vessel, steam generator, and associated plumbing (carrying cooling water) are often further protected within a meter-thick concrete *containment building*. Not all nations require containment buildings, which points out the key role that government regulation plays in protecting public safety of the global community.

- In order for fission to begin in a nuclear reactor, the neutrons bombarding U-235 must be slowed down by a substance called a *moderator,* most often water or graphite. Also, excess neutrons produced when uranium nuclei split must be absorbed by *control rods* in order that the fission reaction is maintained at the desired rate.

Figure 20.5 Nuclear Reactors Produce Electricity

- **Major advantages:** Using fission, nuclear power plants generate electricity without creating the air pollutants (the *most important* of these is the greenhouse gas CO_2, as well as SO_2 and particulates) generated from burning fossil fuels. Additional advantages include fewer chronic health risks than are associated with living downwind from power plants burning coal. Also, because uranium generates far more power than coal by weight, less uranium needs to be mined, so there is less damage to landscapes and less solid waste than produced by coal mining.

- Today, when considering climate change, the main advantage is that nuclear power avoids CO_2 emissions. The International Atomic Energy Agency (IAEA) has estimated that the United States avoids emitting 600 million metric tons of CO_2/yr, equivalent to the CO_2 emissions of almost all passenger cars in the nation and 11% of the total U.S. CO_2 emissions.
- **Major disadvantages:** The main disadvantage is the problem of safe storage and disposal of the radioactive waste generated and the very long half-life of most nuclear waste isotopes. A second serious consideration is the potential for catastrophic nuclear plant accidents. A third consideration is the high cost of building new nuclear power plants and the relatively low EROI value of 14:1 for nuclear power, versus the approximately 45:1 energy return on investment for coal.

The specifics of the debate over nuclear power

- Although nuclear power delivers energy more cleanly than fossil fuels, the possibility of catastrophic accidents has caused a great deal of public debate and anxiety over nuclear power.
- Three events have been influential in shaping public opinion about nuclear energy: in Pennsylvania, the **Three Mile Island** plant partial meltdown (1979); in the Ukraine, the **Chernobyl** plant explosion (1986); and the **Fukushima Daiichi** nuclear facility accident involving six nuclear units in Japan. This latest accident resulted from the magnitude-9 earthquake on March 11, 2011, and subsequent 14-m tsunami that flooded the plant's emergency power generators required for core cooling.
  - It is estimated that decades will be required to fully clean up the site because of radioactive contamination.
  - The most notable finding by researchers, in the aftermath of the Fukushima accident, is that the disruption caused to people's lives from stress, fear, and the health effects arising from evacuation have been far worse than predicted.
- Even if nuclear power could be made completely safe, we would still be left with the serious problem, yet to be solved, of what to do with spent fuel rods and other radioactive waste. Currently, all nuclear waste from power generation in the United States is being held in temporary storage at 120 sites spread across 39 states.
  - Most U.S. plants now have no room left for this type of on-site storage.
  - **Yucca Mountain,** a remote site in the Nevada desert, was chosen as the final repository for U.S. nuclear wastes; however, in 2010 the Obama administration ended support for the project, and an alternative site has yet to be agreed upon.

- Some citizens voiced concern that the Yucca Mountain site was prone to seismic activity and water infiltration. In addition, the need for highly radioactive wastes to be transported on public highways from the approximately 120 U.S. nuclear facility storage areas has posed additional risks and concerns.

- With all the concerns over waste disposal, safety, and expensive cost overruns, nuclear power's growth has slowed. Electricity from nuclear power today remains heavily subsidized and continues to be more expensive than electricity from coal and other sources.

- However, with increased concern over climate change, carbon emissions, and the Kyoto Protocol agreement, some European nations that had planned to phase out nuclear power have now reversed their decision.

  - Sweden's government has shifted policies from vowing to shut down all nuclear plants by 2010 to now advocating the use of nuclear power as a "bridge" to fight climate change while new renewable energy sources are being developed.

  - The United States halted construction of nuclear plants following the Three Mile Island accident in 1979. At its peak in 1990, the United States had 112 operable plants; today it has 99, with no plans for constructing new nuclear facilities.

  - After the Fukushima accident, the developed countries of Europe, specifically Germany and Sweden, have reassessed their nuclear programs and are beginning to phase out nuclear power. Japanese citizens remain opposed to restarting their nuclear plants, and most plants will not come back online until after 2025.

The major sources and impacts of biomass

- **Bioenergy**—also known as **biomass**—is energy obtained from organic matter (biomass) derived from living or recently living organisms. Bioenergy is theoretically renewable and adds no net carbon to the atmosphere because the carbon in biomass fuels may have been captured as recently as months ago (in the case of a corn plant) or perhaps up to a few hundred years ago (in the case of the wood in a tree). Therefore, carbon in biomass is often referred to as *modern* carbon, in contrast to the carbon stored in fossil fuel, which is referred to as *fossil* carbon.

- Bioenergy can come from many different types of plant matter, including wood, charcoal, and agricultural crops, as well as from combustible animal waste products such as livestock manure.

- Fuelwood, charcoal, and manure account for fully one-third of energy used in developing nations; however, in these poorer countries, problems have arisen from overharvesting fuelwood at unsustainably rapid rates, leading to deforestation, soil erosion, desertification, and ultimately diminishing biodiversity.

- New bioenergy strategies, such as burning forestry residues (particularly in Sweden), agricultural residue from cornstalks, animal waste from feedlots, and even organic wastes from landfills (bacterial breakdown of organic matter produces methane, or *biogas*), are being utilized in many industrialized countries today. This latter waste-to-energy process, where biogas is being produced as a fuel that can be burned to generate electricity, is another innovation being employed by Sweden. We are also beginning to grow certain types of plants as crops to generate **biopower,** including fast-growing grasses such as bamboo, fescue, and switchgrass.

- **Advantages of biomass:** Biomass power helps to mitigate climate change by reducing CO_2 emissions, reduces emissions of SO_2 because plant matter (unlike coal) contains no appreciable sulfur content, and enhances energy efficiency by recycling waste products. Capturing landfill gas to use as a fuel reduces emissions of methane, a potent greenhouse gas.

- **Disadvantages of biomass:** The main disadvantage occurs when crops or plant matter is burned for power, as the soil is deprived of nutrients that would otherwise be returned for future plant growth. The depletion of soil fertility is a major long-term problem for bioenergy and the main reason for its weakness in long-term sustainability.

- **Biofuels,** including **ethanol** and **biodiesel,** are used to power automobiles. Ethanol is an energy-rich alcohol produced by fermenting biomass, generally from carbohydrate-rich crops such as corn or sugarcane.

  - About 40% of the U.S. corn crop today is used to make ethanol. At this current level of production, ethanol competes with food production and drives up food costs in many locations.

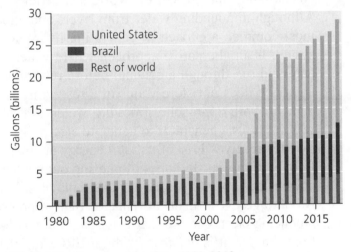

(b) Global ethanol production, 1980–2018

Figure 20.16b Ethanol Production 1980–2018

  - Growing corn for ethanol also requires substantial inputs of energy, with an EROI ratio of only 1.3:1.

- **Biodiesel** is a fuel produced from vegetable oil, used cooking grease, or animal fat. Using waste oil as a biofuel is sustainable; however, most biodiesel today, like most ethanol, comes from crops grown specifically for the purpose (soybeans in Brazil and the United States, oil palms in Southeast Asia, and rapeseed in Europe), all of which take up large areas of land for growing.

- Because the major crops grown for biodiesel and ethanol exert heavy impacts on the land, research is underway on a variety of alternative crops, from wheat, sorghum, cassava, and sugar beets to lesser known plants such as *Jatropha* and the grass *Miscanthus*.

- Theoretically, energy from biomass is **carbon-neutral,** releasing no net carbon into the atmosphere. Burning biomass for energy is *not* carbon-neutral *if* natural forests are destroyed in order to plant bioenergy crops, because forests sequester more carbon than do croplands.

- Biodiesel, oil sands, and ethanol are at the low end of EROIs, at 2:1, 4:1, and 5:1, respectively. EROIs for fossil fuels were historically very high but have been dropping because we now need to expend more energy to reach the less accessible deposits.

The scale and impacts of hydroelectric power

- **Hydroelectric power,** or **hydropower,** uses the kinetic energy of moving water to turn turbines and generate electricity. Next to biomass, we draw more renewable energy from the motion of water than from any other resource. Hydropower accounts for 2% of the world's energy consumption and 16% of the world's electricity generation.

- Although impounding water from rivers and streams behind dams is the most common approach to generating hydroelectricity, a "run-of-river" system is an alternative approach where water is retained behind a low dam and run through a channel before returning to the river. This latter approach does not store water in a reservoir, as would be the case in a dam. In both approaches, moving water turns the blades of a turbine, which causes a generator to generate electricity.

- Sweden receives 11% of its total energy and nearly 50% of its electricity from hydropower. In hopes of phasing out nuclear power, many Swedish citizens had hoped hydropower could play a still larger role.

- **Advantages:** The main advantages of hydropower over fossil fuels for producing electricity are that it is *renewable* as long as precipitation falls from the sky, it is *efficient* (with an EROI of 80:1, higher than any other modern-day energy source), and *no carbon compounds are burned* in its production of energy. However, fossil fuels *are* used in constructing and maintaining dams, and recent evidence indicates that large reservoirs release the greenhouse gas methane as a result of anaerobic decay in deep water.

- In terms of efficiency, hydropower has the highest EROI ratio, averaging 80:1. Biodiesel, oil sands, and ethanol are at the low end of EROIs, at 2:1, 4:1, and 5:1, respectively.
- **Disadvantages:** Adverse environmental impacts of hydropower and damming rivers include destruction of habitat for wildlife, disruption of a river's natural flooding cycles, entrapment of sediment behind dams, and the possibility of thermal pollution because water downstream becomes unusually warm if water levels are kept too shallow.
- China's **Three Gorges Dam,** recently completed, is the world's largest hydroelectric plant. Its construction displaced 1.3 million people; however, the dam is now generating as much electricity as dozens of coal-fired or nuclear plants.
- Hydropower may not expand much more because most of the world's large rivers that offer opportunities for hydropower are already dammed. An increased number of people have also become aware of the ecological impacts of dams, and some dams in the United States have actually been dismantled in recent years.
- Although some nations such as Sweden already rely heavily on the use of hydropower, biomass, and nuclear energy, it appears that all countries will need to focus on developing a greater reliance on renewable energy sources in order to move toward a more sustainable energy future.

Chapter 21: New Renewable Energy Sources

YOU MUST KNOW

- The major sources of renewable energy and their potential for growth.
- The basics of solar energy, including both passive and active solar designs.
- The major advantages and disadvantages of solar energy.
- The basics of wind power including its advantages and disadvantages.
- The basics of geothermal energy including its advantages and disadvantages.
- The potential of ocean energy sources and how they are harnessed.
- The approaches for energy storage and the potential of hydrogen fuel cell technology.

The major sources of renewable energy and their potential for growth

- The **"new renewable" energy sources** include **solar, wind, geothermal, and ocean energy sources.** These energy sources are "new" in their current rapid stage of technological growth and development; however, they have been utilized by humans for centuries with very simple technology.
- Today, just under 2% of our global energy comes from these "new renewable" energy sources, as compared to the contribution of fossil fuels (81%), nuclear power (8.6%), and the conventional renewable energy sources of hydropower and biomass (10%).
- Although they constitute a minuscule proportion of our energy budget, the new renewable sources are growing at much faster rates than all conventional energy sources. The long-term leader in growth is wind power, which has expanded by *nearly 50% each year* since the 1970s. In recent years, solar power has grown even faster than wind power.
- Today, electricity from wind power and from utility-scale solar power is cheaper than electricity from fossil fuels, across large portions of the United States.

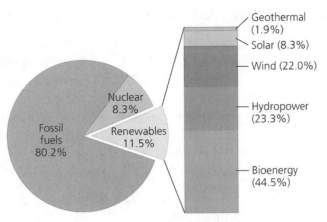

(a) U.S. consumption of renewable energy, by source

Figure 21.3a Renewable Energy Sources Contribute Small but Growing Portion of U.S. Energy Consumed

- Growing concerns over the diminishing quantity of fossil fuels and their negative impacts on the environment and human health are the main reasons for the growth of wind, solar, and geothermal energy technologies.

- Although government subsidies have long favored fossil fuels (together, oil and gas have received 75 times more subsidies, and nuclear power 3 times more, than renewable energy sources), new public policies such as Germany's use of **feed-in tariffs** are promoting and accelerating a transition to greater use of new renewables. As of 2019, nearly all the world's nations and 31 U.S. states have set increased targets for renewable energy use.

  - In a feed-in tariff system, utilities are mandated to buy power at guaranteed premium prices from anyone who can generate power from renewable energy sources and feed it into the electric grid. Feed-in tariffs apply to all forms of renewable energy, including solar, wind, and biomass power.

  - For example, German homeowners and businesses have installed more and more **photovoltaic (PV) solar panels** each year, subsequently selling their extra electricity to the utilities at a profit.

  - Germany has now installed nearly half the world's total PV solar technology and obtains more of its energy from solar power than any other nation. Germany also established itself as the world leader in wind power in the 1990s until being overtaken by the United States in 2008 and more recently by China in 2009.

  - Germany's success with feed-in tariffs is serving as a global model for other nations. Boosted by domestic demand, German renewable energy industries have become global leaders, designing and selling technology around the world. By 2050, Germany aims to obtain 80% of its electricity from renewable energy sources.

The basics of solar energy, including both passive and active solar designs

- On average, each square meter of Earth's surface receives about 1 kilowatt of solar energy, which is approximately 17 times the energy of a light bulb. As a result, a typical home has enough roof area to meet all its power needs with rooftop solar panels.

- **Passive solar energy** collection is an approach in which buildings are designed and building materials are chosen to maximize their direct absorption of sunlight in winter and cool the building in summer. Specific features of passive solar energy design can include the following.

  - Installing low, south-facing windows to maximize the capture of sunlight in winter
  - Overhangs to shade these south-facing windows in summer, when cooling, not heating, is desired
  - Using construction materials (thermal mass) for floors, roofs, and walls that absorb heat, store it, and release it during the night, when the sun's radiant heat is not available
  - Planting vegetation around a building to buffer or shade the building from temperature swings (evergreens on the north side and deciduous trees on the south)

- **Active solar energy** collection is an approach in which technological devices are used to focus, move, or store solar energy. These devices are often used to heat water or air in our homes and businesses and include a variety of approaches such as the following.

  - Installing **flat-plate solar collectors** on rooftops that consist of dark-colored, heat-absorbing metal plates mounted in flat, glass-covered boxes. Water, air, or antifreeze runs through tubes in these collectors, transferring heat to the building or its water tank for later use. Solar water heating for providing domestic hot water and heating swimming pools is the largest application for this rooftop collector approach in the United States. China is the leader in this technology, having installed 70% of the world's solar collectors.

Figure 21.9 Flat-Plate Rooftop Solar Collector System Provides Heating

- **Photovoltaic (PV) solar cells** capture energy from the sun as *light,* not heat, and convert it directly into electrical energy. Certain semiconductor materials (silicon) can generate a low-voltage direct electric current when exposed to direct sunlight. This low voltage is usually converted into higher-voltage alternating current for domestic and business use. The vast majority of PV systems are grid-tied, meaning that any extra electrical energy is sent directly to the utility company, which buys it or gives the homeowner or business credit toward future energy use, in a process called **net metering.** Researchers are experimenting with variations in PV technology, including thin-film solar cells that are lightweight and less bulky than standard silicon cells and may be a promising direction for the future.

- **Concentrated solar power (CSP)** systems are a large-scale application of solar electricity generation, using mirrors or lenses and a tracking system to focus the sunlight from a large geographical area onto a receiver atop a "power tower." From this point, the CSP system operates like a conventional fossil fuel plant in that the heat from the highly focused beam of concentrated sunlight will heat water (or synthetic oil) in a steam-driven generator that produces electricity; however, no air pollutants result. The mirror arrays required are large, so CSP power plants are best constructed in expansive desert areas where open space and sunlight are plentiful (for example, Germany's $7.75 billion CSP DESERTEC facility in the Sahara Desert and the Solar Tres facility being built in Spain).

- **Solar cookers** also use the principle of concentrated solar power to cook food. These simple devices use reflector surfaces in a box-like design to focus sunlight onto food. They are able to raise and maintain temperatures up to 350°F and are proving extremely useful in the developing world. In many places they are replacing the use of already scarce fuelwood supplies, reducing deforestation impacts.

The major advantages and disadvantages of solar energy

- The fact that the sun will continue burning for another 4–5 billion years makes it practically inexhaustible as an energy source for human civilization.
- **Advantages:** A major advantage of solar energy over fossil fuels is that solar energy uses no fuel and does not produce air pollutants, greenhouse gas emissions (CO_2), or water pollutants during the *generation* of heat, hot water, or electricity. However, the *manufacture* of photovoltaic cells does currently require water and fossil fuel use and some toxic materials, but once up and running, a PV system produces no emissions.
- Solar systems allow for local, decentralized control over power without being near a power plant or connected to a grid. This is especially helpful in developing nations, where solar cookers enable families to cook food without gathering fuelwood, lessening people's daily workload, and also reducing deforestation.
- The development and deployment of solar systems are producing many new "green collar" jobs. PV technology is the fastest-growing power generation technology today.
- A standard 5-kW PV system in Ft. Worth, Texas is estimated to save $833 on energy bills and prevents more than 5 tons of CO_2 emissions per year.
- **Disadvantages:** Location and initial cost are currently the two major disadvantages to solar energy. Not all regions are sunny enough to provide adequate and constant power; however, the primary disadvantage is the up-front cost of much of the solar technology hardware (other than solar cookers and passive solar home design/orientation). Because of investment cost, solar power remains the most expensive way to produce electricity.
- Largely because of the lack of U.S. government investment or supportive subsidies, currently solar energy accounts for only 0.93% of our energy supply and just 1.6% of U.S. electricity generation. Even in Germany, which gets more of its energy from solar than any other nation, the percentage is only 7%. However, worldwide solar energy use has grown by 30% annually in the past four decades, and it continues to have a large potential for future growth.

The basics of wind power including its advantages and disadvantages

■ **Wind energy,** derived from the movement of air, is an indirect form of solar energy because it is the sun's unequal heating of air masses on Earth that causes wind movement.

■ The power of wind can be harnessed by using **wind turbines,** mechanical assemblies that convert wind's kinetic energy into electrical energy. Wind turbines are mounted on towers ranging from approximately 150 to 350 ft in height. Turbines are often erected in groups called wind parks or wind farms and are located in areas on land or offshore where optimal wind conditions exist. Texas has five of the world's ten largest wind farms; the largest contains 627 turbines spread across 250 mi^2 of land.

■ Denmark is the global leader in obtaining the greatest percentage of its energy from wind power (wind power supplies approximately 50% of Danish electricity needs).

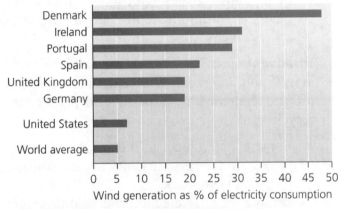

(b) Leading nations in proportion of electricity from wind power

Figure 21.16b   Leading Nations in Proportion of Energy from Wind Power

■ Offshore sites hold the greatest promise for future growth because wind speeds are roughly 20% greater over water than over land and there is also less turbulence. Denmark erected the first offshore wind farm in 1991, and over the next decade many more came into operation across northern Europe where the North Sea and Baltic Sea offer strong winds. By 2019, more than 4500 wind turbines were powering 105 wind farms in the waters of 11 nations in this region.

■ In the United States, a small project consisting of five turbines off Rhode Island is the nation's first commercial offshore wind farm. As of 2019, 20 more offshore wind developments are in the planning stages, mostly off the North Atlantic coast.

■ **Advantages:** A major advantage of wind is that it is completely nondepletable. The amount of wind available in the future does not depend on how much we use today. Other advantages include the following.

- Like solar energy, wind power produces no emissions once the equipment (turbine, tower, and infrastructure) is manufactured. The EPA has calculated that running a 1-megawatt wind turbine for 1 year prevents the release of more than 1500 tons of CO_2, 6.5 tons of SO_2, 3.2 tons of NO_x, and 60 lb of mercury.
- Wind power also appears considerably more efficient than conventional power sources in its energy returned on investment (EROI). The EROI of wind power is 20:1, as compared to a coal-powered electrical power plant's 11:1.
- Unlike conventional fossil fuel or nuclear power plants, wind farms can share the land or offshore waters with other uses, such as grazing of animals, commercial fishing, or recreational activities.
- Wind turbine technology can be used on many scales, from a single tower for local use to fields of hundreds that supply large regions or whole cities.
- Wind power creates "green jobs." More than 100,000 Americans and nearly 1.2 million people globally are employed in jobs related to wind power.

- **Disadvantages:** The intermittent nature of wind causes unpredictability in its supply and requires storage batteries for residential systems that are off-grid. Batteries are expensive to produce and hard to dispose of or recycle.

  - Some people object to the noise and aesthetic impact produced by large wind farms, leading to the so-called **not-in-my-backyard (NIMBY)** syndrome.
  - If thorough site selection and wildlife migratory routes are not fully considered, wind turbines may pose a threat to birds and bats.
  - Good wind resources are not always located near population centers that need the energy; thus, transmission networks often need to be expanded in order to get wind power to where people live.

The basics of geothermal energy including its advantages and disadvantages

- **Geothermal energy** is thermal energy that arises from *beneath* the Earth's surface and not from the sun. The radioactive decay of elements under high pressures deep in the interior of our planet generates heat that rises. Where this energy heats groundwater, natural spurts of heated water and steam are sent upward from below and may erupt at the surface as geysers.
- In California's Napa Valley and in Iceland, geothermal energy is available for development. Geothermal energy can be harnessed directly from surface geysers, but most often wells must be drilled down at great depths toward the heated groundwater. This heated water can then be used directly for heating homes and offices and for driving industrial processes.

- Geothermal power plants harness the energy of naturally heated underground water and steam to turn turbines and generate electricity. The world's largest geothermal power plants, the Geysers, in northern California, provide enough electricity to supply 725,000 homes.
- **Advantages:** A major advantage includes greatly reduced emissions relative to fossil fuel combustion; however, geothermally heated water can release dissolved gases in small quantities, including CO_2, methane, ammonia, and hydrogen sulfide.
- **Disadvantages:** Geothermal power's major disadvantage is the fact that sources may not always be truly renewable if a geothermal plant uses heated water more quickly than the groundwater is recharged. Many geothermal plants worldwide are now injecting water back into aquifers to help maintain pressure and sustain the geothermal resource. The greatest limitation of geothermal power is that it is restricted to specific regions where we can tap energy from naturally heated groundwater.
- **Enhanced geothermal systems (EGS)** are an approach where engineers drill extremely deep into dry rock, fracture the rock, and pump in cold water that then becomes heated. This heated water is drawn up through an outlet well and used to generate power.
- **Heat pumps** make use of temperature differences above and below ground. Operating on the principle that temperatures below ground are more stable than temperatures in air, **ground-source heat pumps (GSHPs)** harness the geothermal energy from just below Earth's surface by circulating a fluid through pipes buried underground. In winter, this fluid absorbs heat from underground and then distributes it throughout the home. In summer, when the underground temperature is lower than the air temperatures, the fluid is cooled and pulls heat from the house as it circulates.

The potential of ocean energy sources and how they are harnessed

- The oceans are home to several underexploited sources of energy—several sources involve the motion of ocean water, and one source involves temperature gradients.
- **Tidal energy** is energy harnessed by erecting a dam across the outlet of a tidal basin. Water flowing with the incoming or outgoing tide through sluices in the dam turns turbines to generate electricity.
- The rise and fall of ocean tides twice each day move large amounts of water past any given point on the world's coastlines. The world's largest tidal-generating facility is South Korea's Sihwa Lake facility, opened in 2011. The La Rance facility in France, which has operated for over 50 years, is the second largest. Many other coastal locations, including San Francisco, New York City, and nations such as China and Canada, are considering further development of their tidal energy potential.

- **Wave energy** involves floating devices that move up and down, harnessing the motion of ocean waves to convert energy to electricity. Scotland is now utilizing this form of wave energy to generate electricity.

The approaches for energy storage and the potential of hydrogen fuel cell technology

- Each renewable energy (solar, wind, and geothermal) can be used to generate electricity more cleanly than from fossil fuels; however, it is challenging to store this electricity for use at a later time, or for a distant location. The following are methods of energy storage of electricity for use at a later time:

  1) **Batteries** are devices that employ chemical reactions to generate electricity. Current research in improvements is beginning to make possible the kind of large-scale storage necessary to convert electrical grids to accommodate rising amounts of solar and wind power.
  2) **Pumped storage hydropower** is currently our primary means of energy storage.
  3) The development of **fuel cells** and fuel consisting of hydrogen shows promise to store energy conveniently, in considerable quantities, and to produce electricity at least as cleanly and efficiently as renewable energy sources.

     A fuel cell is a device that operates much like a battery, where electricity is generated by a reaction between two chemical reactants. Unlike a conventional nickel-cadmium battery, in a fuel cell the reactants are never used up because they are added continuously to the cell, so the cell produces electricity for as long as it is supplied with fuel. Hydrogen is the main reactant in a hydrogen fuel cell, and electricity is generated by the process of combining hydrogen and oxygen atoms to form the waste product, water.
  4) **Hydrogen gas,** usually compressed and stored in an attached fuel tank, is allowed into one side of the fuel cell, whose middle consists of two electrodes that sandwich a hydrogen-permeable membrane. On the other side of the cell, oxygen molecules from the open air are split into their component atoms. These oxygen and hydrogen ions then form water molecules that are expelled as waste along with heat.

3 The electrons move from the negative electrode to the positive electrode, creating a current and generating electricity.

Hydrogen fuel, H₂

Oxygen, O₂

2 The protons traverse the membrane.

4 Water is formed when oxygen combines with the protons and electrons that flow from the positive electrode.

1 Hydrogen molecules are stripped of electrons at the negative electrode, leaving hydrogen ions (protons, H⁺).

H⁺

Negative electrode

Proton (H⁺) exchange membrane

Positive electrode

Water, H₂O

Figure 21.27 Hydrogen Fuel Drives Electricity Generation in a Fuel Cell

- The major drawback for fuel cell technology at this point is a lack of infrastructure. To convert a nation like the United States, Iceland, or Germany to hydrogen as an energy source would require massive and costly development of facilities to transport, store, and provide the hydrogen fuel.

- Hydrogen's benefits include the fact that we will never run out of it because it is the most abundant element in the universe. It is clean and nontoxic to use, and, depending on its source, it may produce few greenhouse gases and other pollutants. Pure water and heat may be the only waste products from a hydrogen fuel cell.

- Hydrogen fuel cells are energy efficient. Depending on the type of fuel cell, 35–70% of the energy released in the reaction can be used.

- Fuel cells are also silent and nonpolluting. For these reasons, modest fleets of hydrogen-fueled buses are now operating in cities in Germany, Japan, China, Brazil, the United Kingdom, and the United States.

■ The increasing concern over global climate change, air pollution, human health impacts, and security risks resulting from our dependence on *finite supplies of fossil fuels* has convinced many people that we need to shift to the renewable energy sources of solar, wind, and geothermal energy. Moreover, by using electricity from these new renewables, we will be helping to create a less-polluting global energy market, particularly now that global climate change is at the forefront of environmental concerns for the planet.

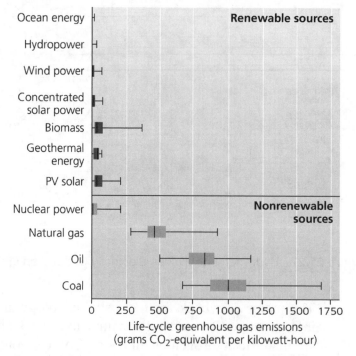

Figure 21.4 Comparing Greenhouse Gas Emissions for Power Sources

Multiple-Choice Questions

***Use the following figure to answer
questions 1 and 2.***

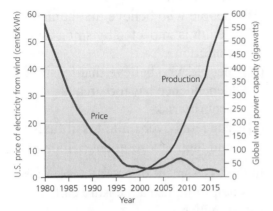

1. Global production of wind power
    increased by what percent, between the
    years 2010 and 2015?
    (A) −2.5%
    (B) −50%
    (C) +100%
    (D) +225%

2. The greatest decline in the price of
    electricity from wind power in the
    United States occurred between
    (A) 1980 and 1985.
    (B) 1985 and 1990.
    (C) 1990 and 1995.
    (D) 2010 and 2015.

3. Which of the following *best* describes
    U.S. energy consumption?
    (A) The transportation sector utilizes
        the greatest amount of energy.
    (B) Sources of fossil fuels are
        declining, while renewables are
        increasing.
    (C) Most of the electricity generated in
        the United States comes from
        nuclear energy.
    (D) Fossil fuels continue to be the
        major energy source for all sectors
        of our economy.

4. Nuclear energy's most *serious*
    environmental and health concerns focus
    on the *unresolved* issues surrounding
    (A) the results of a runaway chain
        reaction.
    (B) the habitat destruction involved in
        the extensive uranium mining
        process.
    (C) the short half-life of most of the
        radioactive isotopes.
    (D) the issue of permanent waste
        disposal.

5. Which of the following *best*
    demonstrate(s) the use of passive solar
    energy?
    (A) south-facing windows with stone
        floors on the inside of the home
    (B) photovoltaic cells on the roof of an
        ecologically designed home
    (C) a home with deciduous trees
        planted outside north-facing
        windows
    (D) a home with evergreens planted
        outside south-facing windows

6. Which of the following sources of
    energy *cannot* be connected to the
    sun's energy?
    (A) biomass
    (B) passive solar energy
    (C) geothermal energy
    (D) wind power

7. For the United States, the *primary* fuel
    that we use for our energy is
    (A) natural gas.
    (B) coal.
    (C) oil.
    (D) nuclear.

8. When we burn fossil fuels,
   (A) the resulting carbonic acid leads to acid rain.
   (B) the greatest environmental impact is the impact on the ozone layer.
   (C) the greatest environmental impact is increased greenhouse gases.
   (D) the greatest environmental impact is the local damage from resource extraction.

9. Which of the following *best* describes global energy use?
   (A) Electricity generation is powered mainly by nuclear energy.
   (B) Electricity generation is powered mainly by coal.
   (C) Biofuels and biomass energy represent the least CO_2 emissions of any energy source.
   (D) Transportation is the largest end use of energy in the world.

10. Worldwide, what is the most widely used *renewable* energy resource?
    (A) solar
    (B) hydroelectric
    (C) biomass
    (D) wind

11. Solar PV-generated electricity as a power source is generated by
    (A) the sun's heat striking solar panels.
    (B) the orientation of the solar panels on a home's rooftop.
    (C) mirrors and lenses that focus the sun's light on a power tower.
    (D) sunlight striking a semiconductor and generating an electrical current.

12. The *primary* motivation to develop the new renewable energy sources comes from
    (A) people who believe conservation is essential.
    (B) people who believe that human health is impacted by smog and pollution.
    (C) people who believe that fossil fuel dependence has too great a security risk.
    (D) concerns over finite fossil fuels and their environmental impacts.

13. In the assessment of energy resources, it is helpful to use a measure called EROI, which is
    (A) energy returned minus energy invested.
    (B) energy returned divided by energy invested.
    (C) amount of energy invested minus heat released into the environment.
    (D) money invested in extraction and processing minus money in sales.

Use the following figure to answer question 14.

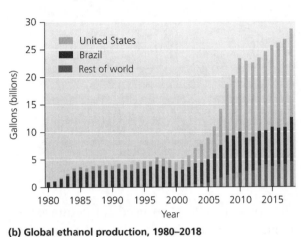

(b) Global ethanol production, 1980–2018

Figure 20.17b   Global Ethanol Production, 1980–2018

14. The recent increase in U.S. production of ethanol is due to
    (A) the dwindling supplies of fossil fuels.
    (B) raising increased amounts of corn for ethanol production.
    (C) more cars requiring ethanol as a fuel.
    (D) using increased amounts of waste biomass for ethanol production.

15. Which of the following represents the correct ranking of the world's total primary energy sources from the most used to least used?
    (A) fossil fuels, biomass, nuclear, hydroelectric, new renewables
    (B) fossil fuels, biomass, hydroelectric, nuclear, new renewables
    (C) fossil fuels, biomass, hydroelectric, new renewables, nuclear
    (D) fossil fuels, nuclear, hydroelectric, biomass, new renewables

16. Ultimately, all biofuels are ___ because they are the result of ___.
    (A) geologic; sedimentation
    (B) solar; photosynthesis
    (C) inefficient; decomposition by microorganisms
    (D) synthetic; chemical interactions of hydrocarbons

17. Currently, the fastest-growing source of electricity generation using new renewable energy sources is
    (A) passive solar.
    (B) wind.
    (C) hydroelectric power.
    (D) hydrogen fuel cells.

18. The Keystone XL Pipeline project refers to the
    (A) removal of coal from Canada's Alberta province.
    (B) extraction of oil from the Gulf of Alaska.
    (C) open pit mining of tar sands in northern Canada.
    (D) hydraulic fracturing of Pennsylvania's Marcellus Shale deposits.

19. Coal continues to be the main fuel to generate electricity in the United States primarily because
    (A) the reserves of coal are not found in environmentally sensitive areas.
    (B) coal deposits in the United States lie very close to the surface and are easily extracted.
    (C) compared to natural gas and oil, coal contains very little sulfur, mercury, and arsenic.
    (D) the country has such large reserves of coal.

20. The practice whereby utilities are mandated to buy power from anyone who can generate power from renewable energy sources, passing the excess to the electric grid, is
    (A) net metering.
    (B) referred to as "living off the grid."
    (C) a feed-in tariff system.
    (D) a renewable subsidy system.

Free-Response Question

Although wind power and solar power have been used for centuries as energy sources, people frequently refer to them as "new" renewable energy sources because they are not yet used on a wide scale in modern industrial societies. Both continue to be in a rapid phase of development and will likely play a much larger role in our future energy use. Photovoltaic (PV) cells, concentrated solar power (CSP) technology, and wind turbines are three of these new renewables receiving much attention. The following table shows the approximate net generation of electricity from wind and solar (PV solar and CSP solar are combined) in the United States from 2012 to 2015 (in million kWh):

Energy source	Year			
	2012	**2013**	**2014**	**2015**
Wind	140,000	168,000	182,000	191,000
Solar	12,700	21,000	33,000	44,300

(Source: The National Renewable Energy Laboratory, www.nrel.gov; 2015 Renewable Energy Data Book, November 2016, 29.)

a) Calculate the average growth rate for both wind and solar electricity generation for the period between 2012 and 2015.

b) Provide one specific explanation for the *difference* in these two growth rates.

c) In the United States, the state of Washington currently has a feed-in tariff system of $0.15/kWh in place for solar PV. This rate would increase to $0.54/kWh if components are manufactured in the state. Explain the feed-in tariff system and its goals.

d) Electricity from wind energy was estimated to cost $0.38/kWh in 1980, and at several U.S. wind farms it is currently $0.03/kWh. Other than this economic advantage, describe two major *environmental advantages* of wind energy.

e) Describe the main reason why wind power continues to represent less than 2% of all U.S. energy sources.

Part III

Answers and Explanations for Topics 1–9

Part III includes the answers and explanations for all multiple-choice and free-response questions found in Part II. Each set of questions is organized according to the nine major environmental science topics discussed in ***Environment: The Science behind the Stories,*** Seventh Edition. The text chapters included in each topic can be easily referenced by referring to the *Brief Overview of Topics* on page **iii** of this AP Test Prep Study Guide.

Each type of multiple-choice question that a student would most likely encounter on the AP Exam is included (both individual and set-based questions), and a concise explanation is provided for each correct response.

One free-response question (FRQ) with accompanying explanation is also included for each of the nine Study Guide topics. Examples of each of the three types of FRQs (experimental design; environmental problem analysis including solution proposal; and environmental problem analysis with solution proposal involving calculations) are included, in order that students gain experience and confidence with the specific problems and challenges encountered on the AP Exam.

Multiple-Choice Questions

Topic 1: Environmental Science and Sustainability

1. (C) is correct. Unaltered ecosystems provide the greatest value; however, once external costs and benefits are factored in, the economic value of sustainably managed ecosystems exceeds that of converted ecosystems, and they have the potential to provide more value for the long term.

2. (A) is correct. Currently we are running a global deficit, depleting renewable resources by using them 69% faster than they are being replenished. Comparing the world's 2.7 ha/person ecological footprint with the U.S. average of 8.1 ha/person produces an impact that is 3 times greater.

3. (C) is correct. Given that the 2005 global footprint was approximately 1.4 (number of planets) and the 1985 global footprint approximately 1.1, the difference is 0.3. Converting this value to a percent (multiply by 100) results in an approximate 30% increase during this 20-year period (33% is the closest choice).

4. (C) is correct. This answer requires a direct reading from the intersection of the 1.2 global footprint value (on the vertical axis) with the ecological footprint graph line, then dropping down to the horizontal axis to read the year, which is closest to 1980.

5. (C) is correct. Controlled scientific experiments involve manipulating one independent variable at a time. There is no preference for quantitative over qualitative data, and new hypotheses are not always generated; however, the experimental design does involve testing the validity of hypotheses.

6. (D) is correct. Ecosystem services are those produced by natural systems, without human intent, but most often with great economic value for humans.

7. (C) is correct. Well-designed and controlled scientific experiments must include a testable hypothesis, one independent variable (that which the scientist manipulates), replication, and several quantifiable dependent variables (that which the scientist measures). Although only one independent variable can be manipulated at a time, several parameters can be measured (dependent variables) as a result of this manipulation.

8. (C) is correct. A sustainable world culture involves the essentials of reducing overall natural resource consumption and halting population growth—both factors are causative agents for the increasing deterioration of the world's natural resources and systems.

9. (D) is correct. An ecological footprint represents the total area of biologically productive land and water necessary to produce the resources needed, and absorb the wastes generated, from a given person or population.

10. (C) is correct. Leadership in Energy and Environmental Design (LEED) is the leading set of standards for sustainable building.

11. (B) is correct. Environmental science includes all the sciences (an interdisciplinary science) and also includes aspects of economics, politics, and the social sciences.

12. (B) is correct. By definition, the independent variable is the variable the scientist manipulates/changes during a controlled experiment; the dependent variable is that which is measured and affected by manipulation of the independent variable.

13. (C) is correct. Current (2019) world population estimates are closest to 8.0 billion.

14. (A) is correct. Forests, water, and soil resources are all potentially renewable. Oil, mineral resources, mineral ores, and natural gas are finite/nonrenewable resources.

15. (A) is correct. Carbon-neutrality approaches involve reducing greenhouse gas emissions (specifically CO_2) and/or employing carbon offsets, with the effect of adding *no net carbon* to the atmosphere.

16. (D) is correct. Water conservation and recycling cost nothing; bicycling is much less expensive than transportation requiring fossil fuel or biodiesel; and consuming local produce also greatly reduces the transportation/fossil fuel costs of shipping food.

Free-Response Question/Explanation

a) There are several important ecosystem services connected to forests (choices follow). The *primary* ecosystem services provided by forests are (1) CO_2 removed from the atmosphere, stabilizing global temperature, (2) nutrient cycling, and (3) reduction of soil erosion. As a part of the global carbon cycle, forests take up CO_2 from the atmosphere during photosynthesis, storing it as organic compounds (biomass). This removal of carbon helps to slow projected climate change. By holding soil in place through their extensive root systems, forests keep soils intact so that plant biodiversity is maintained. This intact soil/plant community also aids in (4) water purification, cleansing the water as it moves through the soil profile.

b) Given that the original ecological services valuation in 1997 of forests was approximately $4.7 trillion, dividing $4.7 trillion by 4 results in **$1.17 trillion per year** as the approximate economic valuation of forests at that time. To check this answer, $1.17 \times 400\% = \$4.7$ trillion per year. In other words, the value of forests in providing *ecosystem services* ($4.7 trillion) is much greater than the value of forests for the direct economic gain ($1.17 trillion) of harvesting for wood products.

c) Sustainability is the approach that focuses on conserving Earth's functioning ecosystems intact for the long term, taking no more potentially renewable resources at any one time than can be replenished by these fully functioning ecosystems. It also includes not overloading the capacity of the environment to cleanse and renew itself of wastes by natural processes. Therefore, by removing forests for economic gain, the beneficial ecosystem services provided by these forests become altered. For example, the forest's ability to recycle essential nutrients, purify air and water, stabilize soil, and store atmospheric carbon become greatly diminished, resulting in a planet's reduced ability for sustainability and increased susceptibility to global climate change.

Topic 2: The Living World: Ecosystems and Biodiversity

1. (D) is correct. Almost all organisms use the solar energy stored in food to fuel their life processes. Autotrophs convert solar energy to glucose, an organic compound useful to both plants and animals. At each successive trophic level, less energy is available, as energy is always degraded to less useful forms (heat). Energy cannot be recycled.

2. (C) is correct. The unseeded plots eventually attained 40% plant cover as compared to approximately 70% plant cover by the plots that were seeded after the volcanic eruption. These data demonstrate that sufficient plants survived the catastrophic eruption to permit significant growth (40% plant cover in 30 years) without seeding.

3. (A) is correct. Percent change is calculated using the following formula:

(Final value – Initial value) ÷ Initial value × 100 = % change

Given that the plant cover 15 years after eruption was 60%, and the plant cover at 10 years after eruption was 30%, use these values in the % change formula: $(60 - 30) \div (30) \times 100 = 100\%$.

4. (A) is correct. The eruption of Mount Saint Helens offered ecologists a rare opportunity to study succession. Most scientists initially presumed that life had been completely eradicated over a large area, that pioneer species would eventually colonize, and that over many years a community would be established in a predictable manner. Instead, researchers discovered that some plants above ground survived the blast, while others were dormant underground. These survivors played a key role in reestablishing the community, demonstrating that succession is not a simple and predictable process that always begins with pioneer species (lichens and mosses) and is often determined by elusive survivors, even in a catastrophic disturbance.

5. (A) is correct. Type III organisms produce a large number of offspring with the graph line declining precipitously when these organisms are young (indicating high mortality). This results in very few of the original young surviving to old age.

6. (A) is correct. Polar bears are mammals, bearing one or two young per breeding season, which usually survive to old age as a result of extensive parental care. Type I survivorship curves are characteristic of humans (also mammalian) and the most similar survivorship curve to the polar bear. Humans also bear few offspring and provide extensive parental care, ensuring survival of their young to old age.

7. (D) is correct. Specialists succeed over evolutionary time by being extremely good at the things they do, but they are extremely vulnerable when conditions change and threaten the resource on which they have specialized.

8. (B) is correct. Climatographs are graphs depicting the annual temperature and precipitation of a biome. The only answer that discusses precipitation is (B); both deserts and tundra have low precipitation, are quite dry, and support less plant life than other terrestrial biomes. Although some high-altitude deserts have seasonally low temperatures, the tundra's temperature is low year-round.

9. (B) is correct. Trophic cascades are defined by top carnivores (tertiary consumers), occupying the fourth trophic level. When present, these top predators keep the carnivores in the third trophic level (below them) in check, and thus members of the second trophic level (primary consumers) will increase in numbers, in an effect known as a trophic cascade.

10. (B) is correct. In general, eutrophication is a result of over-enrichment by nutrients, primarily nitrates. In the case of the Gulf of Mexico, specifically, since it is connected to the Mississippi River watershed, the primary cause of eutrophication is the nitrate enrichment found in fertilizers used in modern agriculture. Answers (A) and (E) are the *results* of nutrient enrichment, not the cause.

11. (C) is correct. Positive feedback loops act to further enhance a particular effect, driving the system toward one extreme or another. If the climate warms enough to melt Arctic ice and snow, darker surfaces of land and water will be exposed, which will then absorb more sunlight, causing even further melting. As a population of prey increases, this expands the food supply for predators, but as the predators increase in number, they catch more prey and the number of prey decreases, an example of a negative feedback loop.

12. (C) is correct. A location where two ecosystems meet (a forest and a coastal marsh) is a transition zone, also known as an ecotone. An ecotone contains elements of both ecosystems and has higher biodiversity than either of the separate ecosystems.

13. (D) is correct. Island biogeography explains how species come to be distributed in "habitat islands," and today these "islands" are best represented by national parks and other protected areas located in vast areas of development. Species richness, immigration, and extinction rates can be predicted from the island's size and its distance from the larger/main reservoir of species. Although Wilson and MacArthur's research originally took place on islands, the implications today for informed development of protected areas (particularly with regard to size and the adequacy of wildlife corridor locations) is the main application of their research.

14. (B) is correct. Second-growth forests are forests that grow back after the primary/virgin forest has been cut. Second-growth forests continue to grow in abundance worldwide and are more prevalent today because of extensive global deforestation. Forests cannot be cut in wilderness areas; hence (C) is incorrect.

15. (A) is correct. As scientists have continued to study forest fragmentation, especially in the Amazon rainforest where forest studies have been going on since the early 1970s, they have found that small fragments lose more species, and lose them faster, than larger fragments. This is because smaller fragments contain fewer species, making these small areas more susceptible to outside threats because food chains are fewer, less complex, and less stable. Climate change has only exacerbated forest fragmentation issues, often eliminating higher elevation species that need cooler temperatures. Forests play a large role, not a minimal role, in the water, nitrogen, and carbon biogeochemical cycles.

16. (D) is correct. Normal ecosystem functioning requires that matter always recycle (it can never be destroyed, according to the law of conservation of matter) and energy be able to flow (according to the second law of thermodynamics, in all energy transformations between trophic levels, energy is degraded and can never be recycled). All ecosystems require a constant input of energy, usually from the sun.

17. (B) is correct. According to the 10% law, assuming an energy content of 500,550 kcal in the autotrophs located in the first trophic level, then organisms in the third trophic level would contain 1/100th of this amount, or 5,005 kcal of energy. At most, only 10% of the energy at any trophic level can be passed up to the next higher level.

18. (B) is correct. Cellular respiration is the energy-releasing reaction of living organisms in which O_2 is required to break down the glucose molecule, also releasing CO_2 and H_2O in the process. CO_2 is then released back to the atmosphere, where it can become available to plants as one of the necessary requirements for photosynthesis.

19. (C) is correct. Density-independent factors are limiting factors whose influence is not affected by population density. Catastrophic events (floods, fires, etc.) and temperature extremes can eliminate large numbers of individuals without regard to their density. Density-dependent factors increasingly slow population growth as that population's density increases.

20. (C) is correct. Introduced species that are successful and become invasive are usually generalists, having a broad niche. They can outcompete endemic species (those native species found in a given area) because the introduced species often do not have predators in their new environment. Successful introduced species are also often r-strategists, having a large number of offspring in a short period of time; they are not K-strategists.

21. (D) is correct. An ecological niche reflects a species-specific use of resources and the role of this species in a community. Niche includes habitat and *all* relationships/roles of the species (symbiotic and feeding relationships, to name just a couple).

22. (B) is correct. Producers are the source of all usable energy in an ecosystem, as they are able to incorporate the sun's energy into organic molecules through photosynthesis, thus making that energy available to other individuals occupying higher trophic levels. As this energy is passed up food chains, the energy content diminishes by approximately 90% at each trophic level.

23. (B) is correct. The Florida Everglades has recently undergone widespread water depletion due to overdrawing of this natural wetlands area for irrigation, development, and flood control. Restoring historical water levels is the goal of this project.

24. (A) is correct. When members of the same species are competing for limited resources, the competition is intraspecific. Interspecific competition is between members of different species.

25. (A) is correct. Productivity is defined as the total rate of photosynthesis, or the rate at which autotrophs convert energy to biomass. This question is specifically comparing gC/m^2 of the various ecosystems, *not* the total area devoted to each of these ecosystems. In terrestrial ecosystems, productivity tends to increase with temperature and precipitation. In aquatic ecosystems, productivity tends to rise with light and availability of nutrients. Water is often limiting in grasslands and deciduous forests, nutrients are limiting in the open ocean, and temperature is limiting in boreal forests. In swamps and marshes, there are large amounts of nutrients, water, and light.

26. (D) is correct. With the advent of modern fertilizers high in nitrogen (ammonia), humans have doubled the rate of industrial nitrogen-fixation processes. These N fertilizers are often eroded into waterways, producing eutrophic conditions in aquatic systems. In the past, the large reservoir of nitrogen (78% of the atmospheric gases) only slowly moved into terrestrial systems through microbial nitrogen fixation or lightning strikes.

27. (D) is correct. The rate at which biomass becomes available to *consumers* is defined as net primary productivity (NPP). Gross primary productivity is the conversion of solar energy, CO_2, and H_2O into organic molecules ($C_6H_{12}O_6$) by *autotrophs*. The energy that remains after cellular respiration is net primary productivity: $GPP - R = NPP$.

28. (D) is correct. The graph indicates that the forest was isolated/broken into fragments in 1984–85. After 1985, the species richness declined dramatically (from 60 to 30 species), demonstrating that species richness is adversely affected by forest fragmentation.

29. (C) is correct. Percent change is calculated using the following formula:

(Final value – Initial value) ÷ Initial value × 100 = % change
(20 – 60) ÷ (60) × 100 = –67%   (a decline of 67%).

30. (D) is correct. The definition of a species is based upon the reproductive compatibility of individuals—not only whether they will mate/breed, but also whether individuals are genetically compatible, producing fertile, viable (living) young, which can then carry on the next generation. Similarity of physical appearance is not a criterion, nor is having similar or even the same food requirements.

31. (D) is correct. Wilderness areas are the most protected federal land designation. No hunting, new road building, development, permanent structures, or harvesting of timber is permitted; however, low-impact recreation is allowed.

32. (C) is correct. When a species is displaced from its habitat of origin to a new habitat, it will survive if it is a generalist with regards to food or if it has a wide range of tolerance to abiotic factors. Often these introduced species do not have predators in their new location, since they did not evolve there, and the result can be an increase in their population; they often outcompete the native species.

33. (B) is correct. Climate change scientists are concerned with the increasing levels of greenhouse gases in our atmosphere, primarily CO_2. Because of their involvement in photosynthesis, forests have the potential for consuming large amounts of CO_2, thereby sequestering (storing) carbon and removing it from the atmosphere. Although (A) and (C) are ecosystem services performed by forests, they are not as directly connected with climate change. Forests do not store methane (D) although it is a greenhouse gas.

34. (A) is correct. To obtain the population growth rate one must take into consideration the birth and date rates. Crude birth and death rates are an abbreviated form (the number of births or deaths per 1000 members of the population). All of the factors mentioned help to determine a population's *total value* (migration, limiting factors, and the organism's survivorship curve type); however, growth rates are determined more simply by birth and death rates alone.

35. (B) is correct. Zebra mussels are filter feeders, consuming phytoplankton and small zooplankton in the water column. The recent decline of zooplankton since introduction of the zebra mussel has been a direct result of predation by zebra mussels.

36. (D) is correct. Net primary productivity (NPP) is calculated using the following formula: NPP = gross primary productivity (GPP) minus respiration. Since it is given that in this New England forest respiration represents 30% of GPP (70 $g/m^2/day \times 0.30$), respiration would equal 21 $g/m^2/day$. It then follows that NPP = 71 $g/m^2/day$ – 21 $g/m^2/day$ = 49 $g/m^2/day$.

37. (C) is correct. Keystone species are those that have strong or wide-ranging impacts far out of proportion to their actual abundance. They are not dominant in numbers, are never producers, and don't cause removal of a whole trophic level, but they are most likely top predators whose presence can often cause a trophic cascade.

38. (B) is correct. Although all answers are true at some level, on a scale of importance, the overdrawing of groundwater for modern agriculture, industrial, and drinking water purposes is considered the most critical. Usable, potable fresh water represents less than 1% of all water on Earth, and these resources are dwindling at an alarming rate.

39. (C) is correct. The largest carbon reservoir was deposited over millions of years by dead plants and animals, buried by sediments, and turned into sedimentary rocks and ultimately fossil fuels. The atmosphere and hydrosphere both contain small amounts of carbon (as CO_2). The abundance of plants and the fact that they take in so much CO_2 for photosynthesis make them a major reservoir of carbon, but not as large as sedimentary rock.

40. (D) is correct. "Dead zones" are hypoxic areas resulting from eutrophication processes that were initiated by nutrient enrichment, usually nitrates in marine ecosystems. Negative feedback loops (A) enhance ecosystem stability and are not characteristic of processes operating in dead zones. There is no evidence that hypoxic zones are caused by introduced species (B).

41. (C) is correct. When oceans become acidic, the pH is *lower,* not higher (B). Ocean acidification *decreases* the availability of carbonate ions necessary for shell building. The lowering of pH due to increased carbonic acid formation (atmospheric $CO_2 + H_2O \rightarrow H_2CO_3$) has the ability to dissolve invertebrate shells and dramatically decrease productivity of coral reefs; however, it is not the dissolving of shells that *causes* ocean acidification (E).

42. (D) is correct. Biodiversity results from the sum of speciation minus extinction. High rates of mutation alone do not necessarily produce greater speciation, as it could be followed by high rates of extinction. A wide variety of habitats does not necessarily mean that all habitats will be filled.

43. (D) is correct. Of the choices provided, habitat destruction is the most critical factor in determining species extinction rates. Overharvesting, introduction of invasive species, and global climate change all have the potential to cause species extinction; however, habitat destruction (due to growing human populations and their need for food and energy) is today's number one threat to species.

44. (D) is correct. A community is made up of numerous populations of different species in a given area. The ecosystem level would include the community of different populations plus the specific environmental factors (temperature, soil, moisture, light, etc.) in that specific area.

Free-Response Question/Explanation

a) *Three characteristics* of a species that would make the species particularly susceptible to extinction are (choices follow): (1) **low reproductive rate** (one to two offspring, possibly not every year, i.e., K-strategist), (2) **slow maturity** (taking many years to reach sexual maturity; thus any mortality is not easily recouped), (3) **highly specialized food/resource requirement** (e.g., bamboo food requirements for Giant Panda), or (4) **highly specialized physical habitat requirements** (e.g., many of Hawaii's native forest birds are restricted to a very small range where specific moisture requirements are at their extreme tolerance level).

b) The main hypothesis that is being tested at the Hakalau Forest National Wildlife Refuge: Does forest fragmentation over the past 25 years affect the population size of the native 'apapane? In order to thoroughly test this hypothesis, one needs a control section of the forest (where no fragmentation has occurred) to compare 'apapane population size and change. In order to test a hypothesis regarding whether introduced species have been affecting the native 'apapane, one would need data on the actual numbers and diversity of introduced species. There are no actual data being collected and reported on introduced species; therefore, one must assume that this hypothesis is not being tested.

c) *Percent change* is calculated by the following formula:

$$\% \text{ change} = \frac{\text{Final value} - \text{Initial value}}{\text{Initial value}} \times 100$$

% change = (40,000 − 30,000) ÷ 30,000 × 100 = 0.33 × 100 =

~33% increase in density

d) The 'apapane population may not have increased as much as originally predicted even with complete forest protection because of several possibilities (choices follow). Climate change may be adversely affecting the growth and productivity of the Hakalau Forest, reducing the insect species that are food for the 'apapane. Also, climate change and warming temperatures may be bringing a number of avian diseases to the area, infecting the native forest birds and reducing their overall population size.

e) *Three* strengths of the experimental design for this field study are as follows:

1. Extensive *replication:* with a 25-year study, there was more than one year of field data in order that long-term trends could be adequately assessed.
2. Fifteen transect lines were established throughout the refuge, with over 20 observation points along each transect. These *same transect lines and observation points were returned to each year* of the study.
3. *Standard observation length:* an 8-minute bird count was taken at each observation point, no matter who the trained observer was.

Topic 3: Environmental Decision Making

1. (C) is correct. Since the Global Warming Solutions Act was passed in 2006, it is necessary to examine the direction of the two graph lines *after* that year. Greenhouse gas emissions were not in a steady state (B), and although reduced, greenhouse gas emissions were not reduced by 50% (A). These emissions were reduced from approximately 95 per capita values to 75 per capita values, while GDP rose from approximately 128 to 138 per capita values.

2. (B) is correct. The % change formula is

(Final − Initial) ÷ Initial × 100 = % change

(128 − 95) ÷ (95) × 100 = 34.7%. Making certain to *use the GDP graph line* for the approximate values, 34.7% is the correct calculation.

3. (C) is correct. The National Environmental Policy Act (NEPA) is the cornerstone of all U.S. environmental laws and requires that an environmental impact statement (EIS) be prepared for each project or action planned by the federal government.

4. (D) is correct. Cap-and-trade systems are a kind of permit trading where an acceptable level of pollution has been determined by the government, which then issues permits to the various polluters/industries. An industry can receive credit for amounts it does not emit and can then sell this credit to other industries that are not able to meet the pollution limit.

5. (A) is correct. A cost-benefit analysis always includes internal costs, as these are the ones most easily estimated since they occur between the buyer and seller. External costs (B) are much more difficult to estimate (costs affecting a member of society other than the immediate buyer or seller) and are sometimes purposefully omitted in order to make the cost of a development project appear more environmentally friendly and economically feasible. The GDP (C) and GNP (D) have nothing to do with cost-benefit analyses.

6. (D) is correct. Federal environmental legislation always takes precedence over state laws whenever they come into conflict on a specific issue.

7. (C) is correct. All "tragedy of the commons" scenarios involve a "commons" (a natural resource able to be utilized by everyone because of public "ownership"). The "tragedy" results from overutilization of the resource by the public, with everyone seeking to maximize their personal gain. With no limits to utilization, pollution and/or depletion of the resource results. Strip mining is not allowed in national parks; (B) and (D) involve *private* resources; (C) involves a *public* resource (the atmosphere) and the current pollution of this natural resource.

8. (B) is correct. In 1996, when the PSA program (Costa Rica's program to pay landowners for ecosystem services) was introduced, the graph bar denoting deforestation in the decade *prior* had already dropped dramatically, indicating that other factors were responsible. In particular, Costa Rica's Forest Law 7575 had banned forest clearing nationwide, although the PSA program continued to further reduce deforestation.

9. (A) is correct. Paying landowners not to harvest timber from their land, allowing the forests to remain intact in order to carry out beneficial ecosystem services, promotes an intrinsic value (the value of something for its own sake). An external cost is one borne by someone not involved in an economic transaction, such as harm to citizens from water pollution. Ecosystem services are natural capital, occur naturally without human involvement, and are *not* anthropocentric (human-centered), although humans definitely benefit from all ecosystem services.

10. (B) is correct. The Montreal Protocol (1987) is considered the most successful effort to date in addressing a global environmental problem (stratospheric ozone depletion). CFCs have been dramatically reduced, and all major countries producing CFCs have ceased production. The Kyoto Protocol has not been as successful because many countries (including the United States) have not yet signed on. CITES has also had problems with enforcement. Choice (D) applies only to the United States and not to international environmental law.

11. (C) is correct. The GPI (Genuine Progress Indicator) differentiates between desirable and undesirable economic activity and better indicates a society's well-being. GNP (Gross National Product) refers to the amount of goods and services purchased by households in a year, and GDP (Gross Domestic Product) includes only the goods and services produced within national borders; however, neither accounts for nonmarket benefits of factors such as volunteerism or external costs such as environmental degradation.

12. (A) is correct. Modern environmental policy aims to promote fairness among people and groups in the use of resources. Too many competing interests need to be addressed in order to preserve natural areas in the most pristine condition possible (D). Natural resources are used for many purposes (aesthetic, ecosystem services, recreational), not just for economically important industrial products (B). Protecting the values of the landowner (C) is always balanced with competing needs, as sometimes a regulatory taking occurs when the government deprives landowners of some economic use of their private property.

13. (B) is correct. The 1997 study published in *Nature* estimating the economic value of ecosystem services was the work of Robert Costanza. Aldo Leopold (A) was a pioneering environmental philosopher promoting his "land ethic"; John Muir (C) was known for his preservationist ethic, was the founder of the Sierra Club, and was an early promoter of wilderness areas; and Gifford Pinchot (D) was known for his conservationist ethic and was the first chief of the National Forest Service.

14. (C) is correct. The timber industry is regulated by the Department of Agriculture, since the U.S. Forest Service is under the authority of this federal department. The Department of the Interior has jurisdiction over the National Park Service and all endangered species. The Environmental Protection Agency is charged with setting standards for environmental quality, but does not have the authority to enforce. Enforcement is left up to the appropriate federal department.

15. (D) is correct. Cap-and-trade is an emissions trading system in which the government determines an acceptable level of pollution and then issues polluting parties permits to pollute. A company or industry receives credit for amounts it does not emit and can then sell this credit to other companies willing to "pay to pollute."

Free-Response Question/Explanation

a) Conservationists could point to an **economic gain** with this federal decision because protecting this intact ecosystem would allow the entire population, not just the timber industry, to continue to realize and experience the value of the many ecosystem services. The value of the intact forest in preventing soil erosion, regulating oxygen/carbon dioxide and water cycles, storing and regulating water supplies in the region's watershed and aquifers, providing habitat for organisms to breed/feed/migrate, producing fish and game, and providing recreation such as ecotourism to one of the last remaining habitats of old-growth forest are just a few of the "hidden" **nonmarket values.** These ecosystem services are often not included in a cost-benefit analysis proposed by commercial interests because they are **external** to the immediate buyer-seller relationship.

b) The 1973 **Endangered Species Act,** prohibiting the government or private citizens from taking actions that would destroy a listed species or its habitat, is the central piece of legislation involved in this conflict. Even if no northern spotted owl is directly killed in the logging process, this act also protects the *habitat* of the species and requires that a *recovery plan* for the restoration of the species be instituted.

c) An **internal economic cost** is defined as one that is directly experienced by either the buyer or seller involved in the given transaction and is typically passed along to the consumer. In this case, the internal economic cost consists of the initial cost of all logging equipment, wages paid to the loggers, worker's compensation and insurances involved in the logging industry, and the fuel costs required for the continued operation and maintenance of the logging equipment. An **external economic cost** (externality) is one that affects other members (not only the buyer and the seller) of the society. The effects of water pollution (increased sediment) and air pollution (increased CO_2, NO_x, and SO_x) coming from this logging enterprise, as well as declines in desirable elements of the environment (fewer fish and wildlife), are the most obvious external economic costs.

d) Many possibilities exist; however, the challenge for any solution would be to protect endangered species (in this case, the northern spotted owls) and also to maintain jobs for a healthy economy. A first step might be to acknowledge that the ecosystem services provided by intact forests are natural capital, worth millions annually in the benefits provided to humans—carbon sequestration combating global climate change, soil conservation, water purification, and providing habitat for biodiversity. Secondly, the federal and state governments could promote a "green jobs economy" in these northwestern states, providing subsidies to the timber industry as they transition away from timber harvesting, moving to new jobs involved in a much-needed sustainable energy economy (solar and wind technologies). With global climate change as a major lens through which all environmental solutions should be viewed, the above solutions would have great potential for contributing to both biodiversity preservation and a sustainable, green economy.

Topic 4: Human Population Dynamics

1. (C) is correct. Multiplying the growth rate (which is a percentage) by the original population size results in the number of individuals that will be added to a population. When this resulting number is added to the original population, the final population size will result. Birth rates and immigration are always taken into consideration in determining the growth rate, but by themselves they cannot determine the exact number of individuals added to a population.

2. (D) is correct. A pyramid-shaped age structure diagram indicates that most of the population is pre-reproductive and that there is significant momentum for continued and future population growth. The population is expanding and will continue to do so for more than one generation. A stable population diagram would generally have vertical sides, with equal numbers in each of the major age classes.

3. (B) is correct. The rapid growth of human population since the industrial revolution has been primarily due to technological advances in agriculture (the ability to raise more food) and improved medical care (reducing death rates and ultimately reducing birth rates as a result of lower infant mortality). Environmental resistance definitely applies to humans. Climatic change is only a very recent phenomenon, and although other species have been adversely affected, it has not affected human population size to date.

4. (C) is correct. Industrialization initiates the transitional stage of demographic transition. Declining death rates, which are due to increased food production and improved medical care, are the first significant change that occurs in a population. Birth rates decline *after* these falling death rates. Technological advances, although an important cause of increased food production and medical advances, do not immediately lead to population decline and improved status of the population. Although death rates and birth rates initially diverge, this change leads to a population increase because death rates decline first.

5. (A) is correct. The global growth rate is determined by considering only birth and death rates, since immigration and emigration are not factors on a global scale. The formula for global growth rate is $(CBR - CDR) \div 10$; $(15 - 12) \div 10 = 0.3\%$.

6. (A) is correct. Decreasing the average number of births per woman, the total fertility rate (TFR), is the most critical factor in controlling human population growth. The remaining choices, (B), (C), and (D), are each important in controlling population growth; however, the TFR is the *most* critical and influential.

7. (B) is correct. With the world's fastest-growing economy over the past two decades, China is "demonstrating what happens when large numbers of poor people rapidly become more affluent" (Lester Brown). New material wealth and the resulting resource consumption are bringing unprecedented environmental challenges to China. Although population size continues to be large, China's actual growth rate has declined considerably (*P*). Technology has improved China's ability to grow more food and have improved medical care (*T*), but overall, *P* and *T* have not been as important as China's increasing affluence, resulting in increased resource consumption (*A*).

8. (C) is correct. The age structure diagram of Nigeria (b, with its very broad base, indicates that this population is growing rapidly because there are large numbers of individuals in their reproductive years and even more in their pre-reproductive years, showing much future potential for growth. The age structure diagram of Canada is fairly stable (equal numbers in various age cohorts) and shows a population that is not aging rapidly. Age structure diagrams do not indicate anything about a country's progression through demographic transition.

9. (A) is correct. Nigeria, a developing country with most of its population below 40 years of age, will likely experience resource depletion and decreased quality of life due to a population that is growing rapidly and has great future momentum.

10. (A) is correct. The balanced age structure diagram of Canada suggests that its total fertility rate (TFR) is less than the 2.1 replacement level value. Answers (C) and (D) indicate a high or increasing TFR, which the diagram does not indicate. With a zero TFR, there would be a very small to nonexistent base, which is not the case.

11. (A) is correct. The size of the U.S. population (P) is fairly insignificant compared to the great importance of affluence (A) and technology use (T). The addition of 1 American has as much environmental impact as the addition of 3.4 Chinese, 8 Indians, or 14 Afghans, all because individuals from affluent societies leave a considerably larger per capita ecological footprint.

12. (D) is correct. Replacement fertility is equal to 2.1 in stable populations. It takes two children to replace the mother and father, and the extra 0.1 accounts for the risk of a child dying before reaching reproductive age. If the TFR drops below 2.1, population size (in the absence of immigration) will shrink. With the growing populations in Africa, Latin America, and the Caribbean, the TFR is considerably greater than 2.1.

13. (B) is correct. The doubling time formula is: $DT = 70 \div \%$ growth rate. Transposing this formula, % growth rate $= 70 \div DT$.
Hence, % growth rate $= 70 \div 30 = 2.3\%$.

14. (B) is correct. All of the factors listed have an influence on a population's growth; however, the total fertility rate (the average number of children born per female during her lifetime) has the greatest effect on the potential growth of a population. For humans, replacement fertility roughly equals a TFR of 2.1. If the TFR drops below 2.1 population size in a given country (in the absence of immigration) will shrink.

15. (B) is correct. Using the % change formula:
(Final − Initial) ÷ Initial × 100 = % change
$(1.4\% - 2.7\%) \div (2.7\%) \times 100 = -0.48 \times 100 = -48\%$, a decline of 48% in India's growth rate.

Free-Response Question/Explanation

a) $\text{Percent change} = \dfrac{\text{Final value} - \text{Initial value}}{\text{Initial value}} \times 100$

In this case, $\% \text{ change} = \dfrac{(13.9 \times 10^8) - (5.0 \times 10^8)}{(5.0 \times 10^8)} \times 100 = \dfrac{8.9 \times 10^8}{5.0 \times 10^8} \times 100$

$\% \text{ change} = 1.78 \times 100 = 178\%$

b) China has experienced the first two stages of demographic transition.

In phase 1, **the pre-industrial stage**, high birth rates and death rates are characteristic and the country experiences very slow growth rates. This was during China's subsistence and predominantly agricultural years, up to approximately 40 years ago. Once industrialization and modern medical advances began to affect China's economy, phase 2, **the transitional stage,** began, with the lowering of death rates followed by a very rapid growth in overall population size. It was at this time (in the 1970s) that China instituted the one-child policy in an attempt to reduce their very high TFR from 5.8 down to below replacement level (2.1). Economic incentives such as better access to schools, medical care, housing, and government jobs also were given to one-child families.

Most demographers hypothesize that China is currently in the third phase, industrialization. However, even though the growth rate for the country has dropped dramatically (0.5%), the country is still experiencing significant population growth—even a small percent of a very large number, 1.39 billion, results in significant growth!—adding millions to the population each year. Therefore, some demographers feel that a few regions of China remain in stage 2, the transitional stage.

c) China's age structure base (0–15 years) is currently **more narrow** than the reproductive age classes (15–45) above it. The evidence for this is that the total fertility rate (TFR) in China is currently 1.5 children, significantly below the replacement level of 2.1, as a result of China's one-child policy reforms, producing many fewer children born today. The post-reproductive age classes farther above in the age structure diagram are pyramid-shaped and narrower than the reproductive age classes.

d) In order to determine the number of additional people that will join China's population, one must utilize the current growth rate (0.5%) and the current population size (~1.39 billion):

$$1{,}390{,}000{,}000 \times 0.005 = 6{,}950{,}000$$

$$1.39 \times 10^9 \times 5.0 \times 10^{-3} = \textbf{6.95} \times \textbf{10}^{\textbf{6}} \textbf{ additional people}$$

e) Doubling time = 70 ÷ % growth rate

$$70 \div 0.5 = \textbf{140 years}$$

Topic 5: Earth's Land Resources and Use

1. (C) is correct. The B horizon, the subsoil, is located below the following layers: the O horizon (litter layer composed of decomposing organic material), the A horizon (topsoil), and the E horizon (leaching layer). The B horizon, located directly below the E horizon, accumulates the minerals and organic matter from the E horizon located directly above.

2. (A) is correct. No-till agriculture is the ultimate form of conservation tillage in which the land is left with a ground cover and crop residues after the harvesting process. To plant a subsequent crop, a "no-till drill" that cuts furrows through the O horizon of dead weeds, crop residue, and upper levels of the A horizon is employed. There is minimal disturbance of the soil.

3. (B) is correct. GM organisms involve the processes of recombinant DNA, whereby genes of organisms as different as viruses and plants or bacteria and humans are combined in the same species. The genes for various desired traits exist in nature and are not artificially created in a lab (C); however, they can be isolated from the species where they exist and placed into species lacking this trait, but do not necessarily carry bacterial resistance genes (D).

4. (D) is correct. The initial application of the pesticide does not kill every individual, and the small number of survivors are the strongest/most pesticide resistant, having genes that allow for their survival. When these survivors mate and pass their genes for resistance to their offspring, the next generation will have an even greater resistance to the pesticide. This is the natural selection process of evolution.

5. (D) is correct. As water used in the fracking process returns to the surface, it is contaminated with salts and radioactive elements. Disposal involves injecting this wastewater back into porous rock formations thousands of feet underground (below the local aquifer). As hydraulic fracturing activity has increased, the underground rocks have become saturated with water and pressure grows in these rocks, expanding the rock layers, causing them to push against existing faults, resulting in earthquakes. These areas had not experienced faulting or earthquakes prior to this new fracking activity (note the dramatic upswing of the graph line beginning around 2010).

6. (D) is correct. The frequency of earthquakes in 1995 was 500 and increased to approximately 2750 per year in 2015. Using the % change formula:

(Final value – Initial value) ÷ Initial value × 100 = % change
(2750 – 500) ÷ (500) × 100 = 450% increase in frequency.

7. (D) is correct. Mining for coal and copper often occurs through strip mining, which removes surface layers of rock, exposing sulfide minerals that then react with oxygen and rainwater to produce sulfuric acid. As the sulfuric acid runs off, it can leach heavy metals from rocks, many of which are toxic to organisms. This process is referred to as acid drainage and is a significant water pollution by-product of strip-mining.

8. (A) is correct. Concern over declining crop diversity (because of the monoculture approach used by modern agribusiness) has led to the establishment of seedbanks, with the hope of preserving Earth's genetic assets for future agriculture.

9. (D) is correct. Overfertilization can easily lead to inorganic plant nutrients (primarily N and P) getting into waterways, where they stimulate algal growth, promote the eutrophication process, and result in hypoxic aquatic ecosystems. Adding too much fertilizer to cropland doesn't promote future fertile soils because the irrigation process and normal rainfall will usually leach these excess nutrients into waterways.

10. (B) is correct. Using the % change formula:

(Final value – Initial value) $\div$ Initial value $\times$ 100 = % change

$(31 \text{ m}^2/\text{metric ton} - 15 \text{ m}^2/\text{metric ton}) \div 15 \text{ m}^2/\text{metric ton} \times 100 =$

$1.06 \times 100 = {\sim}100\%$ increase in land area disturbed.

11. (C) is correct. Mountaintop removal mining has greatly increased the area of land disturbed as several hundred vertical feet of mountaintop may be blasted off to enable strip-mining of the now-exposed resource. Since 2010, the data show a steep increase of land disturbance in order to secure a metric ton of coal, indicating increased use of this destructive mining approach to large areas of habitat.

12. (B) is correct. Integrated pest management makes use of many varied practices used in combination. However, one of the central approaches involves using the natural enemy of a pest species to control the pest. IPM does not rely on methods of GM agribusiness, which are the focus of answers (C) and (D).

13. (C) is correct. The Green Revolution began in the 1940s at the end of World War II, when some areas of human population appeared to be outgrowing their available food supply. The Green Revolution techniques of improved seed varieties and fertilizers paved the way to produce food for the increasing population growth, especially in developing countries.

14. (B) is correct. Raising livestock has a significant environmental, social, and economic impact. The FAO (Food and Agriculture Organization of the United Nations) has estimated that livestock account for 55% of the U.S. soil erosion, 37% of the fertilizer application, and one-third of the N and P pollution in waterways.

15. (D) is correct. The Surface Mining Control and Reclamation Act (1977) mandates restoration efforts requiring companies to post bonds to cover reclamation costs before mining can be approved. This ensures that if the company fails to restore the land, the government will have the money to do so.

16. (A) is correct. IPM is the agricultural approach known as integrated pest management. It incorporates numerous *sustainable* farming techniques including biocontrol, use of limited chemicals when essential, crop rotation, and alternative tillage methods. Roundup Ready crops (D) are employed by modern agribusiness, where monocultures are the focus. CAFOs (C), concentrated animal feeding operations, are another modern agribusiness approach that is in contrast to sustainable agricultural techniques because of its negative effects on soil, water, and atmosphere.

17. (D) is correct. The process of leaching removes water-soluble minerals, in this case plant nutrients, from one location and transports them to another. The plant nutrients arising from the decomposition of organic matter in the O horizon can be leached out of the topsoil (where they would normally promote plant growth) under *un*sustainable agricultural practices such as overirrigation.

18. (B) is correct. Plate tectonics is the process by which Earth's surface is shaped by the extremely slow movement of tectonic plates, or sections of Earth's crust (approximately 15 major plates). Their interaction gives rise to the processes that build mountains, cause earthquakes, and otherwise influence the shape of the landscape and thereby the location of living organisms on the planet.

19. (D) is correct. Since most plants cannot fix their own nitrogen, the addition of fertilizers is required to provide the plants with sufficient nitrogen for growth. GM crops that can now fix nitrogen into a usable form would require less application of chemical fertilizers.

20. (C) is correct. Although the Green Revolution increased agricultural yields, the effects on the environment have not been as positive. The planting of crops in monoculture, large expanses of single crop types, has led to the need for increased pesticide use, as all plants in a field are genetically similar and equally susceptible to viral diseases, fungal pathogens, or insect pests. The Green Revolution did not employ methods of genetic engineering; thus, answer (D) is incorrect.

21. (B) is correct. The bar graph comparing various parameters of organic and conventional farming clearly shows that the energy input is lower with organic farming techniques (approximately 3200 megajoules/acre/yr required for organic farming versus 4500 megajoules/acre/yr required for conventional farming).

22. (D) is correct. Conventional farming techniques produce *more* greenhouse gas emissions, not less. Therefore, one needs to analyze the graphs quantitatively in order to determine exactly how much more greenhouse gases are generated. According to the data, conventional farming generates approximately 1400 lb CO_2/acre/yr, and organic farming generates approximately 900 lb CO_2/acre/yr. This is a 500-lb CO_2/acre/yr difference; 50% of 1400 lb is a 700-lb difference, and is a larger than accurate difference.

23. (D) is correct. (Final − Initial) ÷ (Initial) × 100 = % change. Substituting in values from the graph, (170 − 140) ÷ (140) × 100 = 21%, with the answer (D) being the closest to this calculated value.

24. (B) is correct. By comparing the graph lines for industrialized and developing nations, one can see that the darkest line, representing developing nations, has the steepest slope, indicating that there is a greater rate of change (faster growth rate) occurring with GM crops in these countries. There is no information regarding world food supply provided by the graph.

25. (A) is correct. Conservation tillage is an array of approaches that reduce the amount of tilling relative to conventional farming, maximizing ground cover to protect soil erosion. One common definition is any method of limited tilling that leaves more than 30% of crop residue covering the soil after harvest. Although planting of some native grasses and polyculture approaches (the planting of multiple crops in a mixed arrangement) are both involved in some conservation tillage approaches, the remaining portions of options (B) and (D) are incorrect.

26. (B) is correct. Many environmental problems arise from feedlots; however, animal wastes moving into surface and groundwater during rain events is the most significant of the choices given. Animal wastes are rich in nitrates, leading to eutrophication of aquatic ecosystems when allowed to "escape" feedlots. Climate change concerns involve methane and nitrous oxide production from feedlots, not carbon dioxide (C). Use of antibiotics (D) *is* a feedlot issue; however, it involves a *human health problem* (increased antibiotic resistance of virulent microorganisms affecting human health).

27. (A) is correct. Since the pH scale is logarithmic, each unit change is by a factor of 10. An increase of pH means that the solution is more basic and has 100 times fewer H^+ ions, or conversely, 100 times more OH^- ions.

Free-Response Question/Explanation

a)   i.   Several notable examples of GMOs are (choices follow): Golden rice, Bt corn, Bt cotton, and Roundup Ready soybeans.

ii.   Golden rice has been engineered to produce health-enhancing beta-carotene to fight vitamin A deficiency in Asia and the developing world. Bt corn and Bt cotton have been engineered with genes from the bacteria *Bacillus thuringiensis*. The Bt genes kill insects, allowing less pesticide use, while increasing the yields of these plant crops. These last two GMO examples can improve overall environmental quality due to less toxins/pesticides used.

   iii. Roundup Ready soybeans have been engineered to tolerate herbicides, so that farmers can apply herbicides (Roundup) to kill the competing weeds without having to worry about killing their crops. An ecological concern is that herbicide-tolerant GM crops tend to result in *more* use of chemical herbicides because farmers often need to apply increasing levels of herbicides each year, since these weeds are evolving resistance to herbicides through natural selection.

b) One-third of the world's cropland is now devoted to growing food for animals, and 45% of global grain production goes to feeding livestock. As a result, raising beef in feedlots has several significant and negative environmental impacts. The Food and Agriculture Organization of the United Nations (FAO) has estimated that livestock account for over half (55%) of the nation's soil erosion. One-third of the nitrogen (N) and phosphorus (P) pollution in U.S. waterways comes from animal waste runoff from feedlots and from the overapplication of fertilizers to grow the crops fed to livestock. Increased soil erosion leads to an inability to raise future crops (for humans and livestock), and the overapplication of fertilizers leads to nutrient runoff, eutrophication, and the development of hypoxic "dead zones" in waterways, affecting global freshwater biodiversity.

c) In normal ecosystem and food web functioning, only 10% of the energy at any given trophic level is able to be passed along to the next higher trophic level. For example, if the producers (corn plants) in a given agricultural field contain 800,000 kcal of energy, then the cows eating that corn will be able to utilize only 80,000 kcal. The humans eating the beef will have only 8000 kcal available to them, as there is an approximate 90% loss of energy at each trophic level. When humans eat lower on the food chain (a plant-based diet with fewer animal products), a greater proportion of the sun's energy is put to use as food, the ecological footprint is smaller, and a greater number of humans can be supported. Eating lower on the food chain, a vegetarian lifestyle, is much more efficient and allows more energy (as food) to be available to a greater number of humans.

Topic 6: The Urban Environment

1. (D) is correct. According to the graph of U.S. waste generation, one must look specifically at the per capita waste generation line and the appropriate scale, which is on the right side. In the year 2000, per capita waste generation was approximately 2 kg/person/day.

2. (B) is correct. The total waste generated in the U.S. in 1990 was approximately 200 million tons/year, and in 2010 it was 250 million tons/year. When calculating % change, one uses the following formula:

(Final value − Initial value) ÷ Initial value × 100. Therefore, the calculation would be $(250 − 200) ÷ 200 × 100 = 25\%$.

3. (C) is correct. Smart growth is a city planning concept in which a community's growth is managed in ways that limit sprawl and maintain or improve residents' quality of life. The environment, economy, and community residents are all integrated into urban planning. By limiting sprawl, one is limiting impervious surfaces, fossil fuel consumption, and water pollution and increasing use of urban growth boundaries. Open space designation also increases, since urban areas are kept more concentrated.

4. (A) is correct. By definition, an LD_{50} study explores the lethal dose, or amount of toxicant, which will kill 50% of the population. Answers (C) and (D) produce percentages that are not 50% of the population. Answer (B) refers to the threshold effect.

5. (B) is correct. Since the late 1980s, recovery of materials for recycling has expanded, decreasing the pressure on landfills. U.S. waste managers are landfilling 53% of municipal solid waste, incinerating 13%, and recovering approximately 34% for composting and recycling.

6. (C) is correct. In 1980, the U.S. Congress passed the Comprehensive Environmental Response Compensation and Liability Act (CERCLA), which established a federal program to clean up U.S. sites polluted with hazardous waste from past activities. CERCLA now requires that industries monitor their hazardous waste output from "cradle-to-grave," and the past hazardous waste sites have been placed on a National Priority List for cleanup; however, this is not the name of the specific legislation. The EPA (Environmental Protection Agency) is the federal agency charged with conducting and evaluating research, monitoring environmental quality, and setting environmental standards.

7. (A) is correct. Urban sprawl involves increased use of automobiles and fossil fuel consumption. The burning of fossil fuel (gasoline) produces carbon dioxide and nitrogen-containing air pollutants, which lead to acid precipitation, tropospheric ozone, and urban smog, and potentially contributes to global climate change.

8. (B) is correct. Cities and towns are sinks for resources, since they must import from areas beyond their borders nearly everything they need to feed, clothe, and house inhabitants.

9. (C) is correct. Bisphenol A (BPA) is a chemical added to produce polycarbonate plastics, which are hard, clear types of plastic found in water bottles and many food containers. BPA has also been found to be an endocrine disruptor because it mimics the female sex hormone estrogen; that is, it is structurally similar to estrogen and can induce some of its effects in animals.

10. (D) is correct. All pesticides and synthetic chemicals are registered for use through the Environmental Protection Agency (EPA). The Food and Drug Administration (FDA) is charged with assessing the safety of all foods, drugs, and food additives.

11. (D) is correct. Paper products comprise the largest component (27%) of the municipal solid waste stream by weight, followed by food scraps (14.6%) and yard waste (13.5%). Heavy metals (9.1%) comprise a much smaller percentage, as does e-waste (1%), although the electronic waste category is now growing rapidly.

12. (B) is correct. When examining the figure, one should look for the steepest portion of the "Recovery rate" graph line, as that indicates the greatest change over time. The period of 1990–95 in the decade of the 1990s represented this period of fastest recycling growth.

13. (D) is correct. Recycled items are taken to MRFs (materials recovery facilities) where they are sorted for reprocessing into other goods. U.S. recycling rose from 6.4% in 1950 to 35.7% of the waste stream in 2015. However, contamination of the waste stream (food residues on containers and nonrecyclable plastics mixed in with recyclable ones) caused MRFs in China, the largest importer of recyclables, to no longer find it economical to process these materials. This 2018 decision by China has reduced the U.S. market for exporting recyclables and dramatically altered the economics of recycling for the United States.

14. (D) is correct. LEED certification stands for Leadership in Energy and Environmental Design, the leading set of standards for sustainable building construction. LEED certification does not require demolition, require that the construction take place in a greenway, or require that the structure be built entirely of recyclable materials. LEED buildings are often somewhat more expensive and do include designs that minimize water and energy consumption.

15. (B) is correct. Naturally occurring chemicals that are toxic are crude oil and radon gas. (C) and (D) both contain synthetic chemicals, and (A) includes a living organism (*Salmonella*), not a chemical.

16. (B) is correct. Dose-response studies can test for *both* lethal effects (LD_{50}) and sublethal, effective dose effects (ED_{50}).

17. (D) is correct. By EPA definition, hazardous waste is waste that is one of the following: ignitable/flammable, corrosive, reactive/explosive, or toxic. Answer (D) contains three out of these four characteristics, making it a better answer than (C), which has only the toxic characteristic. Although *some* hazardous wastes (heavy metals and pesticides) can bioaccumulate, can biomagnify, and are fat soluble, these are not the EPA standard list characteristics.

18. (A) is correct. Reducing the amount of material entering the waste stream avoids the costs of disposal and recycling, helps conserve resources, minimizes pollution, and can save consumers and businesses money. To reduce waste, reuse and recycling [(B) and (C)] are often main strategies; however, they are only two of many strategies involved in reducing the overall waste stream. Composting (D) also plays a part in reducing the amount of material entering the waste stream. Recycling (C) has grown rapidly, and the EPA calls the growth of recycling "one of the best environmental success stories of the late-20th century."

19. (C) is correct. Examining the pie graph shows that one must *add* 52.2% (compostable materials) and 30.6% (recycled materials), resulting in a total of 82.6% of the materials disposed can be reused. Compostable materials are routinely recycled for organic fertilizers and soil nutrient enhancers.

20. (C) is correct. This University of Washington study included the average contents of material thrown away from *one floor* of a building on the campus. Given the options, this study could best be improved by including *all* the classroom buildings in the study.

21. (D) is correct. Biomagnification is the concentration of toxicants in an organism caused by its consumption of other organisms in which toxicants have bioaccumulated. The higher the trophic level, the more severe the effects. Chemicals that are persistent (nonbiodegradable) and fat soluble are biomagnified. Of the choices given, PCBs are the only synthetic chemicals that have these characteristics.

22. (D) is correct. Synergistic effects are interactive effects between toxicants that result in an effect *greater than or different from* the effect predicted when each toxicant is experienced separately. These unpredictable effects are what make for challenging risk assessment studies, making it difficult to impossible to accurately assess the toxicant's risk.

23. (A) is correct. E-waste, or electronic waste, which is made up of discarded computers, cell phones, printers, hand-held devices, TVs, DVD players, and fax machines, contains heavy metals and toxic flame retardants. Most e-waste is being disposed of in landfills and incinerators, where it has traditionally been treated as conventional solid waste; however, recent research suggests that e-waste should instead be treated as hazardous waste.

24. (B) is correct. Incineration is the controlled burning process in which mixed garbage is burned at a very high temperature, along with metal-free waste. Incinerating waste reduces its weight by up to 75% and its volume by up to 90%. Many waste-to-energy (WTE) facilities use the heat produced by waste combustion to extract heat energy (D) and generate electricity (A); however, in the process of incineration, air pollution (dioxins, heavy metals, and PCBs) can enter the atmosphere. The life of a sanitary landfill is *increased*, not decreased (B), and this has been one of the perceived benefits of incineration, the great reduction of waste weight and volume.

Free-Response Question/Explanation

a) The *annual* cost to dispose of the Jones household MSW:

$$4 \text{ persons} \times 4 \text{ lb/day} \times 365 \text{ days/yr} = 5,840 \text{ lb/yr}$$

$$5840 \text{ lb} \times \frac{1 \text{ ton}}{2000 \text{ lb}} = 2.92 \text{ tons} \times \$100/\text{ton} = \textbf{\$292/yr}$$

b) One specific problem that plastic presents *for the environment* is that it is durable and nonbiodegradable. Because plastics do not decompose, they take up significant volume in landfills, causing landfills to reach their capacity much more quickly. Plastics also pose a significant environmental hazard for wildlife. Some plastics (bags and other packaging) are mistakenly consumed as food by wildlife, leading to digestion obstruction and often death. A problem *for human health* resulting from plastics is their role as potential endocrine disruptors. These are chemicals that interfere with the normal functioning of hormones in an animal's body. Males normally make estrogen and then convert it to testosterone; however, endocrine-disrupting hormones are thought to interfere with this process, resulting in higher concentrations of estrogen in males, producing feminization characteristics and reproductive abnormalities. Bisphenol A is one of many plastic chemicals that appear to mimic the female hormone estrogen. Many plastic products also contain another class of hormone-disrupting chemicals called phthalates. Health research on phthalates has linked them to birth defects, breast cancer, reduced sperm counts, and other abnormal reproductive effects.

c) In toxicology, the standard method of testing with lab animals is by setting up a dose-response experiment. The strength of a chemical's effect is determined by the number of animals affected at different specific doses. Once the dose-response data are plotted, toxicologists can calculate the specific toxicity by determining the LD_{50} value (lethal dose-50%), which is the amount of toxicant it takes to kill 50% of the test organism population. A high LD_{50} indicates low toxicity and a low LD_{50} indicates high toxicity.

d) *LEED certification* (Leadership in Energy and Environmental Design) is the leading set of standards for sustainable building. This certification process focuses primarily on assessing a building's minimal use of water and energy, building with sustainable materials, and recycling a building's wastes. Since the Jones home is a historic home, already built, they could consider retrofitting with low-flush toilets and low-flow showerheads (minimizing water use), increasing insulation, and installing thermal windows and compact fluorescent bulbs throughout their home (minimizing energy usage).

Topic 7: Water Resources: Use and Pollution

1. (D) is correct. Human wastewater/sewage is primarily organic material that will require significant oxygen in order to be decomposed by the bacteria and other microorganisms living in this body of water. This will produce a high BOD, or biochemical oxygen demand. Fecal coliform are bacteria that are indicator species for potentially harmful microorganisms associated with sewage contamination, since they are normally found in the mammalian and bird (warm-blooded) intestinal tracts. (B) is incorrect because human sewage contamination would not produce *low* BOD readings, even though the fecal coliform presence could be due to the local wild bird and mammal presence.

2. (B) is correct. Non-point-source pollutants are diffuse sources, often consisting of many small, spread-out sources such as a residential lawn, golf course, and feedlot. Sediment loading of a tributary (smaller river) would also come from a wide area of land through which the tributary flowed. The effluent from a sewage treatment plant represents a point-source pollutant, as it is a discrete, specific spot where the sewage is discharged through a pipe.

3. (D) is correct. Ocean acidification is the process by which today's oceans are becoming more acidic as a result of increased carbon dioxide concentrations in the atmosphere. Ocean water absorbs CO_2 from the air, forming carbonic acid, which dissociates into increased bicarbonate ions and hydrogen ions. The hydrogen ions then combine with carbonate ions present in seawater. It is these carbonate ions that are essential in the building of calcium carbonate shells of marine organisms and that are being removed by the ocean acidification process. Also, the lowering of the ocean's pH as a result of the presence of carbonic acid is further dissolving the already formed shells of many marine species.

4. (A) is correct. The values for 2015 will be on the right-hand margin of the graph (assuming that time is represented on the horizontal/x-axis from 1975 to 2015) and referring to the shaded "Overfished" area, approximately 25% of the whole.

5. (C) is correct. Again, assuming that the year 1995 is at the mid-point (between 1975 and 2015) on the x-axis, the value representing "underfished" is a small part of the whole, approximately 30%.

6. (B) is correct. The values for 1975 will appear on the left-hand side of the graph. Of the three categories, "Maximally sustainably fished" represents 50% of all fish; "Underfished" represents 40%; "Overfished" represents 10%.

7. (A) is correct. Record-low levels of precipitation coupled with record-high heat have kept California and the American Southwest in drought conditions since 2012. According to a 2015 NASA study, the accumulated precipitation/snowpack deficit in the Sierra Nevada mountains (the source of most of California's water) was 20 inches—the equivalent of an entire year's average rainfall. The El Niño winter of 2015–2016 provided California with only a slight reprieve from the drought in northern and eastern California, but southern California ended the year with lower than average levels of rainfall.

8. (D) is correct. Trees are a natural archive of climate data because they grow at varying rates, depending on moisture, temperature, and other climate factors. Using data from tens of thousands of samples of tree rings from the United States, Canada, and Mexico has provided an archive of past climates, which is now being used to predict future droughts and climates.

9. (B) is correct. The El Niño effect is caused by a systematic shift in atmospheric pressure, the sea surface temperature (exceptionally strong warming occurs in the eastern Pacific), and the overall ocean circulation in the tropical Pacific Ocean is altered. With this warming in the eastern Pacific, the normal upwelling that would bring nutrients to the surface (productive waters for fisheries) off the South American coast is suppressed, resulting in a decline of fisheries.

10. (C) is correct. An oligotrophic pond is one that has low nutrient and high oxygen conditions. In order to maintain these conditions, you would want to *avoid* inputs of nutrients (organic wastes or fertilizers/nutrients). Runoff from an athletic field would most probably contain fertilizers from the lawn-care provider; therefore, the possibility of stimulating algal growth leading to eutrophic conditions would be enhanced. Decreasing the calcium available to bottom-dwelling organisms is a sign of ocean acidification (not in a freshwater pond). Answers (A), (D), and (E) are opposite to what one would want to pursue to maintain oligotrophic conditions.

11. (B) is correct. Bycatch is the unintentional catch of nontarget species in fishing. It can include bottom-dwelling invertebrates (shellfish species), noncommercial pelagic fish, marine mammals (dolphins and smaller whale species), and sea turtles.

12. (D) is correct. Nitrogen flux is read along the right-hand side of the graph. After determining that 1993 was the year in which the nitrogen flux was the highest (following the graph's solid black line), one can then read this value as slightly over 200,000 metric tons, approximately 210,000.

13. (B) is correct. The Gulf of Mexico's waters would be considered an environment able to support a high diversity of fish and invertebrates if dissolved oxygen is not a limiting factor. In hypoxic waters (< 2 mg/L dissolved oxygen), very few forms of aquatic life are able to survive.

Therefore, one needs to find the year in which the bar on the graph is the *lowest* (2000), as the bars indicate the hypoxic area in square kilometers.

14. (C) is correct. Determining the dissolved oxygen (DO) content of a body of water will immediately inform one of the possibility of eutrophication processes. When a lake becomes eutrophic, microbial decomposition of the organic matter results in low oxygen (hypoxic) conditions. Measuring DO will not provide any *direct* information regarding bacterial parasitism of the aquatic invertebrates (D), acid precipitation (A), or aquatic biodiversity.

15. (D) is correct. Red tides are a harmful algal bloom consisting of algae that produce reddish pigments that discolor coastal and open ocean waters. Like all algal blooms, the algae are stimulated to bloom with increased nutrient inputs (fertilizer and feedlot runoff into fresh water that subsequently flows into coastal waters).

16. (C) is correct. Surface ocean waters are at the surface because they are less salty and warmer, both physical conditions that decrease the density of a body of water. With increased salinity and/or decreased temperature, ocean water becomes denser and will sink.

17. (D) is correct. The Great Pacific Garbage Patch is located in a portion of the North Pacific Gyre where surface currents concentrate plastics and other floating debris, posing great danger to marine biodiversity.

Free-Response Question/Explanation

a) Reasons why the advent of industrial trawling would produce the dramatic *increase* in cod harvested are multifaceted but are focused around the increased pressure exerted on the fish stocks resulting from (choices follow):

1) New fishing gear/technologies used to capture fish in great volumes (driftnets, longline fishing, and bottom trawling) are highly efficient in finding and harvesting marine fish.

2) The use of fossil fuels and large factory ships allows the harvesting and subsequent processing/freezing/storing of large volumes of fish before the need to return to shore to offload the harvest.

3) Faster factory ships allow for making return trips to fishing grounds more quickly with fewer hours/days lost to nonfishing activities at port.

b) Based on the data provided by the graph, the 10-year period during which the greatest decline in cod fishing took place was from **1970 to 1980**. This occurred approximately 10 years after the advent of industrial trawling. The rate of decline, or rate of change, is determined by the following formula:

$$\text{Rate of decline} = (\text{Initial} - \text{Final}) \div \text{Time Interval}$$
$$((800,000 \text{ tons}) - (140,000 \text{ tons})) \div 10 \text{ years}$$
$$= 660,000 \text{ tons} / 10 = \mathbf{66,000 \text{ tons/yr}}$$

c) The commercial fishing practice of bottom trawling involves dragging a weighted net along the ocean floor to catch groundfish (cod), which are benthic species. Driftnetting uses long, transparent nylon nets arrayed to drift with currents so as to capture passing fish. These are held vertical by floats at the top and weights at the bottom of nets, and they hang from the ocean surface into pelagic waters. These two fishing methods differ in the deployment location of the nets and, therefore, the targeted species. Driftnetting usually targets schooling species that traverse open water such as bluefin tuna, swordfish, and squid, whereas bottom trawling targets groundfish, such as cod. Both of these methods are similar in their significant impact on bycatch; that is, both of these industrialized fishing methods involve the harvesting of many nontarget species. They differ in that bottom trawling is known to be extremely damaging to ocean bottom habitat. Currently, driftnet fishing is illegal because up to 80% of harvested species can be bycatch.

d) The main categories of marine pollutants are oil, plastic debris, mercury/heavy metals, and excess nutrients. Because this area off the northwest coast of Canada is not a prime agricultural area or offshore oil drilling location, it is less likely that excess nutrients (from agriculture) or oil seepage from offshore drilling would be major pollutant categories. However, because this area experiences such high fishing pressure, plastic, which comes from lost or intentionally discarded nets, could play a large role in harming marine life. Also, since all the world's oceans are interconnected, plastic debris can now be found everywhere, even in the most remote of ocean locations. Because plastic is designed not to degrade, it can drift for decades before washing up on beaches.

In addition, with the use of fossil fuels increasing globally, many of the fastest growing nations are burning coal in order to fuel their industrialization. Mercury and other heavy metals are emitted into Earth's atmosphere during the combustion of coal. After settling onto land and water, mercury bioaccumulates in animal tissues (including invertebrates and fish) and then biomagnifies as it makes its way up the marine food chain. As a result, fish at high trophic levels can contain substantial levels of mercury; hence, it is probable that many fish and shellfish species inhabiting the Grand Banks have experienced mercury contamination.

Topic 8: Atmospheric Science and Global Climate Change

1. (C) is correct. Worldwide, average sea levels have risen 26.0 cm (10.2 in.) since 1880. These numbers represent a vertical rise in water level, and on most coastlines a vertical rise of even a few inches translates into a great many feet of water movement inland.

2. (B) is correct. According to the key provided in the graph, the thermal expansion of warmer water accounts for ~37% of sea level rise. Melting glaciers (~27%) and the ice sheets of Greenland and Antarctica (21%), although significant factors, account for less. The Arctic ice melting does not influence sea level rise, although it does influence oceanic current circulation.

3. (C) is correct. In May 2013, scientists reported that tropospheric CO_2, levels had reached the 400 ppm level for the first time in 800,000 years. These levels have continued to rise and are currently *slightly* over 410 ppm, but are not 450 ppm.

4. (A) is correct. Methane concentrations have increased approximately 150% since 1750, primarily because of livestock metabolic wastes (more feedlots), disposing of more organic matter in landfills, and growing more crops, such as rice, to feed the increasing human population. Although carbon dioxide has also increased, from 280 ppm to over 410 ppm, this change is *much less* than a twofold increase.

5. (C) is correct. All of the responses are primary pollutants, coming directly from a factory's smokestack, except ozone (O_3). This is a secondary pollutant that forms in the troposphere as a result of the interaction of sunlight, heat, nitrogen oxides, and volatile carbon-containing chemicals.

6. (C) is correct. Natural, unpolluted rainfall is slightly acidic as a result of the chemical interaction between the carbon dioxide and water vapor normally occurring in the atmosphere. This reaction produces carbonic acid, a weak acid that raises the pH of most unpolluted rainfall to 5.6.

7. (B) is correct. According to the key provided in the graph, the middle graph line represents the global reduction of "all nations." Reading from the graph, this line is slightly below the –10% reduction value.

8. (D) is correct. The lowest graph line represents "the former Soviet-bloc nations," and this graph line indicates that these countries were not contributing to the global reduction of greenhouse gases, most likely because of their greatly reduced economic status.

9. (D) is correct. In 1997, the Kyoto Protocol mandated all signatory nations (by 2012 and then extended to 2020) to reduce their emissions of six greenhouse gases to levels below those of 1990. Although the

United States still has not signed this international treaty, over 100 developed and developing nations have ratified it and have begun to decrease their emissions, while still maintaining their standard of living and continuing to be competitive on the international world market.

10. (A) is correct. The six "criteria pollutants" are NO_2, SO_2, particulates, CO, O_3, and lead (Pb). Answer (A) includes the first three. Answers (B) and (C) include CO_2, which is *not* a criteria pollutant monitored by the EPA, nor is nitrous oxide (NO), answer (D).

11. (C) is correct. The EPA regulates the six "criteria pollutants" that are judged to pose especially great threats to human health. These are CO, SO_2, NO_2, tropospheric ozone (O_3), particulate matter, and lead. Carbon dioxide, although an emission of great concern because of its role in global climate change, is not currently regulated by the EPA.

12. (C) is correct. Acid deposition has many impacts; however, one of the most significant is that the acids leach nutrients such as calcium, magnesium, and potassium ions from the topsoil, altering soil chemistry and harming plants and soil organisms. Acid precipitation also "mobilizes" toxic metal ions, such as aluminum, zinc, mercury, and copper, changing them from insoluble to soluble forms. The presence of these ions in the soil does not make the soil more productive (A), but actually hinders water and nutrient uptake by plants.

13. (D) is correct. The greenhouse effect is due to certain gases of Earth's atmosphere (water vapor, ozone, carbon dioxide, nitrous oxide, and methane) absorbing the infrared radiation emitted from the surface of Earth. After absorbing this radiation, these gases subsequently re-emit this energy in all directions, with some being lost to space. However, some of this radiation travels back downward, warming Earth's atmosphere, specifically the lowest layer, the troposphere.

14. (D) is correct. The Montreal Protocol is the international treaty ratified in 1987 in which almost 200 signatory nations agreed to restrict production of chlorofluorocarbons (CFCs) in order to forestall stratospheric ozone depletion. This international treaty is considered the most successful effort to date in addressing a global environmental problem.

15. (B) is correct. The IPCC is an international panel, established in 1988, and consists of hundreds of scientists and government officials. It has released numerous reports summarizing thousands of scientific studies, addressing the impacts of current and future climate change. These reports have focused on measuring global and regional physical indicators (such as temperature and precipitation), social indicators (sea level rise), and biological indicators (studies of species range shifts). Oceanic photosynthesis and global productivity have not yet been specifically studied for these reports.

16. (D) is correct. The 2015 Paris Agreement's primary goal was to limit global temperature rise to no more than 2.0°C above pre-industrial levels.

Free-Response Question/Explanation

a) The specific trends that the IPCC 2017 report documents have been categorized according to physical, social/human, and biological/ecosystem effects. They have been further categorized as already observed consequences and future predicted trends and impacts. This question is asking for an explanation of the *already observed consequences/impacts* in the above categories.

Global or regional **physical effects already observed** are (choices follow):

1) Earth's *average* surface temperature increased 1.1°C in the past 100 years.
2) Sea level rose by an *average* of 24.1 cm (9.5 in.) in the 20th century.
3) Ocean water became more acidic by about 0.1 pH unit in the past 100 years.
4) Storm surges have increased over the past 100 years.

Human/social effects already observed are (choices follow):

1) Farmers and foresters have had to adapt to altered growing seasons.
2) Poorer nations and communities are suffering more from climate change because they rely more on climate-sensitive resources and have less capacity to adapt.

Biological/ecosystem effects already observed are (choices follow):

1) Species ranges are shifting toward the poles and upward in elevation.
2) The timing of seasonal phenomena such as migration and breeding is shifting.

b) Achieving **carbon neutrality** is the condition in which no net carbon is emitted by the individual (in this case), business, government, university, or utility. Since electricity generation is the largest source (40%) of U.S. CO_2 emissions, and transportation is the second-largest source, changing human behaviors that will impact electricity usage and transportation are the most important first approaches to take. Specific actions that reduce residential electrical consumption include using natural lighting during the day by turning off all lights, using only essential electrical appliances, using natural cooling by opening windows rather than air-conditioning, and completely turning off electrical appliances to avoid phantom power usage when an appliance is on "standby." Using only newer, energy-efficient technologies such as the EPA's Energy Star–rated appliances (Energy Star washing machines and refrigerators) can cut one's CO_2 emissions by as much as 440 lb/appliance annually, and replacing all lightbulbs with compact fluorescent bulbs can reduce energy use for lighting by 40%. The single most effective action to take regarding transportation would be to choose human-powered transportation methods such as walking or bicycling. The next most effective approach would be to rely on public transportation and to attempt to completely phase out whenever possible the conventional automobile, which is very inefficient (only 13–14% of the energy from a tank of gas actually moves the typical car down the road).

c) A 25% reduction of 20 tons of carbon/yr = 0.25×20 tons/yr = 5 tons/yr

$$(5 \text{ tons/yr})(\$40.00/\text{ton}) = \textbf{\$200.00 savings/yr}$$

d) To calculate the increase in sea level, *in meters,* over the next 50 years:

$$3.4 \text{ mm/year} \times 50 \text{ years} = 170 \text{ mm}$$

$$170 \text{ mm} \times \frac{1 \text{ meter}}{1000 \text{ mm}} = \textbf{0.177 meters over the next 50 years}$$

Topic 9: Energy Resources and Consumption

1. (C) is correct. Percent change is calculated using the following formula:

(Final value – Initial value) ÷ Initial value × 100 = % change
(450 gigawatts – 225 gigawatts) ÷ (225 gigawatts) × 100 = +100% increase.

2. (A) is correct. From 1980 to 1985, the price of electricity from wind power decreased from 55 cents/kWh to 35 cents/kWh—a decline of 20 cents. From 1985 to 1990, the price decreased from 35 cents/kWh to 18 cents/kWh (0.17/kWh decrease). The decrease in the 5-year intervals represented by (C) and (D) were significantly smaller.

3. (D) is correct. With fossil fuels producing approximately 80% of U.S. energy consumption, there is no other fuel source (biomass, hydroelectric, nuclear) that comes close to competing. Electricity generation utilizes *more* (not less) energy than the transportation sector (A), and nuclear energy accounts for only 13% of electricity generation, in contrast to coal's 38% (C).

4. (D) is correct. The long-term, safe storage of the radioactive wastes produced by all nuclear power plants remains the most serious *unsolved* dilemma surrounding nuclear power today. Although nuclear power poses small risks of large accidents, as have been demonstrated by Three Mile Island, Chernobyl, and the recent Fukushima, Japan, accident, it is the permanent waste disposal issue that has not yet been solved by any nation.

5. (A) is correct. Passive solar energy is based on a building's design, orientation to the sun, and the use of construction materials that can insulate and store heat. South-facing windows are necessary to maximize the absorption of sunlight in winter, and stone floors add to the thermal mass required to store the sun's radiant heat for release at night. When evergreens are planted outside south-facing windows (D), the sunlight is blocked from entering, and when deciduous trees are planted outside north-facing windows (C), they have no buffering effect in the winter because they have no leaves.

6. (C) is correct. Geothermal energy is one form of renewable energy that does not originate from the sun. Instead, geothermal energy is thermal energy that arises from beneath Earth's surface due to the radioactive decay of elements amid high pressures deep in the planet's interior.

7. (C) is correct. Oil represents 36.5% of U.S. energy consumption, a significantly greater portion of our energy budget than coal (13%), natural gas (30.6%), or nuclear (8.3%) fuels.

8. (C) is correct. When all fossil fuels are burned, their carbon atoms chemically react with oxygen atoms, producing CO_2 as a waste product from this combustion reaction. CO_2 is the most prevalent greenhouse gas, and its atmospheric concentration has been increasing significantly since 1958 when Charles Keeling began collecting detailed CO_2 data at the Mauna Loa Observatory in Hawaii. Carbon is not liberated back into the carbon cycle (A); however, carbon in the form of CO_2 is returned to the carbon cycle. There are current studies focusing on whether increased CO_2 concentrations will increase plant growth. Normal "unpolluted" rainfall is naturally slightly acidic, with a pH of 5.6, because of the carbonic acid resulting from the reaction of atmospheric CO_2 with H_2O. However, it is the NO_x and SO_2 atmospheric pollutants that significantly lower the pH of rainfall *below 5.6,* qualifying it as acid rain.

9. (B) is correct. Worldwide, approximately 38% of electricity is generated by coal; natural gas comes in far behind, at approximately 23%. Nuclear energy accounts for only 10% (A). Biofuels and biomass produce CO_2 emissions, even though this CO_2 is considered *modern* carbon, in contrast to the carbon sequestered for millions of years in fossil fuels (C). Nuclear fuel produces *no* CO_2 emissions.

10. (C) is correct. Worldwide, the most widely used renewable energy resource is biomass, representing approximately 10% of the total world energy production. Hydroelectric comes in second, with only 2.5% of the market (B). Wind and solar together share less than 2% of the world energy production.

11. (D) is correct. Photovoltaic (PV) cells convert sunlight to electrical energy by making use of the photovoltaic effect. This involves *sunlight* striking one of a pair of plates made primarily of silicon, a semiconductor. The light causes the silicon to release electrons that are attracted by electrostatic forces to the opposing plate, generating electricity.

12. (D) is correct. Nonrenewable fossil fuels provide approximately 81% of the world's energy resources. Concerns over the finite and shrinking quantity of all fossil fuels and their negative environmental impacts, especially with regard to air pollution emissions of CO_2 and the climate change implications, have motivated the development of solar, geothermal, and wind energy technologies.

13. (B) is correct. EROI stands for energy returned on investment and is a ratio that is useful when assessing energy sources. EROI = Energy returned/Energy invested. Higher ratios mean that we receive more energy from each unit of energy than we invest in the exploration, extraction, and transportation costs for the energy resource to get to the market or utilization site.

14. (A) is correct. Liquid fuels (ethanol) from biomass sources are powering millions of vehicles today. Nearly 40% of the U.S. corn crop is used to produce ethanol to add to gasoline, *conserving* oil (a fossil fuel in high demand) and reducing automotive emissions.

15. (A) is correct. Fossil fuels (~81%), biomass (10%), nuclear (4.9%), hydroelectric (2.5%), and new renewables (1.7%) represent the current best estimate for the world's total energy consumption by source.

16. (B) is correct. All biofuels (ethanol and biodiesel) are liquid fuels from biomass sources. All biomass consists of organic material derived from living or recently living organisms and contains chemical energy that originated ultimately with sunlight and photosynthesis.

17. (B) is correct. Over the past several decades, the fastest-growing source of electricity generation using new renewables has been wind power, doubling approximately every 3 years. Denmark is the global leader, supplying 48% of its total electricity needs from its wind farms.

18. (C) is correct. The Keystone XL Pipeline project refers to the Canadian tar sands mining occurring in northern Alberta. The tar sands slurry recovered from the massive open pit mining is being transported via a trans-Canadian pipeline 2200 miles through the central United States to ports in Oklahoma and Illinois, and on to Gulf Coast refineries.

19. (D) is correct. Coal continues to be the main fuel used to generate electricity in the United States primarily because we have such large reserves of this fossil fuel. Coal provides half the electrical generating capacity of the United States and is currently powering China's surging economy.

20. (C) is correct. A feed-in tariff system is the practice whereby utilities are mandated to buy extra power from anyone who can generate it from a renewable energy source and feed it into the electric grid. Net metering (A) is the process by which owners of houses with PV systems or wind turbines can sell their excess solar or wind energy to their local power utility. Whereas feed-in tariffs award producers with prices above market rates, net metering offers market-rate prices.

Free-Response Question/Explanation

a) The average growth rate is calculated using the following formula:

$$\frac{\text{Final value} - \text{Initial value}}{\text{Initial value}} \times 100 = \% \text{ change (growth rate)}$$

For wind energy: $\dfrac{191,000 - 140,000}{140,000} \times 100 = \textbf{36.4\% growth}$

For solar: $\dfrac{44,300 - 12,700}{12,700} \times 100 = \textbf{248.8\% growth}$

b) In the past several years, solar energy (PV and CSP combined) is growing much faster than wind energy in the United States (approximately 200% faster according to the above 2012–2015 data). One reason for this difference in growth is that solar heating systems do not need to be connected to an electrical grid and are thus more useful in isolated locations. This important feature shows that solar energy need not be confined to only affluent suburban communities. A second reason for the difference is that results of recent research have demonstrated a growing concern for noise pollution and wildlife deaths (especially migrating birds and bats) associated with wind turbines. Over the past four decades, solar, wind, and geothermal energy sources have grown far faster than has the overall energy supply. Although the long-term leader in growth over this period has been wind power (growing by nearly 50% each year since the 1970s), *in recent years* (as the above data show) solar power has grown far faster than wind power. Because solar and wind energy both started from such low levels of use, it will take many years for them to potentially catch up with conventional energy sources.

c) The goal of any feed-in tariff system is to promote the use of the new technology with economic incentives. Utilities are mandated to buy power from anyone who can generate extra power (over their needs) from renewable energy sources and then feed it back into the electric grid. Under this system, utilities must pay guaranteed premium prices for this power under a long-term contract. As a result, homeowners in Washington have installed more and more PV panels each year, and they are selling their extra solar power to the utilities at a profit, as feed-in tariff systems significantly award producers with prices *above* the market rate of $0.15/kWh. To further encourage local "green collar" industry in Washington, a rate of $0.54/kWh (for extra electricity generation that can be fed into the grid) will be credited to homeowners using PV solar cells *manufactured in Washington,* rather than the basic $0.15/kWh.

d) The major environmental advantage of using wind energy is that wind power produces no emissions once the equipment (tower and wind turbine) is manufactured and installed. The EPA has estimated that the amount of CO_2 pollution that all U.S. wind turbines together prevent from entering the atmosphere is greater than the emissions from 34 million cars each and every day. Overall, there are no air or water pollution issues associated with wind power. Secondly, wind is a nondepletable resource—the amount of wind available tomorrow does not depend on how much we use today. Wind energy is a clean and free resource.

e) The main reasons why wind power continues to represent less than 2% of current U.S. energy sources include the following choices: (1) wind is an intermittent resource which we have no control over when it will occur; (2) wind also varies greatly with geographic location (most of North America's people live near the coasts, far from the Great Plains and mountain regions that have the best wind conditions); and (3) although there seems to be wide public approval of existing wind projects and the concept of wind power, newly proposed wind projects have often elicited the not-in-my-backyard (NIMBY) syndrome among people living nearby. Also at play is the lack of factoring in of the external costs associated with fossil fuel use (air pollution, habitat destruction associated with mining, and human health issues associated with poor air quality), considerations in evaluation that seem to make conventional energy sources more economically accessible.

Part IV

Practice Test

On the following pages is a practice test that approximates the actual AP Environmental Science Exam in format, types of questions, and content. Set aside 2 hours and 40 minutes to take the test. To best prepare yourself for the actual AP Exam conditions, use only the allowed time for Section I (90 minutes for 80 multiple-choice questions) and for Section II (70 minutes for three free-response questions). A four-function, scientific, or graphing calculator is allowed on both sections of the exam.

Environmental Science

Section I: Multiple Choice

Time—1 hour and 30 minutes

Directions: This section of the examination contains 80 multiple-choice questions. Each question is followed by four suggested answers. Select the one lettered choice that *best* answers each question or best completes the statement. Calculators may be used on the exam.

Questions 1–3
Use the following figure to answer questions 1 through 3.

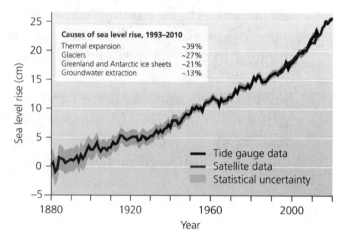

1. Since 1965, the global sea level has risen approximately
   (A) 1.5 cm.
   (B) 15 cm.
   (C) 26 cm.
   (D) 250 cm.

2. The data indicate that the *main* contributing factor of sea level rise has been
   (A) glaciers melting.
   (B) Greenland and Antarctic ice sheets melting.
   (C) thermal expansion of warmer waters.
   (D) heavy rainfalls globally throughout the environment.

3. Sea level rise data represent
   (A) a horizontal rise of ocean water along a coastline.
   (B) the result of storm surges and flooding.
   (C) a vertical rise in water level.
   (D) coastline flooding events resulting in beach erosion.

Questions 4–7
Base your answers to questions 4 through 7 on the following diagram.

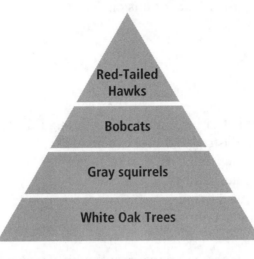

4. The greatest amount of energy present in the above ecosystem is found at the level of
   (A) red-tailed hawks.
   (B) bobcats.
   (C) gray squirrels.
   (D) white oak trees.

5. In the above ecosystem, 250 kilograms of bobcats would require ___ in order to live and grow.
   (A) 125 kg of gray squirrels
   (B) 250,000 kg of autotrophs
   (C) 2,500 kg of gray squirrels
   (D) less than 2500 kg of herbivores

6. The specific tertiary consumers in this ecosystem are
   (A) gray squirrels.
   (B) bobcats.
   (C) red-tailed hawks.
   (D) omnivores.

7. This ecosystem would most likely be found in the biome known as the
   (A) savanna forest.
   (B) boreal forest.
   (C) taiga.
   (D) temperate deciduous forest.

8. A city with a population of 10,000 is experiencing 20 deaths, 40 births, 10 emigrants, and 20 immigrants per year. What is the net annual percentage growth rate of this city?
   (A) 80%
   (B) 1%
   (C) 3%
   (D) 0.3%

9. A country that is beginning to go through demographic transition and becoming industrialized first experiences
   (A) death rates rising as birth rates fall.
   (B) death rates falling.
   (C) death rates rising.
   (D) birth rates falling.

10. A scientist does an experiment with *Daphnia,* a sensitive aquatic organism, to determine the potential toxicity of an herbicide. Eighty individuals were used, and the scientist finds that 10 mg/L kills half the *Daphnia*. The scientist has now determined
    (A) a dose-response curve that can be applied to humans.
    (B) the TC_{50}.
    (C) the potential lethality of this pesticide to humans.
    (D) the LD_{50}.

11. The main chemical *causing* the "dead zone" in the Gulf of Mexico is
    (A) arsenic.
    (B) mercury.
    (C) oxygen.
    (D) nitrogen.

12. The main chemical responsible for acid deposition is
    (A) carbon dioxide.
    (B) sulfur dioxide.
    (C) CFCs.
    (D) mercury.

13. Burning 1 gallon of gasoline in a car releases approximately 20 lb of CO_2 into the atmosphere.

Person X drives 50,000 miles in a car that averages 40 miles per gallon (mpg), while person Y drives 50,000 miles in a car that averages 20 mpg. Over the course of the 50,000 miles, how many fewer pounds of CO_2 are released by the car driven by person X?
(A) 10,000 lb
(B) 20,000 lb
(C) 25,000 lb
(D) 40,000 lb

14. The most productive (g $C/m^2/yr$) ecosystem(s) in the world is/are
(A) temperate deciduous forests.
(B) swamps and marshes.
(C) the open ocean.
(D) temperate grasslands.

15. If a coral reef has an NPP of 5.25 kg $C/m^2/yr$ and a GPP of 7.5 kg $C/m^2/yr$, how much carbon is being used during respiration by the autotrophs in this ecosystem?
(A) 12.75 kg $C/m^2/yr$
(B) 2.25 kg $C/m^2/yr$
(C) –2.25 kg $C/m^2/yr$
(D) 14.95 kg $C/m^2/yr$

Questions 16–18
Use the diagram below to answer questions 16 through 18.

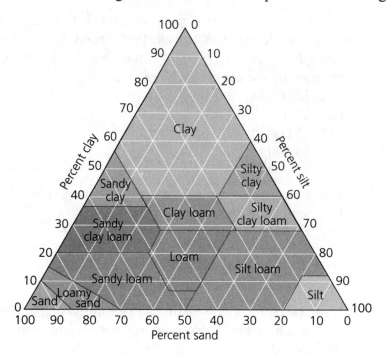

16. If a soil sample was determined to be composed of 40% sand, 20% silt, and 40% clay, the soil type would most closely resemble
    (A) sandy clay loam.
    (B) silt loam.
    (C) sandy loam.
    (D) sandy clay.

17. The soil sample that would have the *largest runoff* after a rainfall event would be
    (A) silty clay.
    (B) sandy clay.
    (C) silt loam.
    (D) sand.

18. The best soil type for most agriculture would be composed of
    (A) 80% sand, 40% silt, 10% clay.
    (B) 40% sand, 40% silt, 20% clay.
    (C) 20% sand, 60% silt, 20% clay.
    (D) 33.3% sand, 33.3% silt, 33.3% clay.

Questions 19–21

Use the graph below to answer questions 19 through 21.

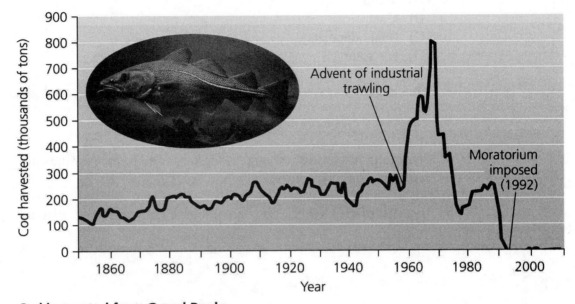

Cod harvested from Grand Banks

19. The cod harvested from the Grand Banks between **1960 and 1980** experienced a
    (A) 200% decline.
    (B) 100% decline.
    (C) 40% decline.
    (D) 20% decline.

20. This initial decline in harvest was attributed primarily to
    (A) foreign fishing fleets in Canadian waters.
    (B) international fishing fleets using bottom-trawling nets.
    (C) large bycatch harvesting.
    (D) driftnet fishing by Japanese tuna fishermen.

21. The current rate of cod harvesting is primarily explained by
    (A) the ability of cod to rebound after the moratorium.
    (B) the overharvesting of bycatch.
    (C) the overharvesting of keystone species on the Grand Banks.
    (D) the collapse of the cod population on the Grand Banks.

Questions 22–25. Match a letter from the following list of energy sources with each of the following questions. A letter may be used once, more than once, or not at all.

(A) Wind
(B) Coal
(C) Shale deposits
(D) PV solar

22. This is the energy source *least* supported by the 2015 Paris Agreement.

23. This is the *fastest* growing renewable source of energy.

24. Hydraulic fracturing is the methodology used to *harvest* the energy reserves from this source.

25. In terms of efficiency, this energy source has the *highest* EROI.

Questions 26–28 refer to the following graph.

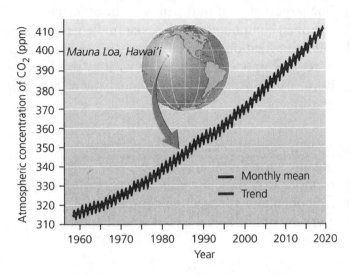

26. The annual fluctuation of the CO_2 concentration is explained by
    (A) annual absorption of CO_2 by the oceans.
    (B) the ozone layer mitigating the annual increase in CO_2.
    (C) seasonal photosynthetic activity of autotrophs.
    (D) annual El Niño events.

27. The data in the graph can be evidence for global climate change when they are combined with
    (A) fossil fuel consumption by the United States.
    (B) the global ecological footprint.
    (C) annual cycles of flooding and drought.
    (D) mean global temperatures.

28. The percent change in CO_2 concentration between 2010 and 2020 is approximately
    (A) 20%.
    (B) 10%.
    (C) 5%.
    (D) –5%.

29. Which of the following is true of nitrogen as it cycles in nature?
    (A) The largest sink of nitrogen is in the atmosphere.
    (B) Nitrogen compounds rarely exist in the gaseous state.
    (C) Nitrogen fixation occurs regularly in ecosystems, producing a nitrogen compound that can be used by primary consumers.
    (D) Denitrifying bacteria live in mutualistic relationships with most consumers.

30. Integrated pest management programs are *primarily*
    (A) organic agricultural approaches.
    (B) methods to completely eliminate agricultural pests.
    (C) a monoculture approach to agriculture.
    (D) a variety of biological and chemical approaches to reduce crop damage to an economically tolerable level.

31. The energy returned on investment, or EROI value, is the lowest for
    (A) nuclear power.
    (B) biofuels.
    (C) hydropower.
    (D) PV technology.

32. Which of the following greenhouse gases has the *highest* heat-trapping ability per molecule in our atmosphere?
    (A) N_2O
    (B) CH_4
    (C) CO_2
    (D) CO

33. Assuming that the human population of Earth is growing at an annual rate of 1.2%, how many years will it take for the world population to double?
    (A) 2.4 years
    (B) 4.8 years
    (C) 58 years
    (D) 100 years

34. When comparing nuclear and coal-fired power plants, a nuclear power plant generates more
    (A) NO_2.
    (B) radon.
    (C) CO_2.
    (D) thermal pollution.

35. Characteristics that contribute to the vulnerability of a species becoming endangered include which of the following?
    I.   having low genetic diversity
    II. having a generalist habitat
    III. being a keystone species
    IV. being r-selected

    (A) I only
    (B) II only
    (C) III and IV only
    (D) I and IV only

36. The international agreement that is widely considered the most important environmental victory for a sustainable planet is
    (A) the 2015 Paris Agreement.
    (B) the Montreal Protocol.
    (C) the Clean Air Act of 1972.
    (D) the Green Revolution.

37. The primary characteristics of sewage treatment plant effluent are
    (A) moderate oxygen, low coliform, and low BOD.
    (B) high oxygen, high coliform, and low BOD.
    (C) low oxygen, low coliform, and high BOD.
    (D) low nitrates, low phosphates, and high BOD.

38. When the I = PAT model is applied to the United States, the *most* important factor in determining the environmental effects of the U.S. population is
    (A) the value of P.
    (B) the value of A.
    (C) the value of T.
    (D) the value of P and T.

Questions 39–41
Use the following figure to answer questions 39 through 41.

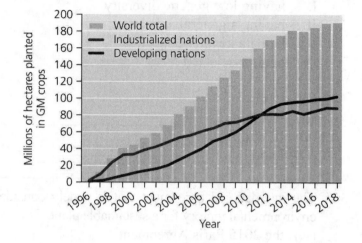

39. The greatest period of global growth for GM crops was
    (A) 1998–2000.
    (B) 2002–2004.
    (C) 2009–2011.
    (D) 2016–2018.

40. The difference in land utilized for growing GM crops by developing nations versus industrialized nations in 2018 is approximately
    (A) 10 million hectares.
    (B) 15 million hectares.
    (C) 20 million hectares.
    (D) 60 million hectares.

41. Since the commercial introduction of GM crops in 1996,
    (A) industrialized nations have questioned their safety.
    (B) the world's total growth rate for GM crops has been approximately 80%.
    (C) the growth rate of GM crops in developing nations has been slow.
    (D) more than half of the world's GM crops are now grown in developing nations.

42. All of the following are examples of GMOs *except*
    (A) golden rice.
    (B) Bt corn.
    (C) Roundup-Ready alfalfa.
    (D) Monsanto meat.

Questions 43–44
Use the graph below to answer questions 43 and 44.

St. Paul reindeer, *Rangifer tarandus*

43. The reindeer's population growth between the years 1920 and 1940 *best*
    exemplifies
    (A) logistic growth.
    (B) demographic transition.
    (C) doubling time.
    (D) logarithmic growth.

44. When examining the entire period between 1910 and 1950, the data *most likely* show that
    (A) the reindeer's environment provided unlimited resources.
    (B) there were other species competing for food resources.
    (C) introduced species arrived in 1930.
    (D) the reindeer's carrying capacity was reached around 1938.

45. A classroom uses eight 60-watt lightbulbs for 10 hours per day. Approximately how many kilowatt-hours of electricity are used per day by the classroom's lightbulbs?
    (A) 4800
    (B) 600
    (C) 480
    (D)   48

46. Crops genetically engineered to fix nitrogen would have which of the following advantages?
    (A) increased disease resistance
    (B) increased tolerance of atmospheric nitrous oxides
    (C) decreased need for chemical fertilizer
    (D) more compatible with organic farming practices

47. When a CAFO (concentrated animal feeding operation) is located in a watershed, a likely effect on the local stream is
    (A) increased oligotrophic conditions.
    (B) increased thermal pollution.
    (C) decreased coliform levels.
    (D) increased eutrophic conditions.

Refer to the countries in the following table for questions 48–49.

Country	TFR	Infant Mortality (per 1000 births)	Life Expectancy (in years)
A	2.2	10	78
B	1.7	45	80
C	3.4	25	65
D	6.3	120	49

48. Which of the countries listed in the table above is most likely in need of improved educational opportunities for women?
    (A) A
    (B) B
    (C) C
    (D) D

49. Which of the countries listed in the table above is most likely experiencing a population decline?
    (A) A
    (B) B
    (C) C
    (D) D

50. Many experts are reporting that the most sustainable path to long-term food security, combined with a significant greenhouse gas reduction, would be to
    (A) increase organic farming productivity.
    (B) decrease livestock as a food source.
    (C) increase grass-fed and free-range livestock production.
    (D) increase GM food production.

51. International seedbanks have been established for the primary purpose of
    (A) preserving declining crop biodiversity.
    (B) finding more available substitutes for scarce agricultural crops in developing countries.
    (C) promoting international cooperation and sustainability.
    (D) increasing agricultural productivity in developed countries.

52. The growing concern surrounding ocean acidification focuses on the main causative agent of
    (A) decreasing calcium in oceans.
    (B) increasing pH in oceans.
    (C) increasing CO_2 in oceans.
    (D) decreasing carbonic acid in oceans.

Questions 53–55
Use the following graph to answer questions 53 through 55.

53. A major conclusion that can be made from the evidence comparing organic and conventional farming is
    (A) conventional farming has a proven history.
    (B) organic farming produces more greenhouse gases.
    (C) conventional farming is more economic yet more environmentally problematic.
    (D) organic farming methods should be more widely considered because of numerous, proven benefits.

54. Environmentally, the *most* significant data provided by the graph, demonstrating the disadvantages of conventional farming, are in the category of
    (A) yields.
    (B) profit.
    (C) energy input.
    (D) greenhouse gases.

55. A *primary* reason for the differences in energy inputs between conventional and organic farming is that
    (A) IPM approaches and animal manure are being regularly employed by organic farms.
    (B) pesticides, herbicides, and inorganic fertilizers are used widely in both conventional and organic farming approaches.
    (C) organic farming routinely uses animals rather than tractors.
    (D) conventional farming saves energy by employing monoculture approaches.

Questions 56–58. The terms listed below refer to important environmental legislation. Match a letter from the list with each of the following questions. A letter may be used once, more than once, or not at all.

(A) Clean Water Act
(B) Resource Conservation and Recovery Act (RCRA)
(C) National Environmental Policy Act (NEPA)
(D) Safe Drinking Water Act

56. Requires cradle-to-grave tracking of hazardous wastes

57. Requires an environmental impact statement and study prior to federal projects that might affect environmental quality

58. Establishes basic coliform levels accepted for human health

Questions 59–61
Use the following figure to answer questions 59 through 61.

59. The above climatograph shows data characteristic of the ____ biome.
    (A) desert
    (B) savanna
    (C) tundra
    (D) temperate deciduous

60. The average annual temperature in this biome is
    (A) above freezing.
    (B) below freezing.
    (C) at freezing.
    (D) approximately 5°C.

61. One of the most distinctive characteristics of this biome is the presence of
    (A) coniferous trees.
    (B) saguaro cactus
    (C) rocky/sandy terrain.
    (D) permafrost.

62. A "tragedy of the commons" scenario is *best* exemplified by
    (A) the U.S. agribusiness in the Midwest.
    (B) the extirpation of cheetahs in Africa.
    (C) overgrazing sheep in a private park.
    (D) acid precipitation falling throughout the northeastern United States.

63. Structures given a LEED platinum ranking are
    (A) exemplary in sustainable design, especially energy efficiency.
    (B) free of asbestos, lead, and radon and therefore made of "green" construction materials.
    (C) especially high in heavy metal content.
    (D) inefficient and need to be renovated in order to meet "green" standards.

64. A trophic cascade is best described as the effect of ___ on ___.
    (A) top predators; top carnivores
    (B) top predators; abundance of lower consumers
    (C) herbivores; carnivores
    (D) autotrophs; herbivores

65. Global climate change could be best thought of as a(n) ___ affecting a population's size.
    (A) logistical growth factor
    (B) endemic limiting factor
    (C) density-dependent factor
    (D) density-independent factor

66. The largest reservoir of carbon in the carbon cycle is
    (A) the oceans.
    (B) freshwater systems.
    (C) plant life.
    (D) sedimentary rock and fossil fuels.

67. If the global population has a CDR of 11 and a CBR of 17, this would result in a growth rate of ___%.
    (A) 0.06
    (B) 0.6
    (C) 6.0
    (D) 28

68. Forests supply us with many vital ecosystem services. The one receiving the most attention currently because of global climate change is the
    (A) photosynthetic contribution of oxygen from the world's forests.
    (B) cap-and-trade potential for global forests.
    (C) moderation of precipitation and climate patterns.
    (D) carbon sequestration potential of the world's forests.

Questions 69–71
Use the age distribution diagram below to answer questions 69 through 71.

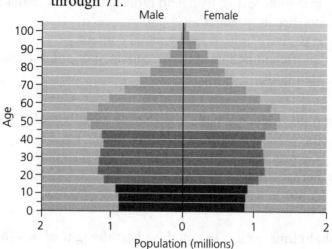

69. Country X has the above age distribution. These data indicate that country X
    (A) is a developing country.
    (B) has 80% of its population over age 50.
    (C) is experiencing rapid growth.
    (D) is experiencing slow or no population growth.

70. Country X is most likely
    (A) China
    (B) Mexico
    (C) Germany
    (D) Canada

71. From these data, this country's growth rate is most likely
    (A) 0.4%.
    (B) 1.0%.
    (C) 3.0%.
    (D) 6.0%.

72. Which of the following is *not* an environmental benefit of smart growth?
    (A) decreased open space
    (B) decreased impervious surfaces
    (C) decreased fossil fuel consumption
    (D) decreased water pollution

73. Humans use fresh water primarily for
    (A) electrical production.
    (B) mining and industrial processes.
    (C) agricultural irrigation.
    (D) residential heating, cooking, and plumbing.

74. Which of the following is not yet regulated by the U.S. Environmental Protection Agency?
    (A) O_3
    (B) CO_2
    (C) particulates
    (D) Pb

75. One's ecological footprint can best be defined as
    (A) the environmental impact on global air and water.
    (B) the effects of the current human population.
    (C) the total amount of waste generated from the human population.
    (D) the area of land and water required to support needs and to absorb the wastes produced.

76. Given that a specific radioactive isotope has a half-life of 30 days, how many days will it take for a 16-kg sample to decay to less than 1 kg?
    (A) 60 days
    (B) 120 days
    (C) 150 days
    (D) 15 days

77. As of 2020, the world human population is approximately
    (A) 6.5 billion.
    (B) 7.3 billion.
    (C) 7.7 billion.
    (D) 10.3 billion.

78. The world's leader in producing and using the most solar power is currently
    (A) the United States.
    (B) France.
    (C) Germany.
    (D) Japan

79. Paleoclimatology data used to study global climate change can be obtained from
    (A) lichens.
    (B) monarch butterflies.
    (C) amphibians.
    (D) Antarctic ice cores.

80. Current sea level rise has been estimated to be closest to
    (A) 0.5 mm/yr.
    (B) 1.0 mm/yr.
    (C) 3.0 mm/yr.
    (D) 10 mm/yr.

Environmental Science

Section II: Free-Response Questions

Time—70 minutes
3 Questions

Directions: Answer all three questions, which are weighted equally. It is suggested that each question will take approximately 22 minutes to answer. Write all answers in essay form. Outline is NOT acceptable. Where calculations are required, clearly show your work. Where explanations are required, support your answers with specific evidence and/or specific examples. It is important that you read each question completely before you begin to write. Calculators may be used in this section of the exam. During the exam, referring back to Section I (multiple-choice questions) is *not allowed* while answering Section II FRQs.

1. Grow-Good Farm, a conventional, industrial farming corporation, has recently purchased a 1000-hectare (ha) plot of land adjacent to the *Islandia Forest Preserve,* a Nature Conservancy–protected temperate deciduous forest. As farmers and ecologists know, understanding ecosystem structure and function is the basis of understanding and solving all environmental issues and potential conflicts of interest.

   a) **Diagram** a specific *temperate deciduous forest ecosystem* with four trophic levels, including one specific species per trophic level.
   b) Assume that the biomass of the organisms at the first trophic level is 6500 kg. **Calculate** and diagram the remaining biomass in all other trophic levels, providing an explanation for the values you determine.
   c) Before Grow-Good Farm can begin actively farming the land, they must determine whether their conventional farming practices will adversely affect the protected *Islandia Forest Preserve.* **Design a controlled experiment** that will address the farm's use of commercial fertilizer *or* pesticides. Include the following in your design:
      1) Formulate a hypothesis.
      2) Identify your independent variable.
      3) Identify your control.
      4) Explain the field procedures that will be followed.
      5) Describe what data you will collect.
      6) Discuss the possible results and relate them to your conclusion.

2. Since the early 1900s, seven U.S. southwestern states and Mexico have removed water from the Colorado River for a variety of purposes, with central California annually removing more than its fair share for

agricultural purposes. As a result of the competing interests of southwestern U.S. states and Mexico, currently only a trickle of the Colorado River reaches the Gulf of Mexico. In response to growing concern over the 4-year drought from 2012 to 2016, California Governor Jerry Brown announced a 25% mandatory water reduction for all California cities and towns.

a) **Explain** how current Colorado River usage is a "tragedy of the commons."

b) In response to the above water issue, **describe** *two specific and feasible* approaches that a U.S. citizen could take to live more sustainably.

c) **Describe** *two* specific ecosystem services connected with the Colorado River.

d) For *one* of the ecosystem services you described, **explain** how this ecosystem service has been compromised by humans.

e) NASA scientists have recently compared the climate of the Southwest over the past 1000 years with their computer simulation predictions for climate for the next 100 years. These studies have concluded that there will be unprecedented levels of drought in the American Southwest through 2100. Surprisingly, the studies also concluded that the drying of soils was *not* being driven by reductions in precipitation, but by increased warmer temperatures leading to higher rates of evaporation. **Propose a solution** that would directly address these recent NASA findings.

3. Like many U.S. citizens, the Jones family committed to making a positive contribution toward reducing climate change effects in 2020. The Joneses currently use an average of 750 kilowatts for their home electricity (hot water, lights, all electrical appliances). Their local utility is charging $0.12/kWh. After researching the new PV solar technology that is increasingly popular in their state, the Jones family decided to install PV solar panels on their roof. These panels will produce an average of 450 kilowatts per month and will cost $3500 to install.

a) **Calculate** how much the Jones family paid for their electricity per month *before* the installation of the solar panels.

b) **Calculate** how many years it will take for the Joneses to break even on the purchase of their solar panels?

c) **Explain** *how* these PV solar panels are making a positive contribution toward alleviating climate change concerns.

d) **Describe** two *passive* solar energy solutions that the Jones family could implement that would further reduce their energy consumption.

e) The Jones family's utility company is currently using natural gas obtained from hydraulic fracturing taking place in their state. **Describe** two *environmental concerns* connected with this approach to obtain energy.

Practice Test Answer Key

__Section I:__ Multiple Choice

1. B	25. B	49. B	73. C
2. C	26. C	50. B	74. B
3. C	27. D	51. A	75. D
4. D	28. C	52. C	76. C
5. C	29. A	53. D	77. C
6. C	30. D	54. C	78. C
7. D	31. B	55. A	79. D
8. D	32. A	56. B	80. C
9. B	33. C	57. C	
10. D	34. D	58. D	
11. D	35. D	59. C	
12. B	36. B	60. B	
13. C	37. A	61. D	
14. B	38. B	62. D	
15. B	39. C	63. A	
16. D	40. B	64. B	
17. A	41. D	65. D	
18. B	42. D	66. D	
19. C	43. D	67. B	
20. B	44. D	68. D	
21. D	45. A	69. D	
22. B	46. C	70. D	
23. D	47. D	71. A	
24. C	48. D	72. A	

Section II: ***Explanations for Free-Response Questions***

Each free-response question (FRQ) can earn a total of 10 points. The following point allocations are those *suggested* for each question part. For some question parts where more than one answer is required, the list of possible responses provided includes the *main/central concepts* but is not necessarily exhaustive of all possibilities.

FRQ 1. a) **1 point** for accurately including temperate deciduous forest species in all four trophic levels (TLs), and **1 point** for accurately including the correct trophic level for each species: an autotroph for the first TL, an herbivore in the second TL, a carnivore in the third TL, and the top carnivore in the fourth TL. Examples follow. No points are earned if the diagram is in the form of a food web with interconnecting arrows, as that doesn't allow one to accurately determine the specific trophic level in which a species is located. A pyramid diagram is the most accurate format, with each trophic level labeled. **(2 points total)**

b) **(1 point** earned for *completely* describing the 10% law; **1 point** for accurately calculating the energy available for all trophic levels: **2 points total)** Merely naming the 10% law does not earn a point.

According to the 10% law, which describes approximate energy transfer between each succeeding higher trophic level (TL), 90% of the energy available at each TL is consumed by the organism's own metabolic processes/needs and is lost as heat energy from the ecosystem. Only 10%, at best, is available to the next higher TL. Therefore:

6500 kg →   650 kg →   65 kg →   6.5 kg

(autotrophs) (herbivores) (carnivores) (top carnivores)

1st TL   2nd TL   3rd TL   4th TL

c) Grow-Good Farm experimental design: According to the question, one must initially choose either commercial fertilizer *or* pesticide effects to investigate. There are many possibilities for designing the experiment, but each design must explain the *specifics* of the following:

1) Hypothesis (**1 point**): States a specific, *testable* explanation for the farm's use of either a fertilizer or pesticide and its possible effect on the forest.

2) Independent variable (**1 point**): This variable is the one that is *manipulated;* in this case, it is the amount of either fertilizer or pesticide.

3) Control (**1 point**): That which is *not* changed; in this case, a portion of the 1000-ha farm plot adjoining the forest preserve, left untreated/undisturbed and used for comparison.

4) Procedures (**1 point**): Outlines a general experimental plan for manipulating the independent variable, describes the control, and briefly describes the overall experiment.

5) Data (**1 point**): Describes the *quantifiable* data (dependent variable) to be collected. In this case, some of the possibilities are forest tree or shrub growth and/or forest biodiversity data (species richness).

6) Results/discussion (**1 point**): Connection of the data collected to the results; what do the data mean? Do data support or refute the hypothesis?

FRQ 2. a) The "tragedy of the commons" is the process by which publicly accessible resources tend to become damaged and depleted through overuse by many separate entities. The Colorado River holds water used by seven U.S. states and two northwestern states of Mexico. If California removes more than its share from the river, less water is left for the other users, tempting them to do likewise for their own state's use and personal gain. This poses threats (depletion, eutrophication, pollution) to the entire riverine natural resource and thus is a tragedy of the commons. (**1 point**)

b) Two feasible approaches that a U.S. citizen could take to live more sustainably with regard to water would be: (**2 points:** 1 point each)

Three approaches are described—only two are required.

1) Increase household water conservation efforts: take shorter showers and install conservation shower heads and low-flush toilets.

2) Plant/restore native plants and vegetation around the home, as arid-adapted and native plants require much less to no additional watering other than what normally is received in this biome.

3) Increase recycling and waste reduction efforts, as manufacture of any new product requires water resources, and recycling of materials requires much less water than the processing of new raw materials.

c) Two specific ecosystem services associated with the Colorado River are: (**2 points:** 1 point each)

Three specific services are described—only two are required.

1) It provides regulation of temperature, precipitation, cloud formation, and climate.
2) It stores and regulates water supplies in watersheds and aquifers, necessary for native biodiversity, agriculture, and drinking water.
3) When native vegetation has enough water to flourish, it provides protection for soils against the storm, flood, and drought damage that occurs.

d) Because large amounts of water are being removed from the Colorado River (thus depleting levels held in Colorado River reservoirs), there is now less water available for supporting natural biodiversity and the normal functioning of the water cycle and climate regulation. Since 2000, reservoirs have been at half-capacity, and climate modelers predict that global climate change will bring increased drought to the American Southwest through 2100. (**1 point**)

e) The recent NASA data indicate that drought and drying soils are being caused by increased warmer temperatures, that is, climate change. Since climate change is driven by increasing levels of CO_2 in the atmosphere, *any solution that decreases CO_2* concentrations would address these NASA findings. Solutions might involve (1) transitioning away from fossil fuels and moving toward increasing alternative energy (solar and wind) use, (2) planting more trees, and/or (3) keeping forests intact for carbon sequestration. (**2 points**)

FRQ 3. a) *Before* installation of the PV panels, the Jones family paid: (**2 points:** 1 point for work/correct setup, 1 point for correct answer. *Correct answers alone do not earn credit for any calculation.*)

$$750 \text{ kilowatts/month} \times \$0.12/\text{kilowatt} = \$90/\text{month}$$

b) The time it will take the Joneses to break even on the purchase of their solar panels (**2 points:** 1 point for work/correct set-up, 1 point for correct answer):

$$450 \text{ kilowatts/mo} \times \$0.12/\text{kilowatt} = \$54/\text{month}$$

$$\$3500 \div \$54/\text{month} = 64.8 \text{ months}$$

$$64.8 \text{ months} \div 12 \text{ months/year} = \textbf{5.4 years}$$

c) Since climate change is driven by increasing levels of CO_2 in the atmosphere, any energy source alternative that *does not* produce CO_2 would be making a positive contribution. PV solar technology collects sunlight and directly converts it to electrical energy. PV solar cells avoid fossil fuel (coal, oil, natural gas) combustion that releases CO_2 in the production of electricity. It is necessary to make the connection between CO_2 produced, temperature increase, and climate change. (**2 points**)

d) Two *passive* solar energy approaches that will further reduce energy consumption:

Passive energy approaches do not have the ability to create electricity; however, through the use of *home orientation* and/or the use of *structural materials* for heat storage, a desired home temperature can be attained from the sun's energy. For any home in a northern latitude, the use of stone floors serving as an internal mass that can directly absorb sunlight's radiant heat is an effective approach. Additionally, *planting deciduous trees* in front of south-facing windows can serve as shading/cooling during the warm summer months, not allowing the direct sunlight into a house. The *planting of evergreens* on the north-facing side of the home shelters against winter storms. (**2 points:** 1 point for each explanation, choices provided)

e) The primary environmental concerns associated with hydraulic fracturing of shale deposits for natural gas are the following: (1) large amount of water usage, depleting groundwater sources needed for other purposes; (2) methane gas contamination of groundwater that is used for drinking water or other domestic purposes; and (3) the need to dispose of the large amounts of contaminated wastewater used in the fracturing/drilling process. (**2 points:** 1 point for each environmental concern; choices provided)